THE INVENTION
OF THE AEROPLANE
(1799–1909)

THE INVENTION
OF THE AEROPLANE
(1799–1909)

by

CHARLES H. GIBBS-SMITH

M.A., F.M.A.,
Honorary Companion of the Royal Aeronautical Society

TAPLINGER PUBLISHING CO., INC.

New York

First American Edition published by
TAPLINGER PUBLISHING CO., INC., 1965

Library of Congress Catalogue Card Number: 65–16662

Made and Printed in Great Britain

TO A LADY

Thou art as fair in knowledge as in hue,
Finding thy worth a limit past my praise.
Yet be most proud of that which I compile,
Whose influence is thine, and born of thee.

— SHAKESPEARE, SONNETS 82 AND 78

CONTENTS

CONTENTS

CONTENTS

FOREWORD

" . . . *That I wouldn't be surprised to see a railroad in the air,*
Or a Yankee in a flyin' ship agoin' most anywhere."
—J. H. YATES

In view of the role which the aeroplane has come to assume in the modern world, it is perhaps curious to find that the process of its birth and coming of age — which spanned the single decade of 1899–1909 — has not previously been examined in the detail it deserves. The present work is an attempt to make such an examination, prefaced by a short survey of the forerunners of the practical aeroplane from 1799 to 1899.

Repetition of historical patterns is often of peculiar fascination, and the history of aviation provides a most remarkable example. For the decade under detailed review, which witnessed the arrival — some would say "intrusion" — in our civilisation of the practical aeroplane, vividly recalls the vital decade of 1799–1809. For it was in 1799 that Sir George Cayley invented the modern aeroplane configuration of fixed wings, fuselage, tail-unit of elevator and rudder, and independent propulsion-system: by 1809 he had built and flown both model and full-size machines incorporating his discoveries, and had completed his epoch-making paper "On Aerial Navigation" (published 1809–10); it was this publication which laid the foundations of modern aerodynamics and practical flight control. It was to take a century of invention and endeavour — much of it wasted in futile projects — for aerodynamics, petrol-engine technology, and pilotage, to join together and produce the successful "hardware" in the shape of the practical powered aeroplane.

Echoing the "Cayley decade" there comes at last the decade 1899– 1909, starting with the Wright brothers' warping kite of 1899, and ending with the first great aviation meeting at Reims in August of 1909; the aeroplane, in biplane and monoplane forms, then flew successfully before great crowds of the general public, before journalists, officials, and the military, and became accepted by the world as the fourth — and somewhat startling — of its newcomers in the realm of transport. It followed the practical bicycle of the 1880's; the petrol-powered automobile, which had been granted the freedom of the French and British roads in 1896; and the dirigible airship, which had grown out of the free balloon, and at last reached a practical stage by 1903. It is this epochal decade which forms the main subject of study in the present book.

FOREWORD

Never before had such a radical departure been made from the traditional methods by which man had transported himself and his chattels over the surface of the earth. Once the wheel had been invented, it seems to us now inevitable that there should have followed the beast-drawn cart and carriage, and their mechanically-propelled descendants which exploited the various prime-movers as soon as they became available. The cycle and motor-cycle were but extensions of the wheel-system. By the same token, as soon as certain kinds of material were seen to float on water, there was bound to follow the discovery of the Archimedean principle of displacement; then propulsion by the paddling hand, the manually operated wooden paddle, the rotary paddle, the screw "propeller" and finally their mechanically operated descendants. But navigation through the incorporeal air, inspired by the clouds which float and the birds that flap, had only hovered as a dream in the minds of men, with little hope of realisation. Then suddenly, in 1783, the Montgolfier brothers had discovered how to "enclose a cloud in a bag", and have it transport passengers through the air. Thus the floaters came surprisingly to beat the flappers in the race to fly.

Envy of the birds had then still to wait for more than a century before it was to be slaked and exploited, despite the brilliance of Cayley's ideas and his achievements. It was lack of a light and powerful prime-mover that was to prove the chief stumbling block. Finally, at the turn of the century, two young Americans — the brothers Wilbur and Orville Wright — proved themselves possessed of those talents of mind and spirit capable of conquering the air. They envisaged the flying machine not as a winged extension of the automobile, to be driven off the ground and chauffeured in churning progression through the air, but as a light and living structure, propelled and manoeuvred about the sky as if it were a bird possessed. To the Wrights, control and manoeuvre were paramount; and they learnt every nuance on their gliders. Power and propellers were but a logical extension, a natural fulfilment of the ability to bank, steer and hold a glider safely in equilibrium against the vagaries of the wind. The Wrights were indeed the mythical "hommes-oiseaux" now come to life at last. They are incomparably the greatest men in aviation; men of absolute integrity, and self-trained men of genius who mastered the design and construction of aeroplanes, aero-engines, and propellers, and the technique of properly controlling an aeroplane in the air. No other pioneers — with the distant exception of Sir George Cayley — can be remotely compared with the Wrights for aeronautical achievement. They first mastered glider flight (1900–02); then made tentative powered flights (1903–04); and by 1905 achieved the world's first fully controllable and practical powered aeroplane which flew for over half an hour at a time.

With the Wrights there began the air age. European aviation, moribund since the death of Lilienthal in 1896, was directly inspired by them — in 1902 and 1903 — to start again. But Europe was lamentably slow to grasp their true message, and it was not until 1908, when Wilbur Wright flew in France, that he then precipitated the second, and decisive, renaissance of European aviation. The Europeans had come to understand something of the lift of wings, the stability of an aeroplane, and the power of engines; but they had clung to the earth-bound chauffeur philosophy, and neglected most of what else mattered, despite the plethora of clues and pointers which surrounded them, but yet went unheeded. It was not until November of 1907 that any European pilot could stay in the air for as long as a minute. For six long years they had neglected research on propellers, and accepted the most primitive of whirling paddles; worse still, they had neglected the pilotage of gliders, and so were taking to the air in powered machines without knowledge or experience of flight control, especially lateral control (control in roll).

Out of Wilbur's brilliant flying at Auvours in 1908, came realisation, action and achievement: the Europeans read, marked, learned and inwardly digested his vital message. Thus freshly alerted and inspired, they exercised the perennial privileges of the pupil, first to learn from the master, then to criticise, and finally to improve on him. The Wrights had adopted the flight philosophy of making their aircraft inherently unstable in the interests of controllability; the Europeans had always clung to the concept of inherent stability. So when they had absorbed the Wrights' message of flight control, as well as their propeller policy, the Europeans — and Curtiss in America — wisely determined upon a combination of stability and controllability: by the summer of 1909, they had achieved this in fair degree in two excellent biplanes (the Henry Farman III and the Curtiss *Golden Flyer*) and two equally excellent monoplanes (the Antoinette and the Blériot XI). Thereafter, although they were to hold their own until 1911, the Wrights were slowly but surely overhauled, when the small stream of successful flying machines had broadened to a swift-moving river.

Records of early aeroplanes and their behaviour exist in profusion, but they are riddled with contradictions and inconsistencies. Even in

FOREWORD

1909, Major B. Baden-Powell, Secretary of what is today the Royal Aeronautical Society, had to write in the Society's Journal: "It is, unfortunately, most difficult to obtain exact details of aeroplane machines. In some instances they are not to be got. Some of them have never been weighed, the engines have not been tested for exact horse-power, and so on. In others, they are only given in general figures. Then, again, the weights may or may not include such items as full petrol tanks, etc. Areas may or may not include ailerons and steering planes. But, above all, the machines were, in many cases, frequently altered in detail . . ." How much more difficult it is for us today to arrive at accuracy may well be imagined. But after many years of sifting contemporary statements, and examining contemporary photographs, I have come to the conclusion that although accurate weights, measures and performances are so difficult to come by, such inaccuracies as we are now forced to accept do not materially hinder one in arriving at a fair assessment of the machines, and of the events, trends and influences in aviation history. I would even suggest that the present vogue for massive documentation of minutiae tends to militate against the understanding of history, owing to its tendency to divert attention away from meaning and significance. It stands to reason that one must at all times attempt to secure and record as accurate an array of facts as possible: but I feel that the wholesale pursuit of minutiae in much technological history today is apt to run wild at the expense of selection and appraisal. Historians are faced with the task of the interpretation of facts, and unless they are to remain content with the role of indiscriminate recorders, they must attempt to select, weigh evidence, and arrive at valid conclusions about both the major and minor matters of history.

The pursuit of minute detail is rivalled, especially in aviation history, by the pursuit of "firsts". Who, it is so often asked, was the first man (or machine) to do such-and-such? Who, for example, was the first Briton to fly (powered)? Who was the first to fly in Britain? Who was the first of British birth to fly? and Who was the first Briton to fly in Britain? Such are the conundrums beloved of this modern variety of sophist.* But however intrinsically interesting such facts may be — and there is certainly an absorbing "cross-word puzzle" type of satisfaction in establishing such points — the devotees seem so often to lack interest in any relative significance among their "firsts":

* For the benefit of such sophists, the answers are: Henri Farman; S. F. Cody; J. T. C. Moore-Brabazon (the late Lord Brabazon); J. T. C. Moore-Brabazon. The general problem of "firsts" is dealt with in detail in my Science Museum handbook, *The Aeroplane: an historical Survey*.

the first pilot to carry a cat across the Channel may even seem to be regarded as of equal significance with the first man who flew the Channel. Moreover, many of the most important firsts pass quite unrecorded, since they often cannot be linked specifically to a single date or person. Thus the first, but very primitive, use of a retractable undercarriage might be recorded (Wiencziers in 1911); but not that it was much later — in the early 1920's — when such undercarriages became practical, and in the early 1930's when they came into common use. Such treatment of a subject must inevitably mislead the reader and give him a distorted view of history.

Hoping to strike a viable balance between detail and generality, between fact and interpretation, I have included a number of general "surveys", each as a prelude to the detailed coverage of a given year or period, which attempt to sum up the chief trends and influences at work. These, if the reader prefers, may be sought out and read as a connected series to gain a general picture of the birth of the aeroplane. To supplement the whole story, a number of appendices are also included. Among these I would particularly mention the table of words and diagrams illustrating the course of powered flying from December 1903 to the end of 1908, and showing graphically both those machines which succeeded and those which failed. I have also included two batches of aviation journalism of 1909, one describing the six chief types of aeroplane flying in August of that year; and the other, *Flight's* excellent coverage of the Reims meeting. These contemporary extracts carry the true flavour of their day, and such "period pieces" are, I feel, of great value in supplementing and enriching the somewhat bare bones of my narrative.

EXPLANATIONS

With ease of reference in mind, I have adopted the practice of dividing the narrative into numbered sections. The illustrations do not bear any Plate or Figure numbers, but are simply lettered A, B, C, etc. within each plate; plates bear, at the top, the number of the text section to which they are matched. It should be noted that the plate to any given section may occur either before or after its text.

I found myself in difficulties when it came to the notes: the publishers and I finally agreed it would be more convenient for the reader if they were not in the form of foot-notes, but were placed en bloc after the appendices.

The weights, measures and performances are given in metric for the Continental machines, and tables of what are hoped will be found convenient conversions are placed after the Bibliography. As mentioned in the Foreword, any detailed accuracy of figures will always be impossible to come by; so for convenience I have generally followed Dumas in his *Ceux qui ont volé* (1909). I have learnt to be very cautious in accepting some of Dumas' information, and have on various occasions discovered him to be wrong. But in general, where figures are concerned, there is no better source, although I have sometimes accepted *L'Aérophile* if special considerations seemed to merit it; but Dumas had access to voluminous and sober reports by technically-minded journalists who witnessed most of the aviation events of those crucial years 1906–09. The times and distances he reported are, of necessity, approximate, as are also the weights and measures; but by comparing him with other sources, the overall picture revealed is remarkably reliable and consistent. The weights of aircraft he quotes — "en ordre de marche" — appear to be "all-up" weights, and I have accepted them as such, after as careful investigation as I could make: so where the word "weight" is given without qualification, it indicates "all-up weight".

Having noted the approximations inevitable in the weights and measures, it is just as necessary to warn against a similar approximation in flight distances and durations. Whichever was available and seemed most reliable, I have entered; and, again, the picture of achievement emerges clearly enough despite the obvious approximations. Incidentally, in the midst of so much lack of detail, one may be excused a raised eyebrow when flight durations are sometimes given to a fifth of a second!

At the end of the book is the customary bibliography, but I hope it will not seem boastful if I say that such a book-list in this particular case is somewhat of a formality, and will not prove very rewarding if the writer is simply looking for confirmation of the facts and interpretations found in my text. There are a few basic sources of text and illustrations, such as the French, English and American periodicals, and Dumas; but none of them have been found to be reliable on their own. There are also the ever-disappearing, but greatly profitable, pioneers themselves and their friends, some of whom I have contacted. A host of facts are, of course, still to be established, and some — I hope not many — of the "facts" I have recorded may be corrected or improved upon by ever deeper research.

"Love of the game" has kept me searching and cross-checking for years, and laboriously establishing point after point: one manages, for example, to pinpoint a date for a particular photograph of one aeroplane: then one finds, often in the most unexpected places, a note that such-and-such a change was made on this machine, which it does not exhibit on that particular dated photograph: this in turn might lead to a renewed scrutiny of all the available photographs and descriptions of that aircraft, to determine whether such a feature was incorporated earlier, and then changed before the dated photograph, or was added later: and so on. In some cases, contemporary information about seemingly simple points is found to differ widely, and only photographic evidence can decide the point. In others, one finds some of the pioneers themselves writing about men, machines, or events, and either forgetfully or intentionally telling demonstrable untruths.

Leaving aside the detailed research necessary to establish so many points, there is always the task of keeping the over-all picture of events in proper perspective, and arriving at a fair assessment of efforts and achievements. This is, perhaps, the most important of the historian's tasks: it is certainly the most exacting and exhausting, and demands, among other things, a constant watch on one's own preferences and prejudices, as well as other people's.

Little is to be found in this work concerning the various controversies — most of them frivolous and ill-motived — about first flights and other problems, since these have been dealt with in detail in my Science Museum handbook *The Aeroplane: an historical Survey* (2nd. edition, 1965). This survey is referred to as "G.S-A" in the text here.

As there are so many aircraft dealt with or mentioned in the present work, the problem of nomenclature has naturally loomed large. To meet the demands of lists, tables, and historical mention in general,

[xx]

the need for standardising the nomenclature has led me to publish —
as another Science Museum handbook — a suggested nomenclature
for all powered aeroplanes (and some gliders) which flew, or made
significant take-offs, from early in 1809 to the Reims meeting of
August 1909; this is entitled *A Directory and Nomenclature of the
First Aeroplanes, 1809–1909*. I have included here as Appendix I an
abbreviated version of this nomenclature, together with a chronological list of first take-offs during the period 1903–1909.

Nomenclature naturally brings to mind the whole question of the
inclusion or exclusion of this, that, or the other aircraft. During the
main period under review in this book — the decade 1899 to 1909 —
there must have been well over two hundred so-called flying machines
actually constructed in factories, workshops and backyards. Of these,
just over a hundred — including the important modifications of some
— made flights, or what were considered at the time to be significant
take-offs: the latter category is, of course, open to question and controversy, but there was general contemporary agreement about most
of them, with which a modern historian can also agree. In the present
work I have dealt with some hundred and fifty machines, including
some of the total failures (a few of which were never even completed),
some models, and even some gliders, if they played a significant
part in history. If the reader finds some of his favourite "freaks"
excluded — and there were many — it is only because I felt they
were less important than the freaks I have included, and because my
space was not unlimited.

To make for easier comparison of certain aircraft, the illustration
pages are sometimes placed opposite one another: this results in one
of such groups of illustrations being found a page or two ahead of its
relevant section of text.

·   ·   ·   ·   ·

A Note on Stability and Control

Stability. There are only two basic kinds of aircraft stability,
longitudinal stability for motion *in* the plane of symmetry, and lateral
stability for motion *out of* the plane of symmetry; the former concerns
rising, falling and pitching movements; the latter, rolling, yawing and
side-slipping movements. Colloquially and descriptively, however,
one may also speak of "directional stability" which is a component of
lateral stability.

Control. Where flight control is concerned, one may speak of "longitudinal control", which is control in pitch; and "lateral control" which comprises control in both roll and yaw. In practice the term "lateral control" is often used to refer to control in roll only, and the term "directional control" for control in yaw. In the present work I have used the term "lateral control" for control in roll, unless otherwise stated.

In early aviation (up to 1908) the Europeans were concerned to ensure:

(*a*) *Longitudinal stability*; *via* a tailplane at the back;

(*b*) *Longitudinal control*; *via* an elevator for control in pitch;

(*c*) *Directional stability*; *via* a keel area and a vertical surface in the rear;

(*d*) *Directional control*; *via* a rear rudder. As the Europeans neglected the proper function and use of warping and ailerons, they found it difficult to control their machines when they attempted to turn them on rudder alone, with the outer wings producing more lift on the turn than the inner; the pilots could only counteract the inwards rolling momentum by putting on opposite rudder to accelerate the lowered wings and lift them, and — in extreme cases — hoping that this rudder action would be in time to stop the machine heeling right over and crashing.

(*e*) *Stability in roll*; *via* a dihedral angle of the wings. Until Wilbur Wright started flying in France in August 1908, the use of ailerons or warping to effect control in roll was neither properly understood nor practised by the Europeans; this was initially due to their remaining ignorant of the necessity to achieve proper control in roll when turning, and their belief that the main function of ailerons or warping was to maintain lateral balance in level flight; then, as a result of these considerations, it was due to their ignorance of the use of the rudder to counteract aileron (or warp) drag.

The Wright brothers, on the other hand, were not concerned with any kind of inherent stability, but much concerned from the first with full lateral control (control in roll, yaw and side-slip).

ACKNOWLEDGMENTS

Debts to friends are, as ever, profound; especially to Mr. Peter W. Brooks, Deputy Managing Director of Beagle Aircraft, who has not only read my typescript but made many valuable suggestions; he has always been ready to discuss controversial points and, even more valuable, has "relentlessly" pursued me into delving ever deeper and wider among the sources when he suspected I was forming judgments on insufficient evidence. Also to Dr. P. B. Walker, C.B.E., of the Royal Aircraft Establishment, Farnborough, who generously acts as my adviser on aerodynamics and structures. Then to my old friend Charles Dollfus, formerly Curator of the Paris Musée de l'Air, and the doyen of aeronautical historians, who has always spurred me to greater efforts, and has — I am thankful to say — approved of most of my assessments.

Bothering librarians is perhaps a legitimate and inevitable proclivity of writers the world over; but I think we all tend to take their long-suffering and ever-willing co-operation too much for granted. When, in Sir Thomas Browne's phrase, I have in my "cooled imagination" contemplated my perennial impositions on Mr. Frank Smith, Librarian of the Royal Aeronautical Society, and his assistant Mrs. L. C. Kay, I not only blush for shame, but count my blessings, and thank my lucky stars for their inexhaustible kindness and patience. Gratitude also goes to my friends at the Science Museum for their continued help and encouragement, especially the Director (Dr. David Follett), then William O'Dea, Brian Lacey, and Commander W. Tuck; to the Editor of *Flight International*, Mr. H. F. King, M.B.E., the most encouraging and history-minded of editors, who has kindly allowed me to use material from contemporary issues of *Flight:* and to Mrs. Phyllis Robson and Mrs. Beryl Edginton for much secretarial, proof-reading, and other help.

Most of the illustrations are taken direct from contemporary books and periodicals, but I am very grateful to the following for the supply of additional, or better, prints: The National Air Museum (Smithsonian Institution), Washington, D.C., and the Radio Times-Hulton Picture Library.

[xxiii]

INTRODUCTION

The practical powered aeroplane took exactly one hundred and ten years to emerge from idea to reality. The process started when Sir George Cayley first formulated its basic nature in 1799, and came to fruition in 1909 when it became a practical and accepted vehicle. Before 1799 there had been an age-old desire to fly; bold but mis-guided attempts to fly by means of wings attached to the body; speculation at all levels of intellect; some few fine flashes of reason or intuition; and — in 1783 — the achievement of air voyaging by balloon.

The hundred and ten years from 1799 to 1909 may accurately and conveniently be divided into two periods; there was first a century-full of forerunners (1799 to 1899), who laboured to bring powered aviation to the threshold of accomplishment; and then ten years in which the practical machine was finally achieved.

The powered aeroplane first became recognised as a practical and established vehicle in the summer of 1909, a stage of achievement heralded by Blériot's Channel-crossing in July, and more particularly by the first great aviation meeting — "La Grande Semaine d'Avia-tion de la Champagne" — which was held on the plain of Bétheny at Reims in August.

Although a considerable variety of configurations had appeared since 1903, including triplane, tandem, canard and even annular, aeroplanes, only two basic types of practical aircraft had crystallised: these were the pusher biplane with forward elevator, represented by the Wright, Voisin, Henri Farman and Curtiss machines; and the tractor monoplane, represented by the Antoinettes and two types of Blériot. All of these machines flew at Reims.

Waiting in the wings, so to speak, and still not matured enough to succeed when it appeared at Reims, was the prophetic tractor biplane, with all control surfaces aft of the propeller, represented by the soon-to-triumph Breguet, and the still tentative Goupy which was not seen at the meeting.

Each of the successful aircraft types at Reims, except the Voisin, possessed the following characteristics:

(*a*) a pair of cambered biplane or monoplane wings as its main lifting surfaces;

(*b*) a horizontal elevator for control in pitch, placed forward of the wings on the biplanes, aft on the monoplanes;

[1]

(*c*) a vertical rudder (aft) for control in yaw, which also provided one component in satisfactory directional steering;

(*d*) a helical twisting ("warping") of the wing-ends, or hinged ailerons, to provide control in roll in combination with the rudder, either for preserving lateral balance or to effect banked turns;

(*e*) a light petrol engine driving one or two propellers — pusher on the biplanes, tractor on the monoplanes — to provide the necessary thrust for forward propulsion;

(*f*) a robust but light construction, including a strong wheeled undercarriage on all but the Wright machines, which had skids.

(*g*) an airspeed of between 35 and 45 m.p.h.;

(*h*) a flight duration of between one and two hours;

(*i*) the ability to maintain satisfactory flight — except as yet in strong winds — and to bank, turn, and circle safely in the air.

All these types, including the Voisin, but excluding the Wright — which was designed as inherently unstable — had a considerable amount of inherent stability built into them, and were thus comparatively simple to fly in favourable weather. The Voisin — safe, slow, but sterile — was alone in possessing no form of lateral control. The prevailing weakness in all the aircraft was the unreliability of the engines, and it was to be many years before this menace to aerial safety and efficiency was remedied.

One other important characteristic to be noted was the ability of the aircraft to carry passengers; among the machines at Reims which showed themselves capable of carrying passengers, the Wright and Blériot XII were the only machines specifically designed for, and capable of, carrying a passenger in comfort as a regular part of their duties.

★   ★   ★   ★   ★

Sir George Cayley dated his first aeronautical activity to 1796, when he heard of, and copied, the Launoy and Bienvenu model helicopter; but it was in 1799 that his first major burst of creativity started with his epoch-making introduction of the modern aeroplane configuration. This phase ended in 1809 with the writing of his classic triple paper "On Aerial Navigation" (published 1809–10), upon which the modern science of aerodynamics is founded. The teachings of Cayley's paper were based on the same outstanding combination of theoretical reasoning and practical verification and correction — with both

[2]

INTRODUCTION

models and full-scale aircraft — which was to characterise the work of the Wright brothers a century later. Then, after a long interval, Cayley came to reinforce and extend the teachings of his first great paper by other important work (1843–53).

Cayley was so far in advance of his day, both in the first and last decades of his creativity, that by the end of the century there had only been a few truly significant advances in practical aviation, chief among which were the achievements of Lilienthal in gliding. Valuable work was carried out in the verification, refining, and extension of Cayley's teachings; this was seen particularly in the emergence of basic configurations for the monoplane and multiplane, in Wenham's and Phillips' new light on the lifting qualities of cambered aerofoils, and Pénaud's demonstrations of inherent stability. There also appeared during the second half of the century a steadily growing number of ingenious designs and flying models, as well as a few tentative full-size machines.

There was, of course, momentous progress through the century in neighbouring fields which the aeroplane would one day have to rely on, such as metallurgy, petroleum technology, and the internal combustion engine.

Among the aeronautical inventors themselves, there began to emerge in the second half of the century three recognisable types of pioneer: (*a*) the "academic" inventors, whose creations — sometimes ingenious, but more often wayward or visionary — were realised only on paper; (*b*) the "model-makers", who were mostly content to experiment only in miniature; and finally (*c*) those pioneers who were willing to risk life and limb in full-size experiments: the latter came to divide into two vitally significant streams, the stream of "chauffeurs" and the stream of "airmen".

Although the aeroplane was not to start proliferating until the 1890's, the "chauffeur's" attitude to aviation was oddly evident long before: this was an attitude which regarded the flying machine as a winged motor-car, to be driven into the air by brute force, so to say, and sedately steered about the sky as if it were a land — or even marine — vehicle which simply became transferred from a layer of earth to a layer of air.

The true "airman's" attitude was evident in the pilot's desire to identify himself with his machine — "je veux faire corps avec la machine", as Françoise Sagan puts it — or ride it like an expert horseman.

The "chauffeurs" came to devote themselves mainly to the pursuit

[3]

of thrust and lift, and thereby proved singularly unfruitful: they invariably tried to take off in powered machines before they had any true idea of flight control. Whereas the "airmen" thought primarily in terms of control in the air, and quickly realised that the unpowered glider was the vehicle of choice, in which a man might emulate the technique of gliding birds, and learn to ride the air successfully before having himself precipitated into the atmosphere in a powered flying machine. This distinction between chauffeurs and airmen was to prove pivotal in the final conquest of the air.*

With Lilienthal's successful gliding from 1891 to 1896, the practical possibility of manned aeroplane flight was forcefully and fruitfully brought to the attention of inventors. What seems strange today is that until the Wrights started gliding in 1900, Lilienthal had only two successful disciples, Octave Chanute and Percy Pilcher; the latter was killed in 1899 when just about to embark on powered experiments.

When the Wright brothers actively entered the aeronautical scene in 1899, practical aviation was all but moribund, with only balloons and airships claiming serious attention; man-carrying mechanical flight still appeared to most inventors as an unrealisable dream.

The Wrights were far from being only the "drawers together" of the technical strands spun by others, or the talented solvers of a technological jigsaw puzzle. They were to triumph as true inventors and pioneers, first in theory, and then in arduous practice. Their key to success was the discovery of the technique of controlling a flying machine in the air, a technique scarcely guessed at before, even by Lilienthal. Furthermore, they had to question and revise most of what they had absorbed from their predecessors, and virtually start again from scratch. In the vital sphere of propellers they had indeed to start right from the beginning, as nothing of note had been done before except to make ingenious but maladroit adaptations of marine practice. Having first mastered gliding flight, they proceeded to build and prove their powered "Flyers". In 1903 they made the world's first powered, sustained and controlled flights: with their Flyer III of 1905 they produced the world's first properly practical aeroplane.

In the first seven sections which follow, a brief illustrated survey is made of the immediate forerunners of practical aviation; then there is presented in detail the evolution of the aeroplane from the Wrights' first machine to the aircraft which flew at Reims.

* Peyrey wrote of Ferber: "il monte, dit-il, des machines volantes tout comme les chauffeurs montent des automobiles."

1

THE FORERUNNERS
Cayley
1799–1809

"The true inventor of the aeroplane and one of the most powerful geniuses in the history of aviation" are the words used by the French historian Charles Dollfus to describe Sir George Cayley (1773–1857), a scholarly Yorkshire baronet who until recently was comparatively unknown to historians of applied science.

Cayley, who lived and did most of his work at Brompton Hall, near Scarborough, first had his aeronautical imagination fired by the invention of the balloon in 1783 — when he was ten — and his active concern with flying lasted until he died in 1857. In the year 1796 he made a helicopter model on the lines of that invented by Launoy and Bienvenu, a device he later improved and modified. Then, within a few years, with no previous workers to guide him or suggest the lines of approach, he arrived at a correct and mature conception of the modern aeroplane, and so laid the secure foundations upon which all subsequent developments in aviation have been built. It was typical of Cayley's genius that, with the central idea of flight in mind, he sought data in whatever fields he saw were relevant, and applied them to his own problems: thus in 1804 he turned to the whirling arm — first used by Robins for ballistic tests in 1746 — and obtained valuable results which he applied to aircraft wings.

But it was in the year 1799 that Cayley took his first and most vital step towards inaugurating the modern aeroplane concept, the proper separation of the system of thrust from the system of lift. This was the crucial breakaway from the ornithopter tradition of centuries; it meant picturing the bird with its wings held rigid as if in gliding flight, and propelled by some form of auxiliary mechanism. This achievement was enshrined on a silver disc, dated 1799, now in the Science Museum (Fig. A) which is in effect the first design in history for a modern configuration aeroplane. There is a fixed main wing; a cruciform tail-unit comprising a combined elevator and rudder; propellers in the form of paddles, aft of the wings; and a nacelle for the pilot. The curvature of the wing was due to air pressure, as Cayley made clear later: he was aware of the superior lifting qualities of the rigid cambered wing, but generally relied on the curvature being effective

[5]

1. THE FORERUNNERS CAYLEY (1799–1809)

A. Drawing of Cayley's silver disc: 1799

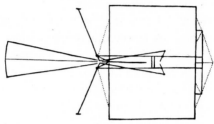

B. Cayley's drawing of his first aeroplane design: *c.* 1799

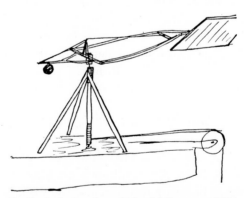

C. Cayley's drawing of his whirling arm: 1804

D. Cayley's drawing of his first glider model: 1804

[6]

aerodynamically with a "sail" wing, rather than with a rigid cambered structure.

To offset the effect of the somewhat crude rendering on the disc — inevitable in an amateur etching on metal — there survives the highly professional plan-view which Cayley drew of the same machine (Fig. B): it shows the paddles operated by an oar transmission from the cockpit, and the tail-unit operated by a tiller.

Although aware since 1796 of the action and potentialities of the airscrew, Cayley preserved just enough links with the past to have a hankering after ornithoptering propulsion systems; and although he steadily progressed from fore-and-aft-moving paddles, through the flapper producing both lift and propulsion (in the manner of a bird's outer primary feathers) to the purely propulsive flapper, this pre-occupation with reciprocating "propellers", and his general aversion to rotating machines, marks one of his few retrogressive traits.

For some time, the subject of bird flight plagued him with its problems, as he was bent on using ornithopter techniques for propulsion. It was not until 1808 that he had worked through Leonardo da Vinci's error of believing that birds flap their wings downwards and backwards like a swimmer; then he came to realise that the outer portions of a bird's wings heel over collectively, or in the form of multiple emarginated feathers, to provide the thrust component as propellers. Cayley was the first to comprehend properly this technique of bird propulsion.

His concurrent aerodynamic experiments formed the outstanding achievement of this 1799-1809 decade. In a now classic pronouncement of aeronautical history, Cayley wrote: "The whole problem is confined within these limits, *viz.* to make a surface support a given weight by the application of power to the resistance of air."

In 1804 he used, for the first time in history, the whirling arm in the service of aeronautics, to test an aerofoil at varying angles of incidence (Fig. C). This was immediately followed by what ranks as the first modern configuration aeroplane of history, although only a small model (Fig. D). It was a simple enough device, but of far-reaching significance: a kite was fixed on top of a pole at a six-degree angle of incidence, with a cruciform tail-unit attached by a universal joint, and lowered to a positive angle of incidence of $11·5°$: a movable weight on the underside of the pole was used to adjust the position of the centre of gravity. In another of his memorable passages, Cayley wrote:

"It was very pretty to see it sail down a steep hill, and it gave the idea that a larger instrument would be a better and a safer conveyance

[7]

down the Alps than even the surefooted mule, let him meditate his track ever so intensely. The least inclination of the tail towards the right or left made it shape its course like a ship by the rudder".

By mid-1809 Cayley had investigated the lifting capacities of cambered wings, the movement of the centre of pressure, longitudinal stability, and the problem of streamlining (his solid of least resistance closely approximating to a modern low-drag aerofoil section): he even came to realise that an area of low pressure is formed above the wing. He had also decided that a dihedral setting of the wings provided a better means than pendulum action of securing lateral stability — although he sometimes returned to pendulum stability in models — and also applied the principle to longitudinal stability. He had advanced from model gliders to the building and successful testing (unmanned) of a full-size glider of 300 square feet; this incorporated the same basic features, except for the dihedrally set wings, that he had laid down at the turn of the century. It was flown in 1809.

Along the way, Cayley had also invented in 1809 the tension (cycle-type) wheel for aircraft undercarriages, and suggested light tubular beam construction for aircraft based on bamboo.

It was inevitably the problem of power which brought him as much disappointment and frustration as his aerodynamic achievements brought him satisfaction. He dismissed the steam engine for its poor power-weight ratio, and experimented briefly with a small gunpowder motor in the hope that fruitful results would develop in the internal combustion field. At the same time (1807) he formulated and published his first specification for the hot air ("calorific") engine of which he is the accepted inventor; he was to pursue this type of motor throughout his life, to the considerable benefit of industrial power supply, but not, as he deeply regretted, of aeronautics.

As his search for a suitable engine was perpetually fruitless, he gave much attention to man-powered transmission systems, although he was later to become aware that sustained horizontal flight by this means was impossible with the materials then available.

But, overall, lay Cayley's supreme confidence in the ultimate success of the powered aeroplane, a confidence preserved throughout his life; it was charmingly summed up in two of his *obiter dicta*:

"I feel perfectly confident, however, that this noble art will soon be brought home to man's general convenience, and that we shall be able to transport ourselves and families, and their goods and chattels, more securely by air than by water, and with a velocity of from 20 to 100

[8]

miles per hour. To produce this effect it is only necessary to have a first mover, which will generate more power in a given time, in proportion to its weight, than the animal system of muscles."

"An uninterrupted navigable ocean, that comes to the threshold of every man's door, ought not to be neglected as a source of human gratification and advantage."

It was in Nicholson's *Journal of Natural Philosophy, Chemistry and the Arts* for November 1809, February 1810 and March 1810, that there appeared Cayley's triple paper "On Aerial Navigation". Ironically, Cayley was here spurred into print by a report that, at Vienna Jacob Degen had flown briefly with wings by his own unaided muscle power. One can only suppose that Cayley was overtaken — no matter how happily for posterity — by wishful thinking; for he swallowed the Degen story whole, and used Degen's alleged flights to bolster his own hopes and aspirations for aviation. Degen relied, in fact, on almost all his weight being supported by a balloon, thus allowing him to perform what today is known as balloon-jumping, aided for a minute or two by vigorous waving of his ingenious clack-valve wings. Most eye-witness reporters, no doubt with an eye to news value, conveniently omitted mention of the balloon.

PS. Degen also employed a hanging counterweight to test his apparatus.

2

THE FORERUNNERS
1809–52

As noted in the previous section, it was Jacob Degen's attempts to fly with his clack-valve ornithopter (Fig. A), and the erroneous reports that he had flown unaided in this machine in 1809, which caused Sir George Cayley to publish in 1809–10 the results of his ten years work in his triple paper "On Aerial Navigation" — the first and greatest classic of aviation — which laid the foundations on which the modern science of aerodynamics is based. Cayley's triple paper, an illustration from which is shown in Fig. B, and his subsequent papers, were to permeate and condition all serious aeronautical thinking thereafter, both in Britain and on the Continent. Henson rightly addressed him, in 1846, as "the Father of Aerial Navigation". Cayley established the basic conception in which the system of lift was separated from the system of thrust; and where a fixed-wing machine, with tail-unit comprising the control surfaces, was propelled by an auxiliary mechanism, with lateral and longitudinal stability obtained by dihedral on the wings, and between the wings and tail-unit.

Thomas Walker published his *Treatise upon the Art of Flying* in 1810, but its chief value was only to fan the then small flame of air-mindedness, especially with the illustrations of his proposed ornithopter (Fig. C). But in 1831 he published a revised edition of the book, which included his design for a fixed-wing tandem aeroplane powered by amidships flappers (Fig.D). Although Cayley had designed a tandem-wing machine in 1815, it was not published; and credit goes to Walker for starting one of the important — although ultimately abandoned — aircraft configurations of history.

Basing his work on Cayley, it was W. S. Henson's design for an "Aerial Steam Carriage" — first published in 1843 — that was to crystallise the fixed-wing monoplane configuration (Fig. E). Through constant publication and description for over half a century, Henson's design was to condition the basic form of the modern monoplane, with main wings, fuselage with wheeled undercarriage, propeller propulsion, and tail-unit comprising elevator and rudder. All this had been envisaged, described and published by Cayley, but he did not enshrine it in a cohesive and memorable form. In 1847 Henson tested a model of his machine, which was unsuccessful; and in 1848 his friend John Stringfellow made and tested an improved model on the

[10]

2. THE FORERUNNERS: 1809–52

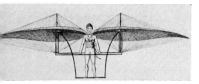

A. Degen ornithopter: 1809

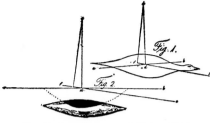

B. Cayley diagram of flight: 1809

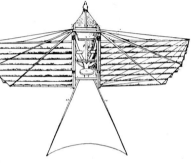

C. Walker ornithopter design: 1810

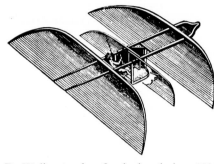

D. Walker tandem fixed-wing design: 1831

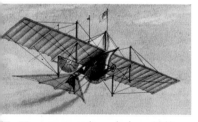

E. Henson aeroplane design: 1843

F. Stringfellow model aeroplane: 1848

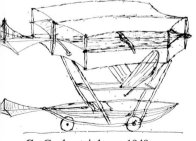

G. Cayley triplane: 1849

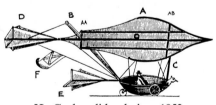

H. Cayley glider design: 1852

[11]

same lines (Fig. F) but with only marginal results: neither model was known to their contemporaries and so had no influence on others.

It was Cayley's fear of large braced surfaces which led him publicly to advocate the multiplane in 1843, a suggestion which directly inspired Stringfellow to build his model triplane of 1868 (see Sect. 3). Cayley practiced what he preached in his own first full-size multiplane of 1849 (Fig. G), a triplane which was flown as a glider in ballast, and with a boy on board for a few yards; but it was not published, and had no direct influence.

In 1852 Cayley published in the *Mechanics Magazine* his design for a glider (Fig. H) accompanied by a detailed description and instructions how to fly it. This machine included most of the basic features of the modern aeroplane except lateral control; *i.e.* wing dihedral for lateral stability; longitudinal dihedral as between the wings and tailplane (which was adjustable); tail fin; pilot-operated elevator-cum-rudder; and wheeled (cycle-type) undercarriage. This prophetic machine, if its message had been realised, could have led to practical controlled gliders in the 1850's or 60's, which in turn might well have precipitated the powered aeroplane by the 1880's or 1890's at the latest. But Cayley's design must have appeared so visionary to his contemporaries that no one is known to have even commented upon it at the time, let alone acted on it, and it was immediately lost to view: no reference to, or comment upon, it is known in nineteenth-century aeronautical literature.

. . . . .

In the sections that follow, only those machines and designs which had a direct bearing on the achievement of heavier-than-air flight are included. For such creditable and interesting items as the first jet aeroplane design (de Louvrié, 1865), the jet designs of Butler and Edwards (1867), and of de Telescheff (1867), etc., see GS-A.

3
THE FORERUNNERS
1853–71

The opening decades of the second half of the century showed three significant trends at work; first, Cayley's basic teachings, which were for the first time translated and published in France (1853), came to condition aeronautical thinking on the Continent, although — as in England — his name was soon lost to view: second, a growing number of technically-minded men began seriously to pay attention to aviation and its possibilities; and third, France now became the dominant influence in the pursuit of aviation.

But the new inventors, preoccupied by their own schemes, suffered from a growing and chronic "blinkerdom", in that they paid far too little attention to — and seldom sought — the writings and activities of their contemporaries, nor did they bother to search out what had been taught or accomplished by their predecessors. Hence the fate of Cayley's published description and illustrations of his glider-design noted in the previous section. The main exceptions to this neglect of their fellow pioneers, were the basic principles laid down by Cayley, which had come to permeate all intelligent writing on the subject — some of which was inevitably read by each newcomer — and the continually revived illustrations of Henson's "Aerial Steam Carriage".

Although not a technical advance, L. C. Letur's parachute-cum-glider (Fig. A) was an ingenious full-size machine, in which he had the confidence and bravery to descend several times from a balloon in 1853–54: then, in 1854, he was dragged over some trees and killed. The publicity attending his descents and his death served in some measure to keep air-mindedness alive.

The first consistent French design for a powered aeroplane appeared in 1853, by Michel Loup (Fig. B): it was a rigid bird-form monoplane with twin propellers let into the wings, a cruciform tail-unit, and wheeled undercarriage.

The French naval officer Félix Du Temple achieved history's first successful (but tentative) powered aeroplane model about 1857–58; and in 1857 patented a remarkable tractor monoplane (Fig. C) which was later (about 1874) to become the first powered aeroplane to take off — probably down a ramp — but not to sustain itself. To Du Temple, and all other early pioneers, the lack of a powerful but light engine appeared as the most persistent obstacle.

[13]

3. THE FORERUNNERS: 1853–71

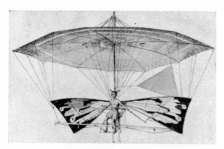

A. Letur parachute-glider: 1853

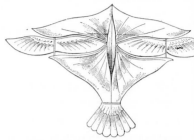

B. Loup aeroplane design: 1853

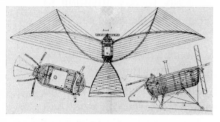

C. Du Temple aeroplane design: 1857

D. Le Bris glider: 1868

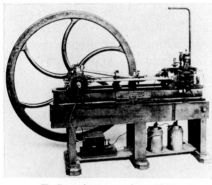

E. Lenoir gas engine: 1860

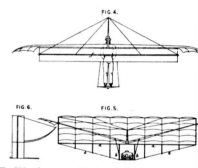

F. Wenham multiplane glider: published

G. Stringfellow model triplane: 1868

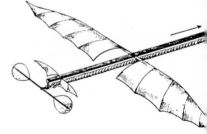

H. Pénaud model aeroplane ("Planopho
1871

THE FORERUNNERS

Between 1857 and 1868, a brave and ingenious French sea captain, J. M. Le Bris, tested two full-size gliders modelled on the albatross, and launched from farm carts driven downhill: in the first machine he made one short glide; and later crashed — breaking a leg — in a second attempt: the second glider (Fig. D) was wisely tested in ballast, and it, too, crashed. The importance of Le Bris, like Letur, lies in the air-mindedness he helped to foster in the pioneers who followed.

In 1860 Lenoir invented the gas engine in France (Fig. E), which was the true beginning of the modern internal combustion engine, a prime mover for which aviation was to wait so long.

About 1858–59, the Englishman F. H. Wenham made tests with a multiplane (five) glider (Fig. F) which, although as a flying machine it was not a success, demonstrated a number of vital points. These were described in a paper he read to the newly founded (1866) Aeronautical Society of Great Britain — now Royal — which was published in their first Annual Report: it was widely read and of far-reaching influence. Wenham followed up Cayley's advocacy of the cambered wing, and demonstrated that such a wing derived most of its lift from the front portion; hence that a high aspect-ratio wing was superior in lifting qualities. He also confirmed Cayley's advocacy of the multiplane.

The most influential exhibit at the world's first aeronautical exhibition — held by the Aeronautical Society at the Crystal Palace in 1868 — was the ageing John Stringfellow's powered model triplane of that year (Fig. G). Derived directly from Cayley's advice, this ambitious machine could not sustain itself: but although not successful, it was to be directly responsible, through widespread publication, for all subsequent biplane and triplane development, inspiring Chanute, Lilienthal, the Wrights, and the rest.

In 1870 there appeared in France one of the great figures of aeronautical history, Alphonse Pénaud, who after preliminary experiments with a model helicopter, produced in 1871 his powered model aeroplane which he called a "Planophore" (Fig. H). It was Pénaud who popularised twisted rubber as an "engine" for models, and thus gave to the young people of the world a power-unit which has played a great part in promoting air-mindedness among boys ever since. Pénaud's great contribution to aviation history was the public demonstration of Cayley's principles of inherent stability (see Notes). His Planophore, with propeller at the stern, had a far-reaching influence and by the constant re-issue of illustrations of it by subsequent writers, kept the idea of inherent stability before the eyes of the influential pioneers. His design for a full-size aeroplane is noted in the next section.

4

THE FORERUNNERS
1871–81

The 1870's continued to see further progress in the practical considerations of heavier-than-air flight. In 1873, Professor Etienne Marey published his *La Machine Animale* (Fig. A) which focussed attention on the problems of bird flight, and was a source of inspiration to many subsequent inventors, including the Wright brothers; to its less mature readers, it unhappily inspired further ideas of ornithopter construction.

In England, D. S. Brown — inspired by Walker — carried out many tests (1873–4) with model tandem-wing gliders (Fig. B), whose chief importance was their later influence on S. P. Langley, who was persuaded to adopt the tandem-wing configuration for both his models and his full-size machine (see Sect. 12). The Du Temple take-off (c. 1874) was noted in the last section.

Thomas Moy's large, but not man-carrying, "Aerial Steamer" (Fig. C), tested at the Crystal Palace in 1875, was a tandem-wing steam-driven machine which just lifted clear of its circular track; but it was chiefly of propaganda value, and did not advance aviation.

In 1876 Pénaud completed and published the design for his prophetic full-size monoplane amphibian (Fig. D), which was never built: it incorporated double surfaced wings, twin tractor propellers, a single control column for combined operation of rear elevators and rudder; glass-domed cockpit, and retractable undercarriage (with ingenious shock absorbers), tail-skid, and wing-tip floats. It played an important part in helping to condition the minds of contemporaries and followers to the idea of the fixed-wing tractor monoplane.

Also in 1876, in Germany, Otto brought the internal combustion engine to its first vital transformation since Lenoir's invention of the gas engine, by introducing the four-stroke cycle (Fig. E). Thus the future power-plant for aeroplanes was being steadily developed through the stages necessary for the perfection of a powerful light prime mover.

In 1879 Victor Tatin in France again reinforced the idea of the tractor monoplane with his ingenious, successful, and much publicised model driven by compressed air (Fig. F); its main value was as propaganda, which had ever to be renewed and kept before the eyes of the pioneers.

[16]

4. THE FORERUNNERS: 1873–84

A. Marey bird-flight test: 1873

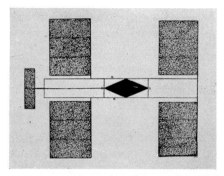

B. Brown tandem-wing glider model: 1874

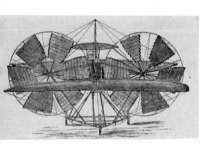

C. Moy "Aerial Steamer": 1875

D. Pénaud aeroplane design: 1876

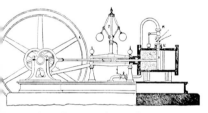

E. Otto four-stroke engine: 1876

F. Tatin powered model: 1879

G. Mouillard bird illustration: 1881

H. Mozhaiski monoplane: 1884

THE FORERUNNERS

When L. P. Mouillard published his book *L'Empire de l'Air* in 1881 (Fig. G), with its new examination of bird flight, it was the accent he laid on soaring and gliding flight that was to prove important in helping direct the attention of later pioneers to the importance of experimenting with fixed-wing gliders in the air, rather than trying to take off in powered machines before becoming aware of the problems of flight control. Mouillard himself had been experimenting with man-carrying gliders since 1856, and, although his own machines were unsuccessful, he became acutely aware of the importance of gliding to the future of aviation. He was one of those — perhaps the most important of them — who created the airman's attitude to flying (see Introduction) as opposed to the chauffeur's.

The second powered aeroplane to leave the ground, but not to fly, was built by the Russian Alexander F. Mozhaisky, whose steam-powered monoplane (with I. N. Golubev as pilot) took off down a ski-jump ramp in 1884 — not 1882 as previously thought — and was airborne for a second or two (Fig. H), but did not sustain itself. Needless to say, the Russians have been tempted to claim this as the world's first flight.

5

THE FORERUNNERS
1881–97

One of the least known, but one of the most important pioneers in the whole history of aviation, was the Englishman Horatio F. Phillips, whose overriding importance was in his experimentation and publications — to be read by all the later pioneers — in the field of cambered aerofoils. He took out his first patent in 1884 for what he called the "Phillips entry", or "dipping edge", wings (Fig. A). Elaborating what Cayley had tentatively advanced, Phillips established experimentally his belief that if a thick (double surfaced) aerofoil is used for an aeroplane's wings, and if it is curved more on the upper than on the lower surface, an area of decreased pressure is created above the upper (more curved) surface, and increased pressure is created on the lower (less curved) surface; with the vital demonstration — also suggested by Cayley — that the major proportion of the lift of such an aerofoil was effected by the low pressure on the upper surface. His patent of 1891 developed these ideas further. Phillips built (and tested at Harrow in 1893) a large powered multiplane model which successfully demonstrated his findings (Fig. D).

One of the most important events in the non-aeronautical world of technology at this time — but which was later to have a profound influence on flying — was the arrival of the petrol-engined automobile, in the form of the Benz vehicle of 1885 (Fig. B). As the automobile developed, so did its petrol engine; and as the petrol engine developed, so did the potential power-plant for the aeroplane.

In 1890 a significant event took place in aviation, which should have led to important developments, but which in fact was to lead nowhere. Clément Ader in France succeeded in taking off in an aeroplane of his own design under its own power on October 9th at Armainvilliers: this was the bat-like steam-powered *Eole* (Fig. C). Unfortunately, Ader was not an airman at heart, and was not — and was never to be — concerned with control in the air. His performance in *Eole*, which no authority either in or outside France claims as a proper flight, was a simple powered take-off, in a completely inadequate aircraft considered control-wise, which covered some 50 m. (164 ft.). Elated by this first effort, he embarked on an ambitious programme (see below).

Meanwhile in Australia there was flourishing a remarkable man,

5. THE FORERUNNERS: 1884–97

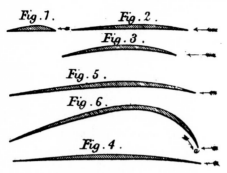

A. Phillips wing sections: 1884

B. Benz automobile: 1885

C. Ader *Eole*: 1890

D. Phillips multiplane: 1893

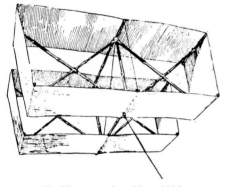

E. Hargrave box-kite: 1893

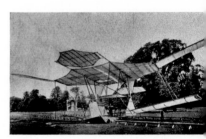

F. Maxim test-rig: 1894

G. Langley model No. 5: 1896

H. Ader *Avion III*: 1897

[20]

Lawrence Hargrave, who, if he had emigrated to Europe, would undoubtedly have been able to absorb the contemporary moods and accomplishments, and progress to important attainments in aviation. Even in such far away isolation, he was later to influence aviation strongly by his chief invention (1893), which he brought to London and demonstrated in 1899: this was the now familiar box-kite (Fig. E) which was to play an important part in the early European development of the inherently stable aeroplane.

The most wasted talent in aviation history was undoubtedly that of Sir Hiram Maxim, wealthy ex-patriate American inventor, whose Maxim Gun made him world famous. For many years he had been interested in the idea of flying machines, but — like Ader, whom he resembled in many ways — he was chauffeur-minded at heart, and his aeronautical efforts were chiefly directed at lift and thrust, not control. He spent nearly £20,000 on his researches, and finally, in 1894, built and tested a huge machine at Baldwyn's Park in Kent (Fig. F). It was a biplane with twin steam-driven propellers, incorporating a dihedral angle of the wings, and both fore and aft elevators: it ran on rails, with wooden guard rails above which permitted a rise of a few inches. On its principal test, it just lifted itself off the rails, broke one of the guard rails, and was brought to a stop. Maxim immediately ceased his experiments and made no other flying machines until his abortive biplane of 1910. This giant 1894 test-rig proved nothing new, broke no new ground, and influenced no one: it represented the greatest amount of wasted money and effort in the history of flying. Maxim was the victim of his mental inflexibility, overweening conceit, and lack of humility which, where aeronautics was concerned, perpetually baulked his undoubted talent: he later made grotesque claims.

The serious study of aviation in the United States, which was soon to flourish so triumphantly, may be said to have started with the work of the eminent astronomer and Secretary of the Smithsonian Institution, S. P. Langley. Unfortunately he, too, was chauffeur-minded, and never contemplated preliminary tests with gliders to learn flight control. He had become interested in mechanical flight in 1886, and by 1896 had produced his first successful powered model, his steam-driven No. 5 (Fig. G). Langley, inspired by Brown's tandem-wing experiments in England, adopted this configuration in his successful models, as well as in his full-size machine of 1903 (see Sect. 12). He called his machines Aerodromes (see note on Sect. 12), and with his models Nos. 5 and 6 he succeeded in making many successful flights, including one of 3,000 ft. and another of 4,200 ft.

[21]

In 1897 Ader appeared again, with his third full-size machine (the second was never completed) named Avion III (Fig. H): of a similar configuration to the *Eole*, it had two steam-engines powering two propellers: there was no adequate flight control system. In neither of its two tests in 1897 did it ever leave the ground for an instant, and Ader abandoned his practical work thereafter. He was too set in his ways after 1897, and was chiefly concerned — like Maxim — with lift and thrust. His idea of flight control was primitive, and he also showed no interest in the rapidly developing petrol engine. Nine years later (in 1906), when he heard of Santos-Dumont's experiments, he pathetically claimed that his Avion III had flown for 300 metres in 1897, despite able and conscientious official witnesses having shown that it never left the ground, and despite Ader himself never previously having claimed a take-off, let alone a flight.

It must regretfully be recorded here that the climacteric year 1896 — which witnessed the successful gliders of Chanute and Pilcher, the death of Lilienthal in his prime, and the certainty of achievement to come — also previsioned the doleful and near-eclipse of British aviation until 1908–10; for it was on December 8th, 1896, that the great English scientist Lord Kelvin, who could easily have satisfied himself of the progress of aviation, wrote: "I have not the smallest molecule of faith in aerial navigation other than ballooning, or of expectation of good results from any of the trials we hear of. So you will understand that I would not care to be a member of the Aeronautical Society."

6

THE FORERUNNERS
Lilienthal
(1891–96)

The key figure in aviation during the last decade of the century, and one of the greatest men in the history of flying, was the German Otto Lilienthal (1848–96). His work led directly to the Wright brothers, whom he resembled in his balanced concern with theory and practice, and he was also the inspiration for many other pioneers. He was a man who, from the first, was determined to get up in the air and fly; and all his models, tests and research were directed to that practical end. His influence was climacteric.

After experimenting with ornithopters, he published in 1889 what became one of the classics of aviation, *Der Vogelflug als Grundlage der Fliegekunst* (Bird Flight as the Basis of Aviation), in which he examined in detail the types and structure of bird wings, the method and aerodynamics of bird flight, and the application of the data gained — especially that dealing with wing area and lift — to the problem of human flight. He was also one of the few investigators, after Cayley, who properly demonstrated that a bird produces thrust by the propeller action of its outer primary feathers. Lilienthal's book was to become one of the chief bibles for the aeronautical world after he demonstrated that his theories could be put into practice. The fact that he concentrated too much on the canopied forms of bird wings at the expense of less natural forms of cambered aerofoil, and that his figures had to be revised later, did nothing to diminish the energising effect which his book, and then his gliding, had on the aviators to come. It was the basis on which the Wrights first started building their aerodynamic work, and they were always high in praise of its pioneering value, even when they were led to modify Lilienthal's findings.

Lilienthal built and flew his first fixed-wing glider in 1891. He thereafter arrived at a more or less standard type of monoplane glider by 1893–94 (Figs. A, B). He also constructed three successful biplane gliders in 1895–96 (Figs. D, E, F). He flew from an artificial hill he had made at what is now Lichterfelde-Ost (Berlin), and from natural heights, especially the Stöllner Hills near Rhinow. In all his gliders the pilot was supported in the centre section frame by his arms, leaving his hips and legs dangling below the aircraft after he had run forward for take-off. Control and stability were effected entirely by

[23]

A. Lilienthal standard glider: 1894

B. Lilienthal standard glider: 1894

C. Lilienthal powered machine flown
as glider: 1894

D. Lilienthal biplane glider: 1895

E. Lilienthal biplane glider: 1895

F. Lilienthal biplane glider: 1895

(Lilienthal is piloting in all the above photographs)

swinging the body in any desired direction — forwards, backwards or sideways — and thus shifting the centre of gravity. From 1893 these "hang-gliders" had cambered wings with radiating ribs — which could be folded for transport — with a fixed rear fin and a tailplane freely hinging upwards to avoid (he hoped) the tail being forced up, and the machine put into a nose dive. With these machines, Lilienthal could make glides ranging from some 300 to over 750 feet, and succeeded in achieving a remarkable degree of control in flight, considering the limitations of the method.

In 1895 he tested — unsuccessfully — a leading-edge flap device to counteract air pressure on the vaulted upper surfaces of the wings, as well as steering air-brakes, and a form of wing-warping. At the time of his death he was developing a body-harness elevator control to augment his body movements.

But his most important departure from the lines he had been working along was the building and testing — with limited success — of a glider with ornithoptering wing-tips operated by a small carbonic acid gas motor (Fig. C). This strange retention of his boyhood ambition, at a time when petrol-motors and propellers were clearly destined to be used in flying machines, marks Lilienthal's historic position as the culminator of the nineteenth-century's efforts in practical flying, as well as the precipitator of the conquering period to come. Before he could develop this powered glider, he crashed in the Stöllner Hills on August 9th, 1896, and died next day in a Berlin clinic. One of his oft-repeated remarks is tragically appropriate here: "Opfer müssen gebracht werden" (sacrifices must be made).

It is hard to over-estimate the vital force which this great pioneer injected into aviation, as much after his tragic death as before. His influence was universal and profound. Extracts from his technical writings were translated and read by all who were convinced that mechanical flight would one day be accomplished; and the overall effect of his work was greatly increased when his successful flights were well photographed, and were published in books and periodicals the world over by means of the then new method of half-tone reproduction, and other techniques. These photographs, and the information which accompanied them, also demonstrated forcibly that it was necessary and possible for a man to be launched into the air and fly — despite the lack of an engine — in order to gain essential experience in the design and flight control of aeroplanes.

THE FORERUNNERS
1896–1901

Before bringing to a close these sections on the nineteenth-century forerunners of aviation, there is a most important automobile date to note: in 1896 the popularity of the new "horseless carriages" had become so widespread that in France and Great Britain they were at last granted the legal freedom of the roads (Fig. A). This led to a vast expansion of the industry, and to the acceptance of the motor-car as an essential means of transport the world over. Automobilism was to produce the necessary reservoir of trained mechanics which was soon to be needed by aviation, and many of its drivers who had taken "mechanically" to the road for sport and adventure, were to take to the air in search of yet new fields. Equally important was the new impetus given to the petrol engine, which now developed more rapidly than ever.

Lilienthal's work directly precipitated the crowning phase of aviation, during which the air was conquered by powered heavier-than-air machines. He directly inspired a number of imitators and emulators, the most important of whom were Percy Pilcher in Britain, Octave Chanute in the United States, and Captain F. Ferber in France.

Lilienthal's work was also to be the direct inspiration of the Wright brothers, but (as will be noted later) they decided from the first to depart from his practice of favouring hang-gliders.

In Scotland there had already arisen the only man who by temperament, training and achievement could have anticipated the Wrights in powered flying. Percy Pilcher built his first Lilienthal-inspired glider in 1895. After twice visiting Lilienthal in Germany, and flying his machines, Pilcher struck out on his own; but he retained much of Lilienthal's configuration and technique, especially in his decision to continue with the "hang" type of glider. In 1896 Pilcher built and flew successfully his most advanced glider, the Hawk (Fig. C): with its wheeled undercarriage and tow-line take-off, it was a much handier aircraft than the Lilienthal gliders, and he made excellent glides of up to some 250 yards. Then, just as he had completed a light oil engine and designed a special machine to be powered by it, he was killed gliding in September 1899. Pilcher did not influence aviation history, as he was working in an all but isolated position in Britain. After his death, British efforts in practical aviation virtually ceased: a whole

[26]

A. Automobiles gain the freedom of the roads: 1896

Chanute Lilienthal-type glider: 1896

C. Pilcher glider (*The Hawk*): 1896

D. Chanute biplane glider: 1896

E. Ferber Lilienthal-type glider: 1901

decade was to pass — 1899–1909 — before even the most primitive British-designed aeroplane could take to the air.

One of the outstanding figures of aviation history was the eminent American civil engineer Octave Chanute (1832–1910), whose importance was threefold: he was the world's chief disseminator of aeronautical information; he finalised the Lilienthal-type hang-glider in biplane form; and he was the most valued encourager of the Wright brothers. Chanute had become interested in aeronautics about 1878, not — as previously thought — after meeting Wenham. At intervals in a very busy life he collected every piece of information available on the earlier history of aviation and on the experiments being conducted in France and England. After sifting and assessing this wealth of material, he wrote a series of articles which he revised and republished in book form in 1894, at New York, entitled *Progress in Flying Machines*. This classic work became, after Lilienthal's *Vogelflug*, the second bible of flying. It presented to would-be experimenters, for the first time, the whole picture of aviation up to date, so that any aviation pioneer could appreciate what had already been accomplished and what directions there were to take in the future. Then, in 1896–97 (inspired by Lilienthal) Chanute publicly exhorted inventors to build full-size gliders and get up into the air to experiment. Although too old to fly himself — he was then sixty-four — he designed and had built a number of man-carrying gliders, and assisted by A. M. Herring and W. Avery, who co-operated in the design of the machines and acted as pilots. Chanute's chief work was accomplished in those years, 1896–97, when the tests of his gliders were made on the south shore of Lake Michigan, near Chicago.

Chanute's ambition was to achieve an inherently stable aeroplane — "an apparatus with automatic stability in the wind" — and to this end, after unsatisfactory results with his first glider (a Lilienthal-type) in 1896 (Fig. B), he built in the same year his "multiple-wing" glider, in which — restrained by rubber — the wings could swing backwards in the horizontal plane under sudden air pressure, in order to adjust the centre of pressure.

Before coming to his classic biplane glider, we may note his "oscillating-wing" triplane glider of 1902, in which the collective angle of incidence of the wings was reduced under sudden air pressure by being pivoted spanwise.

But it was his "two-surface" hang-glider that was to become famous (Fig. D). This was a biplane with wings braced on the Pratt-truss system, with added pendulum stability given by the pilot hanging well below the wings, with his arms on "rail" supports which allowed him to still further adjust the position of the centre of gravity. This would-be stable machine had a fixed cruciform tail-unit, with rubber spring attachments to allow up-and-down flexibility and act as a gust-damper. It was the most successful glider before the Wrights, and made some 700 safe flights of up to 350 ft.

Chanute is wrongly credited with various achievements and ideas (which he himself never even claimed), which have unfortunately gained wide currency. What is now established may be summarised as follows: (1) he aimed at as high a degree of inherent stability as possible ("automatic equilibrium exclusively"); (2) he had the control exercised in both types of glider in the Lilienthal manner, by the pilot swinging his body — although he aimed at reducing the necessary movements by incorporating various types of flexible surfaces to act as gust-dampers; (3) he never used hinged or otherwise movable pilot-operated elevators or rudders; (4) his only major technical contribution to aviation was his excellent bridge-truss method of rigging a biplane; (5) his powerful indirect influence on aviation was in his encouragement, propaganda, and dissemination of information; (6) he intended ultimately to apply power to his gliders, but he did not proceed with the idea.

During his work with Chanute, Herring slightly modified and improved the biplane, but did not materially advance matters. Chanute himself went on to build and test an interesting triplane glider in 1902; but by this time his work was away from the main stream. But, in 1900, at the age of sixty-eight, he had assumed two new and important roles in aviation. In that year the Wright brothers made contact with him: thereafter, for some years, he remained their most trusted confidant and friend. Although he did not contribute anything technically vital to their work, except his bridge-truss method of rigging a biplane, he quickly realised their true merit, and spared no pains — through voluminous correspondence and several meetings — in advising, assisting and encouraging them in everything they did, even to offering financial assistance, which was gracefully declined. "In patience and goodness of heart he has rarely been surpassed", wrote Wilbur Wright, "few men were more universally respected and loved." In 1903, as will be described in detail later, Chanute went to Paris and gave to the Aéro-Club de France an illustrated lecture on his own and the Wrights' gliding. This, together with his own and others' reportage of the lecture, had the extraordinary effect of reviving single handed, so to say, the entire European aviation movement which resulted in the first practical powered aeroplanes on the Continent and in England. Octave Chanute was the most remarkable and productive "middle-man" in the history of flying; his influence was always for the good, and always with the assured faith that mechanical flight would soon be achieved.

The least successful imitator of Lilienthal, who came late on the scene, was the French Captain F. Ferber. For reasons now hard to understand — for ample illustrations and information were available — Ferber constructed a primitive Lilienthal-type glider in 1901, with which he made tentative tests (Fig. E). But, astonishingly enough, Ferber was the only significant aeroplane pioneer active in Europe at the turn of the century, where aviation was all but moribund. But next year (1902) it was to be through Ferber that Europe was to receive the impetus of the Wright brothers, and undergo its slow revival of heavier-than-air flying (see Appendix V).

PS. Pilcher was the first aviator (heavier-than-air pilot) to be killed in Britain. In the same year (1899) the first automobile driver (and his passenger) was killed in Britain, at Harrow: this was E. R. Sewell.

8

The Years 1900–07:
BALLOONS AND AIRSHIPS

At the turn of the century the prospect of achieving a practical powered aeroplane in Europe seemed very remote, and although one or two ingenious inventors were striving for such an ideal (see next section) their efforts were isolated and unsuccessful. Both technical and popular attention was still mainly focussed on the free balloon, until — quite suddenly in 1901 — the Continent became vividly aware of the airship.This awareness may be said to have germinated in 1898, with the first airship built and flown in France by a wealthy ex-patriate Brazilian, Alberto Santos-Dumont, who may fairly be described as a talented amateur aeronaut and, later, aviator. He and his small pressure-ships became growingly familiar to the Parisian public, and the international world of flying.

The first Zeppelin was launched, and flew tentatively, in 1900 (Fig. A) but it did not create much general interest at the time. Then in 1901, Santos-Dumont, in his airship No. 6 (Fig. B) circumnavigated the Eiffel Tower and won not only the Deutsch prize but world-wide popularity and renown. It was Santos-Dumont who, newly and single-handed, thus made Europe "air-minded". This was a Europe well used to balloons, but not to any form of powered aerial navigation.

By 1903 Europe was not only thoroughly air-minded regarding airships, but more than ever aware of aerial "voyaging" as such, by virtue of the now vigorous revival of free ballooning, and its patronage by the wealthy and influential, from about the year 1901. The Aéro-Club de France (founded in 1898) and more especially the Aero Club — later Royal — of Great Britain (founded in 1901), made ballooning fashionable: one of the British club's meetings is shown in Fig. D.

It was in 1903 that the airship first reached a practical stage — Santos' ships could never be described as truly practical — with the French Lebaudy (Fig. C): this dirigible, of 80,000 cu. ft. had been built in 1902, and "matured" in 1903, when it made a successful controlled flight of 38 miles at some 14 m.p.h. on November 12th, and so inaugurated the modern airship epoch.

The Zeppelin was not to achieve a practical stage until the LZ–3 of 1906, after which — despite some setbacks — both civil and military Zeppelins attained a well-deserved success.

The revival of ballooning (widespread until 1910) and the advent of

[31]

A. The first Zeppelin: 1900

B. Santos-Dumont No. 6: 1901

C. Lebaudy dirigible: 1902–3

D. Balloon meeting at Hurlingham: 1908

[32]

the airship, attracted many talented men to the cause of aeronautics, and the air came to share much of the sporting stage with "auto-mobilisme". Both spheres were to prove of vital service to the aero-plane when it arrived, for they supplied most of the pilots, mechanics and patronage that were necessary to the conquest of the air by the powered flying machine.

9

SURVEY OF THE WRIGHT BROTHERS

On December 17th, 1903, the Wright Brothers were the first men in history to make powered, sustained and controlled flights in an aeroplane; both the new machine — Flyer I — and engine were of their own design and construction. The longest of four flights lasted 59 seconds and covered over half a mile through the air. This achievement followed three years during which the brothers had developed and perfected the design, construction and pilotage of gliders.

In 1904, in the second of their powered "Flyers" as they called them — Flyer II — they made about eighty brief flights, including some turns and a few complete circles, the longest lasting just over five minutes, in order to discover and master the basic techniques of controlling a powered machine.

In 1905, the Wrights completed and flew their third Flyer — Flyer III — which was the world's first practical powered aeroplane; during more than forty flights the machine was repeatedly banked, turned, circled and flown in figures of eight; on two occasions it exceeded half an hour in flight duration.

It was in 1902 and 1903 that illustrated information about the Wrights' successful gliding reached France, and directly precipitated the first stage of the revival of European aviation at a time when it was virtually at a standstill, following Lilienthal's death in 1896. The series of events which gave rise to this vital influence on the Europeans is fully documented and established (see Appendix V).

In August of 1908, Wilbur Wright started flying in France, and thereby directly precipitated the second — and decisive — phase of European powered aviation; this resulted chiefly from his demonstrating the technique of proper flight control, especially of lateral control, an essential accomplishment which the slowly developing Continental pioneers, and the A.E.A. in America, had largely neglected.

By character and temperament the Wrights were admirably equipped for their work, being possessed of modesty, pertinacity and a richly inventive talent: in addition, they trained themselves to become both expert engineers and pilots, concerned equally with the theoretical and practical aspects of aviation. They drew their initial inspiration to fly from Lilienthal, and later absorbed a general knowledge of the history and state of their craft; but when it came to the

[34]

specific problems of design and construction — including engines and airscrews — and the pilotage of both gliders and powered aeroplanes, they had to discard much of the accepted data and start virtually afresh.

It is also important to note — albeit with the wisdom of hindsight — three of the Wrights' mistakes, which are dealt with more fully in the Notes. The first of these was in deliberately adopting an inherently unstable machine, instead of a compromise between sensitivity of control and inherent stability. The second was the adoption and retention of the forward elevator, which is always far less satisfactory than a rear one, although there was a good reason for their having such a forward surface in their early days of gliding. The third mistake was to retain the skid undercarriage and accelerated take-off device long after they had outlived their usefulness.

But all great pioneers make mistakes, most of them making many — and often serious — mistakes; but the common denominator of such men is that they make their inventions work; they drive them through to success, despite defects and shortcomings. Their ideas, techniques and configurations are, whatever their faults, workable and successful. This was the case with the Wright brothers. As we see it today, they did not adopt a good configuration, but it was a workable configuration, and a cohesive one, and they triumphed with it. They mastered the theory and practice of aviation, construction and flight control, and — amazingly enough — added the mastery of design and construction of both propellers and engines. No other aviation pioneers came anywhere near such accomplishments.

Mention should now be made here of occasional — but vociferous — claims that some machine or other made a powered flight before the Wrights, the criterion of "flight" being in every claim reduced to the level of absurdity. Such claims are little more than frivolous, and have never been countenanced by any reputable historian: they have been dealt with in detail by the present writer in his Science Museum handbook, *The Aeroplane: an Historical Survey* (in the Commentary, etc.). In this connection it is also worth mentioning that the Wrights' absolute priority in proper powered flight would not be affected in the least, even if their brief flights of 1903 be discounted, as no powered machines other than theirs could remain in the air for more than 20 seconds until November 1906; and it was not until November of 1907 that a full minute's flight duration was attained in Europe. The achievements of the Wright brothers were paramount: to them, and them alone, belongs the credit of inventing, building, and flying the first successful and practical powered aeroplanes in history.

[35]

SURVEY OF THE WRIGHT BROTHERS

The Wright brothers were the sons of a United Brethren Church bishop, and lived at Dayton, Ohio. They had progressed from the selling of bicycles to their manufacture, and thereby made a comfortable living; this business alone provided the funds for their aviation. Their boyhood interest in flying dated from 1878, when their father bought them a helicopter model; but it was the work and death of Lilienthal (1896) that focused their mature attention on aviation. In their subsequent study of bird flight, and of Lilienthal's gliding, they became fully alive to the inefficiency of the latter's method of seeking balance and control solely by body-movements, as well as to the bird's effortless mastery of these problems. They were not, of course, aware of Lilienthal's experiments with warping, which in any case were never conceived of by him in relation to rudder control. Then in 1899* the Wrights made their first two decisive discoveries; (*a*) they observed that gliding and soaring birds, evidenced especially by their local "expert" the buzzard, "regain their lateral balance . . . by a torsion of the tips of the wings"; and (*b*) decided to apply this bird-practice to aeroplane wings. At first they conceived the idea — but abandoned it for structural reasons — of pivoting the wings so that one produced more lift than the normal angle of incidence, and the other (simultaneously) less: then they hit on the technique of a helical twisting of the wings ("warping"), after toying with a long cardboard box. The Wrights' "basic idea was the adjustment of the wings to the right and left sides to different angles so as to secure different lifts on the opposite wings" (Orville): the bare idea, as such, of this adjustment had been previously envisaged, but had never been applied successfully in practice, and never even imagined in combined action with the rudder, as the Wrights were soon both to envisage and accomplish successfully.

* The exact year is still a matter of controversy, but the evidence suggests 1899.

10

THE WRIGHT BROTHERS
1899–1901

Like Lilienthal, the Wrights were true airmen and were determined to get up into the air and fly; but they were also determined to methodically master control in the air on gliders before attempting any experiments with powered machines. They decided to follow Chanute in adopting a biplane configuration: but the general method of biplane bracing was the only technical debt they owed to Chanute.

The Wrights built their first aircraft in August 1899: it was a biplane kite of 5 ft. span, designed to test the efficacy of their technique of wing-warping, but with the added feature of wings which could be shifted forward or backward in relation to one another in order to control the movement of the centre of pressure (Fig. A): there was also a fixed tailplane which, by virtue of its bracing, moved up and down with the shifting of the wings fore and aft, and acted as a semi-elevator.

The effect of the warping was a success, and the brothers decided to build their first full-size glider: this was completed by September 1900 (Fig. B). It was a biplane of 17 ft. span and 165 sq. ft. area, but with a proper elevator ("horizontal rudder") placed out front: there was warping, but no shifting forward or backward of the wings. They mistakenly believed that a front elevator would provide a safer fore-and-aft control than a rear one, especially in the event of a sudden nose-down attitude. The pilot lay prone to reduce head-resistance. Owing to the small wing area, this No. 1 glider was flown (in October 1900) chiefly as an unmanned kite with its controls operated from the ground: only a few manned "pilot-controlled" kite-flights were made, as well as a few piloted free glides. These tests took place over the sand dunes of Kitty Hawk (North Carolina), a desolate location chosen not for its secrecy but for its steady constant winds, along with the soft sand into which crashing would be comparatively painless. They had tried rigging this glider with a dihedral angle for automatic lateral stability, but found it flew badly and was not readily controllable in gusty conditions. So the dihedral was abandoned and seldom used by them again. There was also no inherent longitudinal stability by means of fixed horizontal surfaces.

The basic configuration they had now adopted — with forward elevator and no longitudinal stabilising surface — was a *workable*

[37]

10. THE WRIGHT BROTHERS: 1899–1901

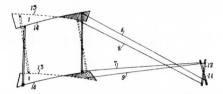

A. Wright biplane kite (shown without the tailplane-cum-elevator): 1899

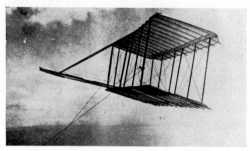

B. Wright No. 1 glider: 1900

C. Wright No. 2 glider: 1901

A. Wright No. 3 glider (first form), with fixed fins: 1902

B. Wright No. 3 glider (modified), with rudder, Wilbur piloting: 1902

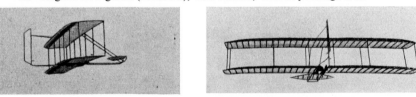

C, D. Wright No. 3 glider (modified) in flight: 1902

E. Launching the Wright No. 3 glider (modified), Orville piloting: 1902

configuration, but far from a satisfactory one; but they wisely "stayed with it" and made a success of it, rather than chop and change and bring nothing to fruition.

Encouraged by their experience with the No. 1, the Wrights were more determined than ever to fly; but they were still determined to proceed carefully and logically. Next year (1901) they built their No. 2 glider (Fig. C), following the same basic configuration as No. 1, but with a wing area increased to 290 sq. ft., a span of 22 ft., a wing camber of 1 in 12, and — for the first time — an anhedral "droop" of 4 in.; also for the first time a hip-cradle was introduced (swung to right or left) to operate the warping cables. They took this new glider to the Kill Devil (sand) Hills, 4 miles south of Kitty Hawk, and tested it in piloted flight during July and August 1901. Finding the wing camber too pronounced (with the centre of pressure moving too rapidly backwards at small angles of attack) they reduced it to 1 in 19, and so improved its performance; glides of up to 389 ft. were made, and control was maintained in winds of up to some 27 m.p.h. But the machine was far from satisfactory.

11

THE WRIGHT BROTHERS
1902

The Wrights began to doubt the accuracy of Lilienthal's calculations, upon which they had relied until now. The 1901 machine had also shown an alarming tendency — when being warped — for the positively warped wings to swing *back*, and for the whole machine to slew round as it side-slipped, and to crash. "Having set out with absolute faith in the existing scientific data", wrote Wilbur, "we were driven to doubt one thing after another till finally, after two years of experiment, we cast it all aside, and decided to rely entirely upon our own investigations."

Between September 1901 and August 1902, the Wrights carried out intensive research, including a thorough re-working of all their aerodynamic problems. The result was their No. 3 glider, built during August and September 1902, and tested at the Kill Devil Hills during September and October. Nearly 1,000 glides were made on this machine. It had a wing area of 305 sq. ft., a span of 32 ft. 1 in., and a shallow camber of 1 in 24 to 1 in 30; the same warping system; the same anhedral droop; and the same type of forward elevator, as the No. 2; but added at the rear was a double fixed fin to counteract (by its weather-vane action) the swing-back of the wings on the positively warped side, in the case either of regaining lateral balance after being gusted out of the horizontal, or of the pilot initiating a bank (Fig. A). The machine was man-launched like its predecessor, and behaved well in some of the glides; but severe trouble arose with deliberate warped banks or gust-produced (non-warped) banks, when the pilot — in trying to hold off the bank or return to the horizontal — applied positive warp to the dropped wings in order to raise them: instead of coming up, these dropped wings would sink or swing back, and the machine would spin and crash.

The Wrights diagnosed the basic trouble as warp-drag (aileron-drag today) where the positive warp increased the resistance of the wings on that side, and the negative warp decreased it on the other, causing them not only to bank, but to turn about their vertical axis in the opposite direction to that originally anticipated. The addition of the fixed fin caused more trouble than it cured. For, in the two classes of banking noted above, the resulting side-slip caused the fin to act as a lever, and rotate the wings about their vertical axis, thus increasing the speed (and thus the lift and height) of the raised side, whilst retarding and lowering the dropped wings. When the pilot applied positive warp on the dropped side, it aggravated the situation, and produced a spin either by swinging back the dropped wings through warp-drag, or by increasing their incidence beyond the stalling angle.

This problem was solved by converting the double fixed fin into a single movable rudder, which — with its cables fastened to the warp-cradle — was always turned towards the warping direction, thus counteracting the warp-drag (Figs. B to E). As the rudder was also (but unintentionally) adjusted to more than compensate for the warp-drag, the machine could also be made to perform a smooth banked turn. Experience with this glider also — unfortunately — persuaded the Wrights that all their machines should be made inherently unstable, to allow of maximum sensitivity and immediate response to the controls: the Wright machines had therefore to be "flown" all the time.

After this vital step, the Wrights had a fully practical glider — the first in history — and with it made some hundreds of perfectly controlled glides.

12

LANGLEY
1901–03

After the success of his steam-driven models in 1896, Langley had intended to give up his experiments and leave further development to others. But in 1898, with the outbreak of the war with Spain, he was asked by his Government to build (with official funds) a full-size Aerodrome, in view of its military possibilities. It is significant that such enlightened patronage could be offered to the generally laughed-at idea of the man-carrying aeroplane, now that a man of Langley's status had taken it up. Langley agreed, and first constructed a quarter-sized model (1901) powered by a small petrol engine, the first petrol-powered aeroplane ever to fly (Fig. A). The man-carrying machine was completed in 1903: it had a span of 48 ft., a wing area of 1,040 sq. ft., and was powered by a remarkably light 52 h.p. radial petrol engine built by Langley's engineer, C. M. Manly, but owing much to its original designer, S. M. Balzer (Fig. D). Two trials, with Manly as pilot, were attempted over the Potomac river (on October 7th and December 8th, 1903), but on both occasions the Aerodrome fouled the launching mechanism — a catapult device atop a house-boat — and plunged into the river, Manly being rescued unhurt in both tests (Figs. B, C). Langley was now subjected to much sympathy and much criticism; but the government lost faith in him and withdrew its financial support, and the whole project was abandoned. In view of the Wright brothers' success on December 17th of that year, it is interesting to consider whether the Aerodrome was at least potentially the world's first successful aeroplane. Technical opinion today views Langley's machine as unsatisfactory and badly underpowered, despite Curtiss' claims after the deplorable story of its secret alteration by him, and the trials of 1914. Langley, in some ways like Maxim, suffered from being "chauffeur-minded", and not basically interested in practical flying; he lacked the flexibility of mind necessary for such a novel sphere of endeavour. He studied the problems of lift, drag, and inherent stability for fourteen years — the Wrights took only four — but was not interested in flight control, and never made gliding experiments; he thus neglected the practical aspects of structure and control. Finally, and also due to his theoretical preoccupations, he made the tragic and incomprehensible blunder of risking the whole enterprise — and his pilot's life — by catapult launchings

[43]

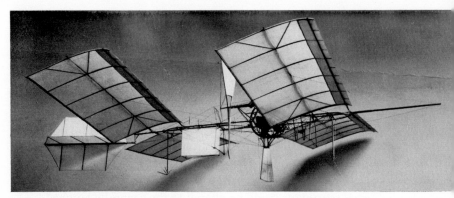

A. Langley quarter-size petrol-driven "Aerodrome": 1901

B. Langley full-size "Aerodrome" on the launching catapult: 1903

C. First unsuccessful launch of full-size "Aerodrome": October 7th, 1903

D. Balzer-Manly radial engine: 1903

over water, when by using a wheeled or skid undercarriage and a flat field he could safely have experimented at his leisure.

Langley exerted a general influence for good on his contemporaries, as his position in the world of science — he was the honoured Secretary of the Smithsonian Institution — made the subject of flying seem almost respectable in an otherwise sceptical environment. Although his models were successful in their limited sphere, his ultimate influence on aviation was slight.

P.S. There has been a firmly held opinion by a number of engineers that Langley's Aerodrome did not actually foul the launching mechanism itself, but broke up under the aerodynamic stresses of the launching owing to its weak structure.

13

THE WRIGHT BROTHERS
1903

Justly elated by the success of their last glider, the brothers (in March 1903) applied for a patent based on it: this was granted in 1906. They had already determined to build a powered aeroplane — they did not, as so often said, put an engine into one of their gliders — and this machine was constructed during the summer of 1903. But they had had to surmount two formidable obstacles before their first "Flyer" (the name they gave to all their powered machines) was ready for testing; (a) the lack of any light, yet powerful enough, engine; (b) the provision of propellers. They thereupon designed and built their own 12 h.p. motor; and — an outstanding achievement — carried out basic and original research to produce highly efficient airscrews.

This first Wright Flyer — Wright Flyer I — was a biplane, on a skid undercarriage, of 40 ft. 4 in. span, a wing area of 510 sq. ft., and a camber of 1 in 20: it had a biplane elevator out front, and a double rudder behind, whose control cables were linked to the warp-cradle: the motor drove two geared-down pusher airscrews through a cycle-chain transmission in tubes, one being crossed to produce counter-rotation (Figs. A–C). The launching technique was as follows: the Flyer's skids were laid on a yoke which could run freely on two small tandem wheels along a 60-foot sectioned wooden rail, laid down into wind; the machine was tethered whilst the engine was run up, and then unleashed; when its speed produced sufficient lift, it rose from the yoke and flew. The Wrights did not use any accelerated take-off device for their 1903 flights: this device was first used in 1904.

14

THE WRIGHT BROTHERS
1903–04

After minor but exasperating set-backs at the Kill Devil Hills, and after brushing up their piloting on the 1902 glider — now fitted with a double rudder — the first attempt was made on December 14th, 1903, with Wilbur at the controls (he had won the toss of a coin): but owing to over-correction with the elevator, the Flyer ploughed into the sand immediately after take-off (Fig. A).

It was on the morning of Thursday, December 17th, 1903, between 10.30 a.m. and noon, that the first flights were made. After five local witnesses had arrived, Orville — whose turn it now was — took off at 10.35 into a 20–22 m.p.h. wind and flew for 12 seconds, covering 120 ft. of ground, and over 500 ft. in air distance (Fig. B). On the fourth and last flight, at noon, Wilbur flew for 59 seconds, covering 852 ft. and over half a mile in air distance. These flights were the first in the history of the world in which a piloted machine had taken off under its own power; had made powered, controlled, and sustained flights; and had landed on ground as high as that from which it had taken off.

This historic first Flyer — following a most regrettable attack on the Wrights — was loaned to the Science Museum, London, from 1928 to 1948. It is now preserved in the National Air Museum (Smithsonian Institution) at Washington, D. C.

The second Flyer — Flyer II — was finished in May 1904; and, through the kindness of their friend Torrence Huffman, an aerodrome was set up at the Huffman Prairie, a 90-acre pasture at Simms Station, about eight miles east of Dayton. The new Flyer had approximately the same dimensions as the first, but had a lesser camber (1 in 20 to 1 in 25) and a new engine of 15–16 h.p.: the pilot still lay prone, and the warp and rudder controls were still linked. From May 23rd to December 9th, some 100 starts were made, and various minor set-backs had to be overcome before consistent and productive flights were achieved: about 80 short flights (Fig. C) resulted from these starts, and the brothers' total airborne time during this 1904 season was about 45 minutes, the longest flight lasting for 5 min. 4 sec. and covering about $2\frac{3}{4}$ miles (November 9th).

On September 7th they introduced for the first time their weight-and-derrick assisted take-off device, to make them independent of the weather, in view of the small area of the pasture, The most important

[47]

A. Wright powered Flyer I (side-view) at the Kill Devil Hills: December 1903

B. Wright powered Flyer I (front view) at the Kill Devil Hills: December 1903

C. Wright powered Flyer I of 1903, when on loan to the Science Museum, London

A. Wright powered Flyer I, after the first — unsuccessful — test (Wilbur piloting):
December 14th, 1903

B. First flight of the Wright powered Flyer I (Orville piloting):
December 17th, 1903

C. Wright Flyer II in flight at the Huffman Prairie (Orville piloting):
November 16th, 1904

[49]

event was their first circuit (by Wilbur on September 20th); this first circuit was the subject of a detailed eye-witness report made and published by Amos I. Root — the first eye-witness report in history of a powered aeroplane flight.* But there was one control problem still outstanding — not to be solved until 1905 — a tendency to stall in tight turns.

It had been early in this 1904 season that two press visits took place: had not the engine failed on both occasions, the history of aviation — and indeed of civilisation itself — might have been transformed. The reporters never came back, despite continual reports by local residents during 1904 and 1905.

* Root's report is reprinted in full in GS-A.

15

The Years 1901–04:
POWERED EXPERIMENTS IN EUROPE

Three dogged but unsuccessful European pioneers — standing outside the main stream of history — deserve particular mention for their work in powered aviation during the opening years of this century: but their work did not influence the course of aviation. The first, isolated in Austria, was Wilhelm Kress who had been experimenting with rubber-driven models since 1877. In 1898–99, curiously paralleling Langley's models, he constructed a full-size man-carrying aeroplane on floats: it was a tandem three-wing machine with rear elevator and rudder, powered by an over-heavy petrol engine driving two propellers (Figs. A and B). Kress had to wait until October 1901 to test it: then, unfortunately, the machine was capsized and wrecked by too sharp a turn while taxying on the Tullnerbach Reservoir before any flight test could be made. Although ingenious, it did not influence the course of aviation.

In Germany, a name comparatively new to aeronautical history has recently emerged — Karl Jatho — to take a small place in the early history of the aeroplane, but did not influence aviation. Jatho was a civil servant in Hanover, and in 1903 completed what was little more than a large powered kite: it had a 9 h.p. petrol engine and a primitive pusher propeller, but there were neither tail-unit nor controls forward of the "planes", and only rudimentary rudder and elevator devices (Fig. C). On August 18th he made a "running jump" claimed to be 18 m.; then in November, with the structure modified to biplane form, the machine made another hop of 60 m. These tests took place on the Vahrenwalder Heide, north of Hanover: they are not claimed as true flights, even in Germany, where the word "Flugsprung" (leap into the air) has been used for them: he therefore may make the minor claim to be the first German to leave the ground in a powered aeroplane, although Lilienthal flew in a power-assisted glider. (*P.S.* It is thought the take-offs were down-hill.)

Third, there reappears the Englishman Horatio Phillips, whose important work on cambered aerofoils and his large model of 1893 were noted in Section 5. In 1904 he tested a multi-wing machine (Fig. D) comprising 20 "slat-wings" similar to his 1893 model: it was fitted with a 22 h.p. engine driving a tractor propeller and weighed, with pilot, 600 lbs. The machine lifted at a velocity of 50 ft. p. sec., but its

[51]

A. Kress tandem-wing floatplane on the Tullnerbach reservoir: 1901

B. Kress floatplane (ditto): 1901

C. Jatho semi-biplane: 1903

D. Phillips multiplane: 1904

longitudinal equilibrium was deficient and it was unsuccessful in its tests. Phillips' last machine of 1907 is noted in Section 31.

None of these men exercised any influence on aviation history with these machines, but Phillips had, of course, previously made highly important contributions to the development of aerodynamics.

16

SURVEY OF THE REVIVAL
OF EUROPEAN AVIATION:
1901–04

The years 1902–04 saw the revival of European aviation, moribund since the death of Lilienthal in 1896. As already noted, there were sporadic attempts at primitive powered flying by such men as Kress in Austria (1901) Jatho in Germany (1903), and Phillips in England (1904): but each was isolated, each was a failure, and none contributed to the progress of aviation.

The true revival of aviation in Europe was due directly to the Wright brothers, as is clear both from the configurations adopted and from the numerous contemporary statements by the pioneers themselves. The revival was effected through the work of four Frenchmen in 1902–04, and resulted in two parallel streams of development of the biplane; and later in the revival and development of the monoplane.

The Wrights precipitated the European revival in two phases, the one reinforcing the other. First to be influenced was Captain F. Ferber, of the French artillery, the only European disciple of Lilienthal still seriously pursuing aviation in 1901: he was experimenting with a hang-glider derived from the great German pioneer. Then, about October 1901, he happened to read a magazine article on gliding: this led to a correspondence with Chanute in America and, in January 1902, to Ferber receiving from him a reprint of Wilbur Wright's first Chicago lecture (given on September 18th, 1901) describing and illustrating the Nos. 1 and 2 Wright gliders of 1900 and 1901. This paper proved decisive for Ferber and thus for European aviation: for he thereupon abandoned the Lilienthal-type glider, and adopted the Wright-type, *i.e.* the 1901 type with forward elevator but no rudder or other tail surface. This was Europe's first Wright-type glider, but it was crudely constructed and did not even incorporate wing-warping. In *L'Aérophile* for February 1903, this machine was well described and illustrated. It was the first piloted Wright-type glider to be properly "seen" by the Europeans (see Appendix V).

In March 1903 Octave Chanute arrived on a visit to Europe, and on April 2nd gave an illustrated talk in Paris at a "diner-conférence" of the Aéro-Club de France, describing in detail his own and the Wrights' gliders; but this time it was the sophisticated No. 3 Wright glider in its final form that received most attention, along with the information — but not raison d'être — of the simultaneous use of warping and rudder.

This pivotal lecture was followed by illustrated published reports of it, and fuller articles written by Chanute and others, including (in August) scale drawings of the Wright machine. It was these new revelations of the Wrights' successful gliding — Chanute's own gliders were largely disregarded — and the excellent accompanying photographs and drawings of the Wrights' No. 3 machine, which precipitated the chief revival of aviation in Europe. This revival had as its mainspring and leader the rich lawyer-sportsman, Ernest Archdeacon, who now (1903) created an Aviation Committee in the Aéro-Club de France to promote heavier-than-air flying; the avowed intent was to beat the Wrights in the race to achieve the powered aeroplane.

Although feeling was running high, as contemporary documents make all too clear, Archdeacon, Ferber and their friends seemed strangely complacent, and were content to make haste slowly; and although Ferber modified his machine, and even made tentative powered experiments in 1902–03, Archdeacon did not have his glider built until March of 1904: this was an attempt to copy the modified No. 3 Wright glider of 1902, but had only limited success. Archdeacon was joined in April by the young Gabriel Voisin from Lyon, who was soon to take on the manufacture, piloting and much of the designing, of aircraft derived from this first Archdeacon glider.

The other significant newcomer was the engineer Robert Esnault-Pelterie, who in May 1904 built and tested without success what he wrongly claimed was a true copy of the Wrights' 1902 glider: equally wrongly, he concluded that the Wrights' claim to full success in gliding was unfounded, and their machine unsatisfactory. This led him later in the year to make what he believed were improvements on the Wrights' glider, chief of these being the abandonment of warping, which he said was potentially dangerous structurally, and the introduction of ailerons (actually elevons), the first in history: but neither the elevons nor the machine were successful. The far-reaching results of Esnault-Pelterie's activities are noted later.

Meanwhile, also in 1904, Ferber introduced a new modification of his Wright-type glider which, although he was never to have much success with his own machines, was later to exert a vital and beneficial influence on all aviation to come: for he now abandoned the Wright concept of inherent instability and — while retaining the Wright forward elevator — added a longitudinally stabilising fixed tailplane, and gave dihedral to the wings for lateral stability.

[55]

Ferber had thus revived the century-old European tradition of inherent stability, recommended by Cayley in 1809, and espoused by all subsequent makers of models and designers of man-carriers on the Continent. The Wrights had thus directly inspired this revival of European aviation; yet, as time went on, the French wisely modified the inspiration by way of the earliest of all aeroplane configurations.

But having recorded both the new inspiration and the tradition-inspired modification, as well as the overt imitation of the Wrights by Archdeacon and Esnault-Pelterie, the historian can only view the general situation in Europe with amazement. Contemporary statements show clearly that the impact of Chanute's talk and his articles was profound, and that Archdeacon and his friends were at first genuinely determined to press ahead with gliding, and then powered flight. Next there is the question of what Chanute said, and what he subsequently published. It has often been assumed that he gave only a sketchy idea of the vital machine, the Wrights' modified No. 3 glider; this assumption is quite incorrect. Chanute not only published detailed descriptions, scale drawings, and excellent photographs of the machine in flight, along with descriptions of the elevator, warping and rudder controls; but actually mentioned the simultaneous use of warping and rudder, the key discovery in the Wrights' control system. The only points Chanute did not reveal — because at that time he did not know them — was how this simultaneous application was effected or its aerodynamic raison d'être.

This description by Chanute was part and parcel of his stressing the mastery of flight control achieved by the Wrights, which was then followed by his statement that they would soon proceed to build a powered machine.

The next consideration is the Aéro-Club de France — which Chanute was addressing, and where the leading French pioneers congregated — which could rightly boast a profusion of talent along with ample finance to encourage experimentation.

We now face head-on, so to speak, the following extraordinary and still largely inexplicable state of affairs.

Chanute had expounded clearly, together with his telling photographs, that the necessity for complete control in the air by the pilot was the message of paramount importance presented by the Wrights, and that mastery of glider flight was the essential preliminary to powered flight; he described the mechanisms whereby such mastery of flight control could be obtained, and gave — in his mention of simultaneous use of warping and rudder — a vital clue to the operation of these mechanisms; and he made perfectly clear the necessity for intensive test flying and modifications, before the problems of flight control could be solved and mastered: *yet the Europeans disregarded or misapprehended every one of these points.* Esnault-Pelterie was the only one who attempted lateral control — the others simply dismissed it — but did not seek to understand what it involved, and did not press on and make it effective until he came to produce his powered machines of 1907–09. The neglect of lateral control by the French pioneers up to 1908 was a thoroughgoing neglect up to mid-1906, then a misconception of it until Wilbur Wright first flew in France in August 1908: this neglect was among the more inexcusable features of early French aviation. Although the lack of gliding experience accounts for some of the neglect, it is extraordinary that not one of these pioneers envisaged its vital role long before they started gliding, just as the Wrights did.

None of the Europeans after Lilienthal and Pilcher spent more than an aggregate of a few minutes in the air in any of their gliders, and indeed none of them were ever to achieve a practical glider. No systematic, persistent and progressive study of the problems of glider control was made, hence no one came near to any kind of proficiency in gliding, let alone mastery; none of them thought out and tested the significance of combined warping and rudder movements. The Wrights, in their determination to master control, made over a thousand gliding flights during their three short seasons "in the field" (1900–02), to say nothing of the model tests they made at home. The Europeans had available all the necessary facts and clues in Chanute's articles, and — if they had troubled to read them — in the two excellent Wright papers of 1901 and 1902, which were easily accessible. Yet during the three years since Ferber heard from Chanute (1902–04), the total produce of European endeavours amounted to only some four ineffectual gliders.

The only significant productive move made in Europe was the espousal of inherent stability, especially longitudinal; but the importance even of this was to lie in the future: it was a case of trying to run before they could walk.

Prolonged search among contemporary statements, records and photographs has led to fairly safe conclusions on some aspects; but much of the overall situation poses an insoluble problem, perhaps the most important and baffling problem of early aviation history.

First to be considered is the general attitude and "flight philosophy" in Europe at this time (1902–04): this attitude may be summed up by what, earlier on, I have called the "chauffeur's" attitude to aviation, where the pilot looks upon his machine as a winged automobile to be driven off the ground and steered about the sky, as if it has simply left the flat layer of earth to move in a slightly less flat layer of air. Aerodynamics and control, conceived in such an attitude of mind, was resolved into brute thrust applied to one or more aerofoils, with the maximum of inherent stability and the minimum of control by the pilot, the elevator and the rudder being the only necessary controls. The strange thing about such a flight philosophy is that it should apply only after proper flight control has been achieved: for until the pilot has experienced and can anticipate and control the behaviour of his machine in the air, he cannot decide what is necessary (or possible) to leave to automatic mechanisms and built-in qualities.

The Europeans had now virtually repudiated the real "airman's" attitude, as championed by Lilienthal, and were only willing — some, of course, more than others — to commit themselves to the air with great caution: they did not see themselves as parts of the machines they flew. Their ideal was to drive an aerial automobile rather than to ride a winged horse.

Secondly, they were only half prepared to believe the story of glider mastery which Chanute had reported of the Wrights ("they soon attained almost complete mastery over the inconstancies of the wind") Esnault-Pelterie for example, showed obvious satisfaction in claiming that he had built an exact copy of the Wright glider (when he clearly had not) and that it would not behave as the Wrights said theirs did; therefore, he implied, the Wrights were making false claims when describing their gliding achievements.

Next, and allied to the last point, there was present in France a very evident jealousy of what they half felt the Wrights had achieved, and a somewhat chauvinistic ambition to rival and defeat them: "Will the homeland of the Montgolfiers have the shame of allowing the ultimate discovery of aerial science to be realised abroad?" asked Archdeacon in April 1903. "The aeroplane must not be allowed to be perfected in America" cried Ferber: to which the editor of the widely-read L'Aérophile added the significant exhortation, "there is still time, but let us not lose a moment".

Fourthly, there is no doubt that the Europeans, to a man, greatly underestimated the complexities of learning to design, build and fly an aeroplane: they had simplified the whole subject in their minds to such a degree that they felt, now that the Americans were getting up in the air in gliders, they would do the same in no time at all, and then progress easily to the triumph of powered flight.

There was not one pioneer at that time — and they all revealingly spoke, wrote, or tried to build flying machines — who had more than a faint conception of the difficulties involved. Their attitude was well summed up by the editor of *L'Aérophile* (January 1904), when he wrote: "gliding flight, so vigorously launched by Monsieur Arch-deacon, will not be long in bearing its own fruit. What do we lack? A few specialists trained in the tricks of the trade."

Fifthly, arising out of the last, was the strange state of mind which seemed collectively to possess the Europeans; this prevented them from arriving at a clear idea of what they were about, from formul-ating the basic problems to be solved, and from methodically going about the solution of them. This state of mind seems to have been an amalgam of over-confidence, inertia and a certain distrait dilatoriness, coupled — incredibly — with an inability to appreciate the essentials of the subject: I say "incredibly" in view of the fact that we are considering Frenchmen of undoubted talent; not only one or two individuals, but a whole group of them ostensibly dedicated to the pursuit of aviation. This extraordinary state of mind among the mem-bers of the French Aéro-Club, and those few outside it, resulted in a persistent but leisurely kind of "slapdashery", despite the aims and protestations of Archdeacon's Aviation Committee. It was this lam-entable attitude and its outcome which was later to lead to bitter self-criticism by the officials of the Aéro-Club for "notre inexcusable torpeur." Perhaps there was no deep will to fly.

The first three leading French pioneers, Ferber, Archdeacon and Esnault-Pelterie, all started by copying (as they thought) one or other of the Wright gliders, and went on to modify them: yet, it must be repeated, by the end of 1904 there had only been some four primi-tive gliders built and tested, and not one of them was a properly flyable machine.

There can be little doubt that if the Europeans had possessed the necessary devotion, humility and pertinacity, they could — with all the information and clues Chanute provided — have speedily dupli-cated the Wrights' gliding achievements, and added far-reaching improvements in stability, by the middle of 1904; successful powered flight on the Continent would have followed rapidly thereafter. With the variety of engineering talent available in Europe, the year 1906 (at the latest) should have witnessed there the full conquest of the air, with inherent stability added to the Wrights' control philosophy.

[59]

SURVEY OF THE REVIVAL OF EUROPEAN AVIATION

In January of 1904, reports of the Wrights' powered flights on December 17th, 1903 appeared in Europe. But only a few believed this news, which was even more unwelcome and less credible than Chanute's report of the brothers' gliding: the powered reports were seldom referred to again in 1904, and faded into the background. But every pioneer was becoming more aware of the Wrights' gliding, as the French imitators were further described and illustrated, although the new recruits were few.

. . . . .

Certain writers still seek to deny the decisive influence of the Wright brothers in reviving European aviation. The contemporary evidence is overwhelming, and a few of the many statements by the European pioneers themselves may be cited.

Ferber, who started the revival of aviation in Europe, wrote that he was "in pursuit of the Wrights from 1902 to 1906", and said of Wilbur Wright that "without this man I would be nothing, . . . without him my experiments would not have taken place."

Archdeacon, who then became the mainspring of the European revival, and organised the Aviation Committee of the Aéro-Club de France, said of his first glider in 1904 that it was a machine "which is — except for subsequent modifications — exactly copied from the Wright brothers' model." And G. Blanchot, writing also in 1904 (in *L'Aérophile*) referred to "the Wright machine, which inspired M. Archdeacon."

Esnault-Pelterie, who followed Ferber and Archdeacon in their efforts to revive European aviation, described his first glider as "absolutely similar (absolument semblable) to that of the American experimenters."

François Peyrey, writing of the Wrights' gliding in 1900–02, said, "the results obtained at Kitty Hawk by the Wright brothers shook the French aviators out of their torpeur."

Victor Tatin, one of the great veteran pioneers, in closing a lecture to the Aéro-Club de France in Paris in February 1904, "protested against the tendency we seem to have in France of slavishy copying (à copier rigoureusement) the gliding machines of the Americans. . . . Shall we some day have to read in history that aviation, born in France, was successful only because of the labours of the Americans, and that only by servilely (servilement) copying them, did the French thereafter obtain any results ?"

17

The Years 1902–04:
THE WRIGHTS AND FERBER

Captain F. Ferber has already been noted as being one of the few active imitators of Lilienthal. He now became a key figure in European aviation, the link between the anticipators and the achievers: for it was through him that the Wright brothers' influence first entered Europe. It was also Ferber who was the first wisely to modify the Wright configuration in the direction of inherent stability by adding a fixed tailplane, and giving dihedral to the wings.

In January of 1902, as noted before, he received his first account of the Wrights after having previously read an article on gliding, and having started a correspondence with Chanute in America; Chanute sent him various material, including information and illustrations of his own gliders; then, in January, he sent Wilbur Wright's paper on the first two Wright gliders of 1900 and 1901, both of which were without rear fin or rudder. Ferber then promptly abandoned the Lilienthal tradition and started making gliders "du type de Wright", the first of which he tested at Beuil in June 1902 (Fig. A). Not having sufficient details of the Wright gliders, Ferber could only copy inadequately what the Wrights themselves felt were as yet inadequate machines. Nevertheless, the Ferber machines were unnecessarily primitive, with non-rigid surfaces, the most sketchy elevator control, and no warping: in 1903 a flimsy triangular vertical rudder was placed at each wing-tip (Fig. C). None of these machines had either rear fin or rear rudder. The results, as might be expected, were poor, to say the least; he seems at that time to have had neither the knowledge nor the experience to make much improvement. Ferber — who was dogged and ambitious — had also made a powered twin-propeller Wright-type glider without an elevator, which he hung and tested on a giant whirling arm at Nice in December 1902: this machine was also a primitive affair, and a complete failure (Fig. B): incidentally it has the odd and quite unimportant distinction of being the first powered "Wright-type" aeroplane.

As a result of Chanute's lecture about the Wrights in April 1903, Ferber's enthusiasm was revived. In 1903–04 he temporarily abandoned his front elevator (having still inexplicably failed to make the wing surfaces rigid): then again fitted one, and made some tentative glides.

[61]

A. First Ferber Wright-type glider (Ferber V–A): 1902

B. Ferber powered Wright-type (suspended on whirling arm): 1902

C. Ferber Wright-type glider: 1903

D. Ferber V–B tailed Wright-type glider: 1904

A, B. Archdeacon No. 1 Wright-type glider: 1904

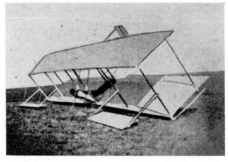

C. Esnault-Pelterie Wright-type glider with elevons: 1904

D. Robart model glider: 1904

E. Solirène glider: 1904

G. Levavasseur powered machine: 1903

F. Lavezzari glider: 1904

Next, in 1904, Ferber made a move which, although it did not much advance his own success, was later to prove vitally influential. He became the first European who — having tried unsuccessfully to imitate the Wrights — rejected their concept of inherent instability, added a stabilising horizontal tailplane to their front elevator configuration, and added dihedral to the wings; he also put ineffectual rudders on the wing-ends (Fig. D). Thus, in returning to the old European ideal and tradition of inherent stability, he now established the basis of the first European biplane configuration, *i.e.* front elevator, wings, and outrigger bearing a horizontal fixed tailplane. The machine was tested with some success from October to December 1904 in straight line glides. Like the other Europeans, Ferber did not go on to master the control of gliders, but he helped to re-establish the European ideal of inherent stability. It was evidently this preoccupation with inherent stability that led him to the complete disregard of lateral control. He seems to have felt that, where lateral control was concerned, the Wrights' deliberate choice of inherent instability, and their reliance on full pilot-control, could be entirely replaced by the inherent stability provided by the dihedral setting of the wings. Ferber's misunderstanding of the aerodynamics of control resulted in his misleading many of his contemporaries and followers on this vital subject.

P.S. A detailed account (by the present writer) of the Wrights' influence, is shortly being issued as a Science Museum monograph, entitled *The Birth of European Aviation.*

The Years 1903–04:
FURTHER WRIGHT INFLUENCE

Although Ferber was first to be swayed by the Wrights, and was ultimately to exert a vital influence on subsequent aircraft configuration, it was Octave Chanute's lecture on April 2nd, 1903 to the Aéro-Club de France that was to precipitate the main revival of European aviation. As already mentioned, Chanute described and illustrated his own 1896 glider, but gave greatest prominence to the key machine of the Wrights, their successful modified glider of 1902. The French pioneers of the time made it abundantly clear that it was the gliding successes of the Wrights that directly inspired them to emulation: not one of these men turned even briefly to the Chanute type of hang-glider, although a handful went off on quite different tacks (see below), it was the 1902 modified Wright machine which, by its success, now came to dominate the French mind, and was to directly inspire and precipitate the main stream of French — and European — aviation, despite the lack of understanding of its control rationale.

The mainspring of this new European movement which, in spite of numerous exhortations, got off to a slow start, was Ernest Archdeacon, wealthy Paris lawyer, automobilist and patron of flying. It was not until next year (1904) that he had made for him at Chalais-Meudon "une reproduction de l'appareil Wright", which was flown with only minor success at Berck-sur-Mer (Merlimont) in early April 1904 (Figs. A and B): the pilots were Captain Ferber and a newcomer from Lyons, a young architectural student-turned-engineer named Gabriel Voisin who had been inspired to enter practical aviation by hearing a lecture by Ferber in Lyons: surprisingly enough, the machine had no wing-warping or other lateral control.

Inspired by Archdeacon to emulate the Wrights, an able engineer named Robert Esnault-Pelterie also built and tested in May 1904 what he absurdly claimed was an exact copy ("absolument semblable") of the 1902 Wright glider except for details; he found it was unsatisfactory and decided to improve it. He clearly could not make the warping work properly, and — like the other Europeans — did not understand the significance of Chanute's description of the simultaneous use of warping and rudder: Esnault-Pelterie asserted that warping was structurally dangerous. In October 1904 he tested a rebuilt version, using — for the first time in history — ailerons, or

[65]

rather primitive elevons, instead of the warping and front elevator (Fig. C): this machine, despite its ingenuity, was a crude affair and a failure, and Esnault-Pelterie — like his friends — would not take the trouble to experiment, modify, and improve. The deplorable influence of Esnault-Pelterie on French aviation did not take effect until 1905, when his lecture was given and later published (see next section).

To indicate what one might call the "fringe" endeavour of 1904 I include here such men as the Messrs. Robart at Amiens (Fig. D), Solirène at Palavas (Fig. E), and Lavezzari at Berck (Fig. F). None of these was to prove of any significance historically.

Standing by himself — and, for the moment, also away from the main stream — was Leon Levavasseur, who had also been inspired by Archdeacon and Ferber to quickly build and experiment with a full-size bird-form machine, back in 1903: the machine (Fig. G) was a failure, but it has the odd distinction of being the first petrol-engined aeroplane in France to make a free-flying test, the engine being made by Levavasseur himself. Levavasseur's Antoinette engines and air-craft were soon to become world-renowned.

THE YEAR
1905

SURVEY OF THE YEAR 1905

The year 1905 saw the Wrights in America achieve the first practical powered aeroplane of history with their Flyer III; and the Europeans continue their slow and confused progression. The only significant feature of European aviation — which in practice still meant French aviation — was in conception, not execution: this was the crystallising of their determination to pursue the inherently stable tailed aeroplane, rather than the inherently unstable machine espoused by the Wrights. In this they were maturing the stability concept laid down by Cayley in 1809, publicised by Henson in 1843, popularised by Pénaud in the 1870's, and perpetuated by most of the model makers and full-size designers in Europe thereafter. In more detail, the European situation may be itemised as follows:

(*a*) the complete abandonment by the Europeans of the Wrights' doctrine of inherent instability;

(*b*) the consequent settled pursuit of inherent stability;

(*c*) the consequent abandonment of the pure Wright glider configuration of forward elevator, wings, rear rudder, and no rear horizontal surfaces;

(*d*) the furthering — following Ferber in the cause of inherent stability — of the Wright-type-glider-plus-tailplane configuration;

(*e*) the inauguration of the second type of European biplane configuration, *i.e.* the Wright-type-glider-cum-Hargrave-box-kite;

(*f*) the final and still tentative European attempts to fly gliders; then the abandonment of this basic flight philosophy of Lilienthal and the Wrights, which postulated that mastery of glider flight should precede attempts at powered flight;

(*g*) the tentative application of power to the first European biplane configuration.

The core of the European situation in 1905 was the final failure of her pioneers to comprehend the Wrights' philosophy and technique of aeroplane flight, which prevented the successful building and flying of Wright-type — or any other type — gliders, despite the descriptions, photographs, and explanations published in 1903. It represented the strengthening of the "chauffeur" attitude of winged automobilism as opposed to the attitude of the true airman. This situation was worsened in 1905 by Robert Esnault-Pelterie lecturing to the Aéro-Club de France in January about his 1904 tests with Wright-type gliders, and the publication of this misleading lecture, with illustrations, in *L'Aérophile* for June 1905. This published lecture did much harm, both short and long term, and was one of the chief factors in the further retarding of aviation in Europe. Its one beneficial result was, by virtue of its large and clear illustrations, to put the visual idea of ailerons firmly in the minds of the pioneers, ready for such time — still far ahead — when they would come to realise the true nature of lateral control. All ailerons used in aviation thereafter can readily be traced back to Esnault-Pelterie's two surfaces as illustrated in that issue of *L'Aérophile* of June 1905.

Meanwhile, Archdeacon proceeded to have built and tested (in March) his second glider, which retained the Wright wings-cum-forward-elevator, but had a tailplane and fins added for stability: this directly followed Ferber's lead, and went to reinforce the concept of a Wright glider rendered stable.

Gabriel Voisin, commissioned by Archdeacon, then took the significant step of marrying the Wright wings-cum-forward-elevator to the Hargrave box-kite to produce a float glider, to make for more — and all-round — stability. The wings were divided by vertical "side curtains" to form the main "box", with a smaller cellular unit added as tail: this machine was flown briefly, towed by an Antoinette-powered motor-boat, in June and July 1905. Voisin also collaborated with Louis Blériot to produce a similar float-glider, but with the outer side-curtains forming a sharp dihedral angle: but the machine was destroyed on its first test in July. These two machines signalled the first practical application of the Hargrave box-kite to full-size aviation. Both tests took place on the Seine.

And so a new biplane configuration was born, the stable box-kite in tandem, with the Wright-derived forward elevator, the wings being a large kite, the tail a small one. Although more rooted than ever in the "chauffeur" tradition, and discouraging true pilotage still further, this configuration did inaugurate a second important stream of European biplanes. Ferber, retaining his tailed Wright configuration, boldly added a small engine and tractor propeller to one of his machines, but it could not sustain itself.

Overseas, the other pioneers worked tentatively and without influence on aviation; S. F. Cody with a manned biplane kite-glider in England, and J. J. Montgomery in the U.S.A. with a balloon-launched tandem glider derived from Langley.

[69]

Meanwhile, at the Huffman Prairie near Dayton, the Wrights had finally perfected their Flyer III, which by the end of their season (in October 1905) had been constantly banked, turned, circled and flown in figures of eight, and had remained in the air for flights of over half an hour at a time. This third Wright Flyer was the first properly practical aeroplane in history.

In a lecture on January 5th, 1905 (published and illustrated in full in *L'Aérophile* for June 1905) Esnault-Pelterie made it clear that he felt the Wrights' gliding claims were suspect. Then he said: (*a*) that to test their claims he had built a replica; (*b*) that this replica wouldn't perform as the Wrights claimed; and (*c*) that even his own improved version was not successful: in effect, the Wrights were said to stand discredited. The publication of these conceited and foolish moves probably did more than anything else to discourage other experimenters from imitating the Wrights, then rivalling and improving on them.

Esnault-Pelterie's damping influence on European aviation, and the poor progress of the other pioneers in France, had for some time been breeding dismay in the Aéro-Club. This delay was transformed into near-despair by the publication in *L'Aérophile* for December 1905 of an eight-page leading article on the Wrights. It included letters from the brothers about their triumphant 1905 season then completed; reports from Chanute and others who had questioned the various local witnesses, and who had been assured that the Wrights had done all they claimed; and a long editorial discussion on the pros and cons for believing the reports. *L'Aérophile* was more than half convinced that the reports were true, but would not commit itself. In his peroration, the editor wrote: "if the results obtained by the Wrights are definitely confirmed, let us not forget that aviation was born in France." Forgetting Cayley — who had already been acknowledged by the French to have founded aviation — the editor finally turned to the possibility that the reports were not true: "If the news that has arrived from America today is not true, it will be tomorrow." He ended the long article with exhortations, and by quoting the brave words spoken back in 1903 by Archdeacon, after hearing Chanute's news of the Wrights' gliding: "Scientists (savants), to your compasses! You, you Maecenases, and you too, gentlemen of the Government, put your hands in your pockets, or else we shall be beaten!" This quotation is rounded off by the editor's final comment — "if we have not been beaten already, we should add."

[70]

20

The Year 1905:
ARCHDEACON; VOISIN; BLÉRIOT

The vital moves of 1905 in Europe were made by Archdeacon and Gabriel Voisin; Louis Blériot also first entered the scene now, but in a somewhat puzzling way.

One of the most interesting — and still insoluble — problems of early aviation, is the amount of credit due to Gabriel Voisin. According to his deplorable autobiography, he not only played the leading part in everything he took on, but was personally responsible for the invention of the practical aeroplane (see Notes). In 1904 he was new to the business, and simply piloted the Archdeacon-commissioned Wright-type glider, having been coached by Ferber. But it would seem that he was mainly responsible, now in 1905, for both the new Archdeacon glider (see below) and for the vitally important Voisin-Archdeacon glider in which, for the first time, the Hargrave box-kite entered full-scale aviation.

But the box-kite float-glider was to be arrived at after a transitional machine had been built — moving away from the Wright-type towards stability — which must first be described: this was the Archdeacon No. 2 (Figs. A, B), in which an engine was later to have been installed: it was of the Wright-type, but with a tailplane and fins to provide inherent longitudinal and directional stability. This machine, unmanned, was towed down a wooden slipway and off into the air by an automobile on March 26th, 1905 at Issy: it seems to have flown well for a short while, but soon suffered a breakage in the tail-unit, and crashed. It may have been again briefly tested on April 2nd, before being finally abandoned. It was largely designed by Voisin.

The Hargrave box-kite first entered full-scale aviation — somewhat similarly to what he himself had envisaged — in the Voisin-Archdeacon float-glider of 1905 (Fig. C), and its sister craft the Voisin-Blériot, in which the Wright front elevator was retained, the biplane wings — with differing camber — were divided by "side curtains" into three box-kite cells, and a two-cell box-kite (one-cell in the Voisin-Blériot) was added on an outrigger as a tail-unit. This configuration, like its box-kite ancestor, was adopted to provide inherent longitudinal, lateral, and directional stability, along with the addition of an elevator and (later) a rear rudder: it also introduced the concept of the "lifting tail", where a considerable portion of the machine's total lift was borne by the tail, as opposed to Ferber's "floating tail"

[71]

 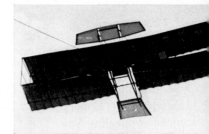

A, B. Archdeacon No. 2 Wright-type glider (tailed): 1905

C. Voisin-Archdeacon float glider: 1905

D, E. Voisin-Blériot float glider: 1905

whose only function was to stabilise. This Voisin-Archdeacon glider was twice towed captive off the river Seine (between Sèvres and Billancourt) by an Antoinette-powered motor-boat, with Gabriel Voisin as pilot; the first time for 150 m. on June 8th, 1905; the second for 300 m. on July 18th of the same year. This machine was later tested without success on the Lake of Geneva (see Notes).

On the latter day, immediately after the second Archdeacon test, Voisin piloted the second machine, the Voisin-Blériot float-glider, which Dollfus has shown was a genuine combination of ideas from the two men. This machine had four significant differences; in the pronounced wing and tailplane camber, the dihedral angle given to the outer side-curtains, shorter span, and the single-cell tail (Figs. D, E). This glider had only just been towed off the water when it suddenly banked, side-slipped, and plunged into the river; Voisin narrowly escaped being drowned: the machine was not tested again. The only movable control surface these two machines had was the Wright-type forward elevator.

21

The Year 1905:
CODY; MONTGOMERY; WEISS; FERBER

The year 1905 also saw three unorthodox gliders, and the first European attempt at powered flight. There was the kite-glider made and piloted by S. F. Cody (until 1909 an ex-patriate American), who later became the first man to power-fly in Britain (Fig. A): in 1901 he had patented a type of man-carrying Hargrave box-kite, with the upper surfaces extended laterally as aerofoils; this type of Cody kite, used in connection with a supporting train of similar kites, was adopted in 1906 by the British Army. Cody's kite-glider, also made for the British Army at Farnborough (Fig. A), was a tentative and unsuccessful machine with a rear fin and no tailplane, but bearing — for only the second time in history — a pair of ailerons: these were of too small a size, and placed too far inboard, to be effective. This type of machine was not developed.

Next to be noted is a tandem monoplane glider built by the controversial "Professor" John J. Montgomery in California (Fig. B). He had built a number of unsuccessful machines before producing this Langley-derived glider in 1905, which he employed a professional parachute-jumper, D. Maloney, to pilot. It was taken up beneath a large hot-air balloon — an ingenious method of launching first suggested in 1852 by Cayley — and on three occasions (March 16th, April 29th and July 18th, 1905) Maloney made perilous descents from some 500 ft.; on the last, the machine crashed and he was killed. The controls seem to have consisted of rudder and elevator, and some sort of primitive wing-warping device derived from the Wrights. A similar tragedy was narrowly avoided on a similar machine in 1911. Montgomery himself was killed on one of his gliders in 1911. He was a brave man, but contributed nothing to the development of aviation.

The French-Alsatian José Weiss made many experiments with models in England, aiming at inherent stability in gliders based on bird-forms: this model (Fig. C) is a development of a type originally shown at the first "Concours d'Aviation" (which was confined to models) held by the Aéro-Club de France in Paris in February 1905. Weiss later (1910) built a full-size powered machine, and also designed one of the early Handley Page machines.

Captain Ferber, in 1905, pursued a highly creditable course along his own lines, being determined to develop his Wright-derived biplane

1. THE YEAR 1905: CODY; MONTGOMERY; WEISS; FERBER

A. Cody kite-glider with ailerons: 1905

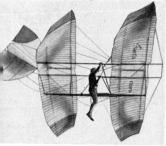

C. Weiss model glider: *c*. 1905

B. Montgomery glider: 1905

Ferber VII–B powered Wright-derived tailed biplane, still with forward elevator: 1905

glider with its fixed tailplane, unmodified by Hargrave features: he built a similar but larger glider this year, with a 12 h.p. Peugeot motor driving a small tractor propeller within the forward elevator outrigger (Fig. D): this Ferber VII–B could only make a powered glide when it was launched from an overhead cable on May 25th, 1905; but here was the first tractor biplane of history, and the start of the longest line of the world's biplanes; also, incidentally, the first time a free "flight" had been made with a powered machine in Europe. It led directly to de Pischoff in 1907, and on to Goupy and the Breguet brothers in 1909, all of whom took the vital step of eschewing the potentially dangerous front-elevator. But Ferber was still, and was always to remain, incapable of arriving at proper lateral control.

22

The Year 1905:
THE WRIGHT BROTHERS

Although the four brief flights of 1903 have naturally invested the Wrights' first Flyer with the greatest fame, it is their Flyer III of 1905 — seldom dealt with in aviation histories — that should stand equally with it; for the 1905 machine was the first practical powered aeroplane of history (Figs. A, B). It was of the same general configuration as the others, but noticeable differences appeared in the placing of the elevator farther forward to improve longitudinal control, and (similarly) the rudder farther back: the span was 40 ft. 6 in.; the wing area was slightly reduced, to 503 sq. ft.; the camber was increased to 1 in 20; and new sets of propellers were used; but the excellent 1904 engine was retained. The prone pilot position was retained, so also — for the start of the season — was the warp and rudder linkage. The speed was approximately 35 m.p.h. Like all the Wright aircraft, it was built to be inherently unstable, and had to be "flown" all the time by the pilot.

The 1905 season at the Huffman Prairie lasted from June 23rd to October 16th, and some 40 flights were made; but the Wrights were now concerned with reliability and endurance. They were airborne this season for just over three hours. In September, the trouble they were having in tight turns was diagnosed as a tendency of the lowered wings to slow up and stall, and the cure was seen to be in putting the nose down to gain speed in the turn. It was while seeking this cause and its cure that the brothers took the important step of unlinking the warp and rudder controls, and providing for their separate — or combined — operation in any desired degree.

With this Flyer III now perfected, the Wrights made many excellent flights, including durations of 18 min. 9 sec., 19 min. 55 sec., 17 min. 15 sec., 25 min. 5 sec., 33 min. 17 sec., and — on October 5th — their record of 38 min. 3 sec., during which they covered over 24 miles.

The description of this machine as the world's first practical powered aeroplane is justified by its ability to withstand constant take-offs and landings; to bank, turn, circle and perform figures of eight; and its reliability in remaining airborne for over half an hour at a time. It is now preserved in Carillon Park, at Dayton (Ohio). Detail photographs are given in the next section.

It was in 1905 that the Wrights first offered their invention to the U.S. and British governments. In January, on the experience they had

[77]

A. Wright Flyer III (Orville piloting) over the Huffman Prairie:
October 4th, 1905

B. Wright Flyer III (of 1905) as now preserved at Carillon Park, Dayton

Wright Flyer III (of 1905) in course of re-assembly at Carillon Park, Dayton. Details of this machine are shown below

B. Rudder

C. Elevator outrigger

D. Elevator

E. Elevator 'blinker'

Port propeller and outrigger

G. Engine and flight controls

had with the Flyer II, an offer was made to the U.S. War Department, which was refused outright without even an attempt at investigation — "a flat turn down", as the exasperated Wilbur called it. They then offered it to the British War Office. The British dilatoriness was as bad as the U.S. refusal; so, with persuasion from Chanute, the brothers again (in October, still of 1905) offered it to the U.S. War Department, with all the added confidence now provided by the performance of their Flyer III. Again it was turned down; for the second time the War Department assumed that the Wrights were asking for financial assistance — whereas they made it quite clear they were offering a finished product — and for the second time the Department made one of the classic statements of aviation history: "the device must have been brought to the stage of practical operation without expense to the United States." [Continued in the next section].

The Year 1905:
THE WRIGHT BROTHERS (contd.)

The Wrights' Flyer III of 1905 is of such importance in aviation history that I have here added various photographs of it where it now lies in Carillon Park, Dayton (Ohio). (See page 79.)

Fig. A shows the machine before the wings were covered, with one of the so-called "bent end" propellers, the most sophisticated of the various kinds built by the brothers.

The double rudder is shown in Fig. B: it was supported on a two-boom outrigger, and braced laterally to the inner rear struts. There were also two diagonal bracing-wires in the vertical plane to preserve the form of the outrigger, but the wire running from near the top of the rudder to the lower rear wing-spar (to which the lower outrigger boom was attached) ended in a strong coiled spring: this allowed the rudder and its outrigger to hinge upwards in case it dragged on the ground at take-off or landing.

The robust forward elevator-outrigger-cum-skids is seen in Fig. C: this basic pattern of members was retained in the subsequent "standard" model A machines.

In Fig. D is seen a side view of the biplane elevator showing the two semi-circular vertical stabilisers known as "blinkers", added to provide forward keel area and make the rudder effective.

One of the "blinkers" is shown in a close-up in Fig. E, together with the actuating lever of the elevator.

One of the propeller outriggers is shown in Fig. F, where the long propeller shaft, sprocket, and chain transmission are clearly seen.

Fig. G shows the offset engine, the sideways-swinging hip-cradle for operating the wing-warping (with the foot trough with its bar to fit the insteps), the horizontal half-disc-cum-tiller to operate the rudder, and the vertical elevator lever. (For a description of the weight-and-derrick launching technique, see Sect. 44).

At the end of 1905 there appeared for the first time in public a crude, but basically correct, sketch of a powered Wright machine (the III of 1905). It was made by a Dayton pressman and was to have appeared in the *Dayton Daily News*; but the Wrights seem to have succeeded in suppressing it. It was then seen in Dayton, and pirated, by the representative of the Paris journal *L'Auto*, and duly appeared in the

December 24th (1905) issue of that periodical. It was the prominent forward biplane elevator shown in the sketch that later led, in 1907, to Gabriel Voisin adopting a similar elevator for his first three machines (see description in Notes to Sect. 33).

THE YEAR
1906

SURVEY OF THE YEAR 1906

Although the Wrights did not fly in the year 1906, it was their unseen presence which pervaded the whole European scene, and underlay every move the Continental pioneers made during the year. This was primarily due, as already noted, to the well-nigh shattering impact of the long article on the Wrights which appeared in the issue of *L'Aérophile* for December 1905. There were other articles on the Wrights at that time — notably one in *L'Auto* — but *L'Aérophile* was by far the most important journal, as it was the official organ of the Aéro-Club de France: all the leading French pioneers were members of the Club, and all of them looked upon *L'Aérophile* as "required reading." It was also read by the serious pioneers in other countries.

As a result of the December article, there had been continual conflict between the doubters and the convinced: and one evening at the Aéro-Club in January the debate was so passionate ("un débat si passionnant") that it went on till midnight. But despite the patriotic scepticism expressed by so many Frenchmen — the British and Germans were, regrettably, still sound asleep — the evidence for the Wrights' claims was mounting. Archdeacon, most deeply involved of those in the controversy, was always to remain stubbornly unconvinced; but the more expert among the older men, such as the veteran Victor Tatin, came to accept the evidence: the latter wrote in *L'Aérophile* for January 1906: "Unfortunately, for some years, and despite all the stimulation received from the news announcing the partial successes and well-founded hopes of the Americans [*i.e.* in 1903 from Chanute, etc.] we have remained in a state of regrettable expectancy ("dans une regrettable expectative") although we have had in France everything necessary to solve, better and more rapidly, the problem whose solution abroad today arouses us ("nous émeut"), alas, a little too late."

In the midst of this mood of despondency and self-criticism, we are faced with yet one more inexplicable problem: for in this same January issue of *L'Aérophile* there was published the basic text of the Wright patent (with illustrations), which had been applied for by the brothers in 1903, and was now granted. The version in *L'Aérophile* was not complete, but it took care to include the Wrights' lucid description both of the means of lateral control — by warping and rudder — and, for the very first time, its aerodynamic raison d'être:

[84]

in other words, here, in January of 1906, was published for all to see, the chief "secret" of the Wrights, and the principal key to their mastery of flight control. Yet no one in Europe took the slightest notice! I can find no informed discussion, let alone appreciation, of the Wrights' flight philosophy in the European writings of the time. We can only surmise that the Continental pioneers were so set in their "chauffeur" attitude of mind, that the passages in the Wright patent describing warp-drag, and its counteraction by the rudder, meant nothing to them: they were simply not thinking along the lines of dynamic flight control at all, and had had so little experience with their gliders that they had never experienced warp or aileron-drag.

To make this whole situation even more extraordinary, we find Archdeacon — in his manifesto of August this year (see below) — saying that the second and greater difficulty about aeroplane flight, after the problem of the light engine which he said had now been solved, was "that of equilibrium and the actual control of the machine", which was "unfortunately far from being solved." One wonders just what he and his friends thought the Wrights were talking about in their patent specification. It is almost inconceivable to us today that such obtuseness should have prevailed among these men, with all the talent and resources they had at their disposal.

Modern readers may wonder why so much surprise is expressed at this European attitude, and the consequent delays. Apart from the same surprise — and indeed exasperation — being shown by the pioneers themselves, one need only consult the periodicals of the day to realise the prodigious amount of time and effort being put into fruitless aviation projects. The technical basis of proper aeroplane flight and control was readily available to all; but a general paralysing malaise seems to have overspread the European pioneers which, as said above, I feel was basically associated with the "chauffeur" attitude. I believe it was this attitude which kept them preoccupied with the machine on the ground rather than control in the air, and resulted in so much wasted effort. There was also, strange to say, no single pioneer who would adopt a given configuration, as the Wrights had done, and then — regardless of whether it was the best one — pursue it methodically and relentlessly to the stages of workability and success.

The manifesto by Archdeacon just referred to, was published in *L'Aérophile* for August 1906, and was preceded by a revealing statement from the President of the Aéro-Club de France, L.-P. Cailletet, in which he said that the purpose of the manifesto was to shake the

members out of their inexcusable torpor ("pour secouer notre inexcusable torpeur"). Archdeacon, who did not admit the Wrights'
claims, exhorted his friends to catch up on the "slight advance (légère
avance) which the Americans have made." He then reminded them of
the existence of the famous "Prix Deutsch-Archdeacon" for the first
kilometre circle (on offer since 1904, and not to be won until January
13th, 1908!); but he said nothing of the two other prizes, also offered
in 1904, for the even more modest distances of 25 and 100 m. respectively, which were at last to be won this year by Santos-Dumont.
Archdeacon concluded his manifesto by declaring, with italicised em-
phasis: "the discovery of aerial navigation is imminent, and there is
just time for us in France to make the first public demonstration."

It is surprising that it was not until August 1906 that the Aéro-Club
made this appeal: it was still, as it had been since 1903, a case of
making haste slowly. No wonder that the more enlightened members
of the Club were becoming ever more fretful and frustrated. It was
now the late summer of 1906: no European powered aeroplane had
yet flown, and no powered machine seemed within sight or hope of
flying. The only hope was that a few hops might be achieved with the
Vuia monoplane or the new Santos-Dumont biplane (see below).
Ferber had been launched into the air last year in his tentative
powered machine, and had reduced the angle of glide by the action of
his engine and propeller; but that was all. The more honest Europeans
realised that the position was well-nigh ridiculous, and as the President
of the Aéro-Club said, "inexcusable".

The most important European achievement of 1906 was the per-
fecting by Levavasseur of his two Antoinette engines, of 24 and 50 h.p.
respectively, both of which, in turn, were to power Santos-Dumont's
machine. First tested in motor-boats in 1903, Antoinette motors were
to become the chief power-plants of European aviation until 1909:
they might even be said to have made European flying practicable.
There was no comparable advance in European propellers, which
remained primitive devices until 1909.

There was another historical consolation — but no consolation to
its contemporaries — in that the tractor monoplane, not seen since
Ader's Avion III of 1897, was reborn in Trajan Vuia's machine, which
from March to October 1906 made some five take-offs, but never
stayed in the air for more than three seconds at a time. Its appearance,
however, was prophetic and influential; and Blériot, who was wasting
this year in fruitless tests of his new and oft-transformed biplane, the
III/IV, was soon to consider Vuia and follow his lead.

[86]

But, to the Europeans, by far the most important events of the year were the hop-flights made by Alberto Santos-Dumont on his ingenious but sterile cellular biplane 14-*bis* (mod). On October 23rd he won the prize for the first machine to cover 25 m. by his flight of 197 ft. (60 m.) and on November 12th he won the prize for the first flight of 100 m. by covering 722 ft. (220 m.) in $21\frac{1}{5}$ sec. These were the first officially recognised flights in Europe, and it was a true measure of Continental desperation that such pathetic achievements — after four years of endeavour — were immediately hailed as outstanding triumphs. After the 60 m. hop of October 23rd, even Ferber was constrained to cry "Une ère nouvelle commence!" Alas, it was a short-lived hope. Not until nearly a year later, in October 1907, was Santos' best duration ($21\frac{1}{5}$ sec.) exceeded; and not until November 1907 that a European machine could stay up for a full minute. The 14-*bis* (mod) was a curious "canard" descendant of the Wrights' biplane (with forward elevator) and the cellular Voisin float-gliders of last year: it was a historical "freak" and led nowhere; but it was a salutary lesson for the other pioneers that an "airship" man could suddenly take to aviation, and could get his first machine into the air, even though it was a matter of "only just".

In Denmark, J. C. H. Ellehammer had taken off in his semi-automatically controlled biplane — his No. II — for some 42 m. (138 ft.) on September 12th, but it "flew" in a circle, tethered to a centre pole, and was never airborne in free flight.

Despite the shock of the Wrights' claims, despite self-criticism, despite the efforts of Archdeacon, Ferber, Voisin and their friends, the Aéro-Club de France had to take a melancholy look back at another long year with little to show on the credit side. Only two powered machines, both built by men outside the main stream of endeavour, had succeeded in taking off; but neither had been able to remain airborne for even half the 59 seconds the Wrights achieved on their first day three years before.

But perhaps the most important "news" of all in 1906 had been the negative news that the Wright brothers did not fly: their last flight in 1905 had been on October 16th, and they were not once to leave the ground until May 6th, 1908, a period of $2\frac{1}{2}$ years. Realising the full epoch-making significance of what they had achieved, the brothers became secretive in face of the efforts they knew were being made to discover their secrets. They felt they could only preserve their patent rights, and their rightful priority, if they came to a clear-cut business agreement with a client — preferably their own or a foreign Government — that such a client must guarantee to purchase their machine provided there was mutual agreement about the desired performance, and provided the machine performed as agreed. But the clients, particularly the U.S. Government, insisted on viewing the machine (or drawings of it) before signing a contract; this was an unreasonable condition, and totally unacceptable to the Wrights, especially in view of the many would-be spies who were out to learn all they could. So the Wrights refused to fly.

The ethics of this strange situation are somewhat confused, and it is all too easy for us today to pontificate on the Wrights, and assert that they should have presented their invention to the world, regardless of reward. Nevertheless, from the historian's viewpoint, their $2\frac{1}{2}$ years interregnum was a major tragedy. It severely retarded the whole develpment of aviation, and the history of the world might well have followed a radically different course — possibly even a better one — had the Wrights made public flights at the end of 1905 with their perfected Flyer III. They would undoubtedly have been copied rapidly and widely, especially in Europe, where there was at that time a talented and receptive audience of men bent on flying, and an excellent reservoir of automobile engineers and mechanics to back up their efforts. The Wrights would also, of course, have received at once the full and universal honour for their achievements which will always be their due, an honour which historians have since had to waste much time in defending against those men of dishonesty and ill-will who even today seek to denigrate the American brothers.

Finally, it is the historian's duty — and a melancholy duty indeed if he is an Englishman — to record the continuing neglect of practical aviation in Britain, a neglect as deplorable, as inexcusable, as it is still inexplicable, in view of the wealth of technological talent then present in the Country. Here is a serious statement from the well-known authority of those days, Patrick Alexander (quoted in the *Daily Mail* of November 24th, 1906) which must surely take the biggest bun for lunacy: "Great Britain and the British Empire stand easily in the van of progress. We know more about the science of aeronautics than any other country in the world. As yet, we have not attempted to apply our knowledge, but silently and quietly we have been studying the subject, exhausting every possible theory and fact, until today our scientists may lay claim to have conquered the air on paper. To achieve the victory in practice will not be a difficult matter." Perhaps the poet Dryden should have the last word here: "I'll sing," he wrote, "that I may seem valiant."

[88]

The Year 1906:
VUIA; ELLEHAMMER

Considering that Europe had seen a continual train of monoplane designs, models, and full-size gliders since Henson's "Aerial Steam Carriage" of 1842–3, it is surprising that when serious efforts at practical aviation were renewed in 1902–3, the conventional monoplane was generally neglected.

It is to the credit of Trajan Vuia, a Paris-domiciled Rumanian (and a Doctor of Law of Budapest) that in 1906 he inaugurated the powered monoplane tradition of today with a machine of simple tractor configuration; but the machine itself was a failure. Vuia's immediate ancestors were Ader and Lilienthal; his immediate descendants, Blériot and Levavasseur's Antoinettes. The Vuia I (Fig. A) was a tractor monoplane, built by the designer, with a wing area of 20 sq. m., a span of 8·70 m. and a weight of 241 kg. The engine was a Serpollet carbonic acid gas engine of 25 h.p. driving a primitive propeller at 930 r.p.m.

The machine, which had a rudder but no elevator, ran on a four-wheel (cycle-type) undercarriage — incidentally the first pneumatic, and the second cycle-type, undercarriage of history — whose front wheels were steered in concert with the rudder. Control, apart from the rudder, was by a primitive type of wing-warping ("une sorte de gauchissement"), and a device to alter the angle of incidence of the wings in flight, in lieu of an elevator. The Vuia I made three take-offs at Montesson, on March 3rd, August 12th and 19th, its best, and last, hop covering 24 m., and ending in a crash landing ("atterrisage brusque").

Vuia was unfortunately no airman, and had no conception of flight control: he was a dogged "chauffeur", bent on driving his machine into the air. It took his "brusque" landing to show him that he had virtually no longitudinal stability or control. So he added a rear elevator of 3 sq. m.; reduced the wing camber; and increased the wing area to 23 sq. m., with a span of 8·70 m. a chord of 2·40 m. and a weight of 275 kg.: the "en route" variable incidence device was abandoned: engine and propeller were the same. This machine was known as the I-*bis* (Fig. B), and was also a failure. Between October 6th and March 30th, 1906, it made a total of 8 take-offs at Issy and Bagatelle, its best hop covering only 10 m. The Vuia II of 1907 was also a failure, and made only two brief hops.These machines are good examples of aircraft which, though failures in themselves, exerted strong influence on others.

A. Vuia I (without elevator): 1906

B. Vuia I-*bis* (with elevator): 1906

C. Ellehammer II in tentative tethered flight: 1906

VUIA; ELLEHAMMER

The name of J. C. H. Ellehammer, the Dane, has often come into prominence as a putative rival to Santos-Dumont for the honour of being first to fly in Europe; but, tentative as Santos' flights were, Ellehammer — in his second machine (Fig. C) — did not even achieve the free flight which his admirers have so often claimed for him. His aircraft was a tractor semi-biplane — a monoplane with a loose sail stretched above — with a 3-cylinder 18 h.p. motor. On September 12th, 1906, tethered to a central post on the small island of Lindholm, the No. II lifted Ellehammer over a circular track for some 42 m.; but the pilot was only a passive passenger, the machine having a fixed rudder and automatic (pendulum) longitudinal control, to say nothing of the advantage of centrifugal force. If Ellehammer had concentrated on his excellent engines, he might have played a major role in history; but his work in aviation was not historically important, and influenced no one.

The Year 1906:
BLÉRIOT III/IV

The case of Louis Blériot offers an excellent illustration of the strengths and weaknesses of early European aviation after it was sparked into revival in 1902 and 1903 by news of the Wrights' gliding. Blériot was an engineer with a flourishing business in the sphere of automobilism; he made admirable acetylene head-lamps of his own design, which were widely used on the Continent, and in Britain. He first became actively attracted to aviation as early as 1901–02, when he built a model ornithopter. In 1905 Blériot had Gabriel Voisin build him a variant of the Voisin-Archdeacon float-glider (noted in Sect. 20). Blériot had little to do with the general design of this machine, but he may have suggested the dihedral on the outer side-curtains.

In 1906, still employing the Voisin factory (as it had now become) at Billancourt on the Seine, he ordered what may be termed the Blériot III/IV, which never succeeded in flying in any of its transformations (the Voisin-Blériot float-glider of 1905 was named by Blériot the Blériot II). The III (Fig. A) was a float biplane with ellipsoidal main wings and ellipsoidal tail-unit of the same size, and a combined lifting surface of 60 sq. m. A 24 h.p. Antoinette engine drove two tractor propellers through flexible shafts. There was a narrow biplane elevator within the front wings, and a rudder within the rear wings. The machine was first tested in May 1906, on the Lake d'Enghien, but never rose. This was the first aeroplane (after Levavasseur's own primitive machine of 1903) to be powered by one of the excellent Antoinette engines which, in versions of 24 and 50 h.p., soon became the mainstay of European flying.

The III was then modified to become the Blériot IV, still on floats, in which the ellipsoidal tail-unit was retained, but in which the front part of the machine was totally transformed: there was now a Wright biplane wing structure (with two side-curtains widely enclosing the pilot), and a biplane elevator out front. A remarkable added feature were the two small and narrow ailerons fitted to the rear struts at mid-wing position, this being the third application of ailerons in history, and clearly inspired by Esnault-Pelterie's which had been illustrated during the previous year. There were also two 24 h.p. Antoinettes driving two pusher propellers. This machine was tested on Lake d'Enghien (in October 1906), but also failed to rise.

The IV was then modified to become a landplane, with wheeled undercarriage (Fig. B) but now with a single 50 h.p. Antoinette driving the two pusher propellers: it was tested at Bagatelle in November 1906, but never flew. So ended Blériot's current concern with biplanes.

Although anxious to get up into the air and fly, Blériot — like most of the Europeans — was still too much of a "chauffeur" to realise that mastery of gliding flight was the best road to powered flight: he was also, one feels, somewhat lacking in original thinking, but he became a talented adapter and courageous pilot later on.

A. Blériot III floatplane on the Lac d'Enghien: 1906

B. Blériot IV, as landplane (with between-wing ailerons) at Bagatelle: 1906

A. Santos-Dumont 14-*bis* being tested under his airship No. 14: July 1906

B. Santos-Dumont 14-*bis*: October 1906

C. Santos-Dumont 14-*bis* (mod) (with ailerons): November 1906

D. Santos-Dumont 14-*bis* (mod) in flight: November 1906

[95]

27

The Year 1906:
SANTOS-DUMONT 14-*bis*

This ungainly aircraft has become one of the affectionately sanctified machines of aeronautical history, owing to its making the first "official" flights in Europe. In sober fact, it was a bastard child and a barren adult; it influenced no one; it had but few merits; and in the nine take-offs of its life, it stayed in the air on one occasion for $21\frac{1}{5}$ seconds, and for never more than $7\frac{1}{5}$ seconds on any of the others. Archdeacon had, in 1904, offered a fine silver trophy for the first flight of 25 m. (82 ft.) along with the Aéro-Club's 1,500 francs prize for the first 100 m. (328 ft.); these were now to be won, more than two years after the vital Wright clues had been given to Europe, and a year after the Wrights themselves had been flying for over half an hour at a time. Their 1905 news now "sparked" Santos-Dumont.

The 14-*bis*, the fruit of Santos-Dumont's advertence to heavier-than-air flying, was so-called because it was flight-tested slung beneath his airship No. 14 (Fig. A). After toying with the idea of a helicopter and with the idea of a monoplane, Santos designed and built at his "aérodrome" at Neuilly-Saint-James (near Paris) a cellular biplane of the canard-type, *i.e.* with fuselage and "tail-unit" forward of the main planes (Figs. B, C, D). A covered-in fuselage extended forward from the wings to support the control surfaces in the form of a single box-cell pivoted to turn up and down as an elevator, and left and right as a rudder. The wings, set at a pronounced dihedral angle, had an area of 52 sq. m., a span of 11·50 m., a chord of 2·50 m., and a wing gap of 1·50 m. There were six side-curtains. A 24 h.p. Antoinette engine (later exchanged for a 50 h.p. Antoinette) was placed in the centre section, driving direct a 2·50 m. diameter metal pusher propeller at 900 r.p.m. The pilot stood in a wickerwork balloon basket in front of the engine. The elevator-cum-rudder was 1·50 m. high, with a 2 m. span, and a 2 m. chord. The machine was built of fabric-covered pine and bamboo (round the basket); had two main wheels (with rubber shock absorbers) and a skid under the forward box. The weight was 300 kg. Its ancestry is evident enough; a basic Wright configuration of biplane wings and forward elevator, combined with Hargrave box-kite modification to form a cumbersome ensemble.

The 14-*bis* was first tested suspended from a pulley running on a wire, the traction being performed ineffectually by a trotting donkey;

[96]

this was at Neuilly. Then in July, the machine was tested suspended beneath Santos' airship No. 14 (Fig. A) also at Neuilly.

It made its first free take-off on September 13th, 1906 at Bagatelle, near Paris, but only covered 7 m. before it made a bad landing. Repairs were accompanied by the installation of a 50 h.p. Antoinette engine, and the machine may now be called the 14-*bis* (mod). On October 23rd, at Bagatelle, the 14-*bis* (mod) made one hop-flight of 60 m. and won the Archdeacon prize for a flight of 25 m.

Santos now added two octagonal (not hexagonal) ailerons, one in each outer wing-cell (Figs. C, D), operated by a body harness. With the machine thus modified, and still with the 50 h.p. Antoinette, and also at Bagatelle, he made his chief series of hop-flights on November 12th, 1906 (Fig. D); first came a run of five brief efforts, varying between 40 and 82 m. covered, with a maximum airborne time in the 82 m. hop of $7\frac{1}{5}$ sec.; and then the sixth and longest achievement on the same day — which overnight brought Santos world renown — of 220 m. (722 ft.) in $21\frac{1}{5}$ sec., keeping about 6 m. above the ground, which won him the Aéro-Club's prize (1,500 Francs) for the first flight of 100 m.

Admirable effort as this was, in face of the general lack of progress on the Continent, it was not of course flying in any true sense of the word, let alone sustained and controlled flying. A "chauffeur" had at last driven his winged automobile off the ground and into the air. But for the first time in Europe the public realised through descriptions and photographs that a heavier-than-air machine had actually lifted itself from the ground and been supported in the air for a number of seconds in free flight. From the tone of contemporary comment it appeared to one and all that the air age had indeed arrived.

The 14-*bis* (mod) made only one more appearance, on April 4th, 1907 at Saint-Cyr, when it covered 50 m. No one copied this first Santos-Dumont aeroplane; no one was influenced by it. Other more promising configurations were already in being, and were soon to mature.

In cold retrospect, Santos' flights now seem scarcely worthy of the title; but public and pioneers alike were so relieved to see an aeroplane leave European soil at last, that they indulged in "une immense clameur d'enthousiasme", for this "nouveau triomphe de Santos-Dumont".

An interesting and significant outcome of Santos-Dumont's performances this year was the offer on December 4th by the oldest firm in the Champagne industry — Ruinart père et fils — of a prize of 12,500 francs (£501) for the first aviator to fly the English Channel, or more properly called perhaps, as it was a French prize, La Manche. In view of the general state of European aviation in 1906, and especially of the minuscule achievements of Santos, it appears to us today as a most admirable act of faith and imagination to envisage and promote a Channel flight by aeroplane as early as 1906. The Ruinart prize was still on offer when Blériot conquered the Channel in 1909, and he would have won it — in addition to the *Daily Mail* prize — had he given the necessary prior notice of attempt, which was a little longer than that required by the *Daily Mail*. This far-sighted offer by the Ruinart firm presaged the extraordinary, and even now generally unknown, role of the Champagne industry in ushering the aeroplane into civilisation by sponsoring, launching, and providing lavish prizes for the first great aviation meeting of history — "La Grande Semaine d'Aviation de la Champagne" at Reims in August of 1909.

THE YEAR
1907

28

SURVEY OF THE YEAR 1907

The year 1907 witnessed the true, but still tentative, beginnings of practical powered flight in Europe, following the "false dawn" of 1906. Three important configurations, all confirming the European inherent stability idiom, became well defined during the year; but only one machine achieved significant flights. These configurations were as follows:

(a) The pusher biplane, Wright-cum-Hargrave-derived, with forward elevator, "open" biplane wings, and box-kite tail-unit, but with no lateral control. This type was represented by the first two powered Voisin machines, the Voisin-Delagrange I and the Voisin-Farman I; the latter, after important modification by Henri Farman, was the first European aeroplane — and the only one in 1907 — to achieve productive flying (October 1907 onwards), and the first to stay in the air for over a minute (November 9th).

(b) The tractor biplane, derived from Ferber, but with no surfaces forward of the propeller: this was first seen in December in the De Pischoff machine which, although itself not successful, was to exert much influence later.

(c) The tractor monoplane with main wings, fuselage, and tail-unit, developing from the Vuia (which itself made some hops in 1907), seen in the promising Blériot VII and the diminutive Santos-Dumont 19, both of November, but both only tentative.

Off the beaten track, and also only tentative, were (1) the Ellehammer III (triplane); (2) the Phillips II multi-slat machine; (3) the Dunne swept-wing tailless biplane (glider and powered), which inaugurated yet another basic configuration; (4) the two Blériot machines which were to lead up to the VII, i.e. the "canard" monoplane (No. V) and the Langley-derived tandem monoplane No. VI (Libellule); (5) the Tatin-De la Vaulx pusher monoplane; (6) the Wels-Etrich monoplane glider; and (7) the unconventional but promising monoplane (REP. No. 1) brought out by Robert Esnault-Pelterie. Standing still farther from the beaten track were the first two helicopters in history to lift — but only just — a man, "flown" by the Breguet brothers in September (but today disqualified as it was steadied from the ground), and by

Paul Cornu in November, now given priority: neither of these creditable efforts had any influence on the early history of the aeroplane.

Despite the talented men who were now growing up in European aviation — many of them attracted away from automobilism — the same basic attitudes and habits of mind possessed them now as had possessed them in 1903. The "chauffeur" philosophy was still dominant, and still no one realised that mastery of glider construction and control — which they could easily have accomplished within a year of Chanute's revelations in 1903 — would have led rapidly to mastery of powered flight. The main reason for this neglect was, as noted previously, their basic mistake of regarding flight control as only passive and corrective — as an extension of inherent stability — and not as both corrective and as a positive dynamic means of manoeuvre. They also failed to realise that even the corrective function of flight control needed a control system which would be instantly effective about all three axes: hence their neglect of proper lateral control. In view of Chanute's partial revelations of 1903, and the explicit revelations in the Wright patent published in 1906, it is well-nigh incredible that this dual function of flight control was not properly comprehended, let alone appreciated and utilised, by the Europeans until Wilbur Wright's display of mastery in August 1908. Nor had the Europeans progressed beyond the most primitive of ungeared propellers. Continental pioneers were understandably unwilling to risk any effective catapult, or other, launching methods with their embryo machines: they would certainly not have known how to control them if they found themselves suddenly committed to the air, and would assuredly have suffered many a casualty. Not having had to face the problems of flight control in gliders, they underestimated or neglected flight control in general — especially lateral control — in their powered machines; they therefore concentrated on forcing them into the air in small straight-line hops. Henri Farman alone had begun to acquire the "airman's" attitude by the end of 1907; Blériot was to embrace this attitude next year.

The only strong suit of the Europeans was their traditional pursuit of inherent stability, and their correct insistence on the adoption of a tailplane to bring it about longitudinally, and wing dihedral for lateral stability. But this persistent pursuit of stability was largely nullified by their equally persistent refusal to appreciate the vital role of flight control. This neglect of control — one of the two chronic European diseases — was worse confounded by the second disease, the refusal by the European pioneers to think out and adopt any definite con-

[101]

figuration and pursue it, through test and modification, until success was reached. Blériot's production of no less than three basic configurations in this one year, 1907, with no proper testing and development of any of them, was typical of the Continental attitude. It was again a question of time-wasting "slapdashery". Blériot had been working at the problem of flight since mid-1905; but only at the end of 1907 had he even arrived at a promising configuration: he was to labour until mid-1909 — two more years — before he could achieve a practical aeroplane. Here we have a typical, and incomprehensible, case-history of European pioneering. Equipped with all the information and clues that anyone could wish for, and with ample funds, a talented and fearless man took no less than four years — forty-eight months, two hundred and eight weeks — to progress from an unsuccessful (but feasible) float-glider to a practical powered machine.

The case-history of the Voisin machines is equally extraordinary and deplorable. Gabriel Voisin was tentatively piloting Archdeacon's Wright-type No. 1 glider in the Spring of 1904; but it was not until November of this year, 1907, that the powered machine he built for Henri Farman (and modified by him), could remain in the air for sixty consecutive seconds; and not until January 1908 that this same machine could make a wavering officially attested circle, yawing round on rudder alone. The standard Voisins were indeed never to have any lateral control, right to the end of their days in 1909–10.

There was, therefore, only one European aeroplane — the Voisin-Farman I — which, by the end of 1907, could remain airborne for a single minute. But at least it was a beginning, and Europe had to be content with small mercies.

P.S. An interesting "comment" on the Europeans' conception of flight control — especially lateral control — as mainly passive and corrective, rather than dynamic and initiatory, was the oft-used term for ailerons, current even up to the latter part of 1909, i.e. "ailerons de stabilisation", and "equilibreurs latéraux", and the English "balancing planes", and "righting planes".

29

The Year 1907:
MONOPLANES — BLÉRIOT V, VI, VII

In the monoplane field, the year 1907 saw the most noteworthy development in the work of Louis Blériot, who — clearly inspired by Vuia — had now abandoned the biplane. Had he been more patient and persevering, he might well have brought European aviation out of the doldrums by 1908, instead of having to wait, along with all his confrères, for Wilbur Wright to fly in Europe in 1908; it was therefore 1909 before he could truly succeed. But he was far too impatient, and in this year 1907 built and tested no less than three monoplanes of totally different configurations.

Blériot's first monoplane — the Blériot V — was a frail canard-type "de forme bizarre", owing its general character to Santos-Dumont and its cambered swept-back wings to some supposed bird-form (Figs. A, B). Its wing area was 13 sq. m., its span 7·80 m., and its weight 236 kg. A small elevator and rudder were placed on the end of the fuselage, and there was also a primitive wing-warping control: a 24 h.p. Antoinette behind the pilot drove directly a two-bladed pusher propeller. This machine made some 4 take-offs in April 1907, but never covered more than 6 m., and was wrecked at the last attempt.

Blériot promptly abandoned the canard-type and built his No. VI, a Langley-derived tandem monoplane called the *Libellule* (Dragonfly) (Figs. C, D). This had a wing area of 20 sq. m., weighed 280 kg. and was powered by a 24 h.p. Antoinette driving direct a two-bladed tractor propeller. The wings, set at a pronounced dihedral angle, had a span of 5·85 m. and a chord of 1·50 m. There was a large fin aft, to which the rudder was hinged; and pivoted wing-tip elevons (used primarily as elevators), derived from Esnault-Pelterie. The Blériot VI made some eleven take-offs in July and August of 1907, its hop-flights including six of over 100 m., the best being 150 m. in 10 sec. The VI was modified at various times — it is still impossible to log the modifications correctly — but it seems to have had its dihedral reduced, a smaller tail-fin, and a 50 h.p. Antoinette installed: the wing area remained the same, but the weight rose to 300 kg. In September 1907 it made six take-offs at Issy, and four of its hop-flights exceeded 100 m. the best was 184 m. (its last appearance) when it crash-landed.

Blériot's third machine of 1907, the VII, was of radically different design, and was to prove prophetic (Fig. E). He returned to the classic

[103]

A, B. Blériot V, canard monoplane: 1907

C, D. Blériot VI, tandem monoplane (*Libellule*): 1907

E. Blériot VII, tractor monoplane: 1907

A, B. Model of the Antoinette I: 1907

C. Esnault-Pelterie REP. 1: 1907

D. Santos-Dumont 19: 1907

E. Tatin-De La Vaulx monoplane: 1907   G.I.A.

type of European tractor monoplane, derived from Henson, Pénaud, and the rest, and revived in 1906 by Vuia; but he realised it in a highly sophisticated form, with dihedrally-set main planes, enclosed fuselage, and an empennage comprising the rudder, and elevons in the form of a "flying tail", with no fixed horizontal surfaces. These elevons represented another stage of Blériot's unsuccessful flirting with the aileron concept, without yet comprehending its full purpose and the necessity for making the surfaces large, and setting them at maximal distance from the fuselage. The VII had wings of 25 sq. m. with a span of 11 m. A 50 h.p. Antoinette drove direct a four-bladed metal propeller. This machine, which weighed 425 kg., made 6 take-offs at Issy in November and December 1907, with two of the hop-flights covering 500 m. The VII, although not in itself successful, was soon to set the basic monoplane style for the world.

30

The Year 1907:
MONOPLANES (VARIOUS)

Leon Levavasseur, creator in 1903 of the Antoinette engine and of the bird-form monoplane it powered, did not again take seriously to aeroplane design until 1907, when he envisaged a pusher monoplane with forward elevators flanking a fixed horizontal surface, and a long fuselage with engine amidships, and rudder, cruciform stabilising surfaces and propeller at the rear: this strange configuration was realised in model-form during the summer (Figs. A, B). A full-size machine — minus the forward elevator — was almost completed in 1908, but was abandoned: it bore the designation Antoinette I. This machine (both model and full-size) in whose design and construction Ferber was said to have had a hand, has always been something of a historical mystery; it was only occasionally mentioned and illustrated in 1907-08, and lost to view thereafter.

Robert Esnault-Pelterie also re-emerged in 1907, as the designer and builder of an excellent 7-cylinder radial aero-engine of 30 h.p., and of an unconventional tractor monoplane powered by it, which drove a four-bladed propeller (Fig. C). This REP. No. 1 had its wings — of 18 sq. m. and 9·60 m. span — set at a slight anhedral angle on a very short fuselage, with a spreading tailplane and elevator, but no rudder: there were two centralised wheels in tandem, and a wheel on each wing-tip. Control was by Wright-derived downward (only) wing-warping (which Esnault-Pelterie had previously condemned) and by an elevator, both operated by a single control column: but there was a serious lack of longitudinal and directional stability. The REP. No. 1 made 5 take-offs from November to December 1907, which produced creditable hop-flights, the best being of 600 m. on November 16th.

Santos-Dumont, like Blériot, had also abandoned the biplane for the monoplane, and produced in 1907 the first of his — and the world's — light aeroplanes, which were later collectively to take the popular name of *Demoiselle*. The first machine was his No. 19 (Fig. D) a diminutive bamboo monoplane of 9 sq. m. wing area, a span of 5 m., a chord of 1·80 m., and a weight of only 110 kg. The engine was a horizontally opposed 2-cylinder Dutheil-Chalmers of 20 h.p driving a two-bladed metal propeller. Horizontal and vertical control surfaces comprised a cruciform tail-unit (on a single bamboo rod) of

[107]

elevator-cum-rudder, and another elevator — working in concert — in front: lateral control was simply by the pilot (sitting beneath the centre section) rocking his body from side to side, almost *à la* Lilienthal. This No. 19 made only 3 take-offs (at Bagatelle, Issy and Buc) in November 1907, covering 190 m., 200 m., and 150 m. respectively, making a crash-landing on the last, and breaking the propeller.

Count Henry de La Vaulx, a well-known balloonist, had an ambitious-looking monoplane made by Mallet to the design of the veteran Victor Tatin. It had a wing area of 40·60 sq. m., a span of 15 m., and a weight of 400 kg. A 50 h.p. Antoinette engine drove two Tatin pusher propellers. This Tatin-De La Vaulx took off twice at Saint-Cyr on November 18th, 1907; it made a hop of 70 m. on the first occasion, and one of 50 m. on the second, when it crash-landed: it was then abandoned (Fig. E).

Vuia, following the poor results with his Serpollet carbonic acid gas motor, re-built his monoplane in 1907 (now called Vuia II) and fitted a 24 h.p. Antoinette. It made two tests at Bagatelle, in June and July, and was then abandoned.

The Year 1907:
MISCELLANEOUS MACHINES

Other interesting but not very fruitful machines also appeared in 1907, as well as one vitally important book on aerodynamics.

I. Etrich and F. Wels completed this year a tailless monoplane powered by a 24 h.p. Antoinette; but it was tested (at Oberalstadt in Bohemia) only as a glider (Figs. A, B), and did not lead to any important developments: it might be compared with Dunne's.

The man-carrying triplane was first introduced into aviation by Ellehammer, who built and tested his machine — his No. III — in 1907 (Fig. C): it had a new Ellehammer 5-cylinder 30 h.p. radial engine, the familiar pendulum system and no voluntary lateral control: the rear undercarriage wheel was filled in to form a rudder. It made many brief hops, but was not successful, and did not influence European development.

The helicopter, whose basic behaviour had been demonstrated in a sixteenth-century model, had been "re-discovered" and again made in model form in 1784; the latter, primarily through Cayley's version of it, had fired the imagination of many inventors in the nineteenth century, and had resulted in a number of successful models. The year 1907 at last saw the first machine to lift a man vertically off the ground in free flight: this was a twin-rotor machine, powered by a 24 h.p. Antoinette, built and first tested by Paul Cornu near Lisieux on November 13th (Fig. D). It is often said that the Breguet brothers' machine of the same year — the Breguet-Richet I — made the world's first helicopter flight on September 29th at Douai; but unfortunately this large machine was steadied by four men during the take-off: although they did not thus aid the lift, they certainly aided stability; and so this machine loses its priority in history. The Cornu machine — admittedly just as tentative as the Breguet — must therefore be adjudged the first to raise a man — just — vertically in free flight.

It was in 1907 that aviation saw the publication of its most important written work since Cayley's triple paper of 1809–10: this was the first volume to be written and published by F. W. Lanchester, entitled *Aerodynamics*, and the first full statement of his theory of circulatory flow which (with the next year's publication of his *Aerodonetics*) laid the foundations of modern aerofoil theory. The illustration from *Aerodynamics* reproduced here (Fig. E) shows a diagram

[109]

A, B. Wels-Etrich monoplane as glider: 1907

C. Ellehammer III (triplane): 1907

D. Cornu helicopter: 1907

E. Wing-tip vortex, from Lanchester's *Aerodynamics*: 1907

F. Phillips II (multiplane): 1907

of a wing-tip vortex. Lanchester's epoch-making work was not to be recognised in Britain for some time to come: it was first appreciated at its true worth by L. Prandtl, in Germany.

Horatio Phillips, following his "Venetian blind" machine of 1904, proceeded to an ambitious but ungainly development of the theme in 1907, the Phillips II (Fig. F) which has a good claim to have been the first powered aeroplane to have flown tentatively in England, piloted also by an Englishman. It comprised a large number of his high aspect-ratio aerofoils fitted in four tandem frames, and powered by a 20–22 h.p. engine driving a 7 ft. propeller at 1,200 r.p.m. The empty weight was 500 lbs. and it lifted off the ground at about 30 m.p.h. It was tested at Streatham in the spring or summer of 1907, and seems once to have been airborne for about 500 ft.: but the machine — both illustrated and described in 1908 — was completely unpractical and outside the main stream of development, and did not influence the course of aviation.

The Year 1907:
BIPLANES (VARIOUS)

Santos-Dumont made one more effort to master the biplane, following his 14-*bis*, and before going on to his No. 19 (*Demoiselle*) which has already been noted. The Santos-Dumont No. 15, a smaller and more frail machine which echoed its predecessor, was a tractor biplane, with cellular wings of high aspect-ratio, set at a pronounced dihedral angle, with a single cell aft comprising the rear stabilising and controlling surfaces combined (Fig. A). Two narrow ailerons in the mid-wing position were to have been added out front, but were not fitted. The wing area was 14 sq. m., the span 11m., and the chord 60 cm. Santos had intended to install the new 100 h.p. Antoinette, but it was not yet available; so the 50 h.p. motor was used, set on the jointure of the upper wings. There was a single-wheel undercarriage (the truck here seen beneath it is the handling dolly). The weight was 280 kg.

After preliminary ground tests, the No. 15 was to be flown on March 27th, 1907; but when taxying to turn into wind on that day, a wing dropped and was badly damaged. Santos seems to have had little faith in this machine, as he promptly abandoned it without further tests. He was to start afresh with his first monoplane, the No. 19 already noted in Sect. 30.

The English pioneer J. W. Dunne (later the author of *An Experiment with Time*) was particularly interested in inherent stability. Inspired by the form of the winged seed of the Zanonia — a Javanese climbing plant — he built his first swept-wing tailless biplane for the War Office in 1907, and tested it that year in Scotland at Blair Atholl. It was designated the D. 1 and was tested as a glider only once; it made a free flight of 8 seconds, after being launched downhill from a trolley (Fig. B) and was damaged on landing. Then two 12 h.p. Buchet engines were fitted; but it was badly damaged at the first take-off attempt. As his machines did not play any significant part in aviation history before 1910, Dunne's still tentative developments of 1908 and 1909 are not included in this book.

The biplane of unequal span designed by de Pischoff, and built in Lucien Chauvière's workshops, was another of those machines which was itself a failure, yet influenced others (Fig. C). Although the "open" configuration of the tractor biplane — with a "floating tail" and no forward control surfaces — was not to be fully established

32. THE YEAR 1907: BIPLANES (various)

A. Santos-Dumont 15 tractor biplane, on handling truck: 1907

B. Dunne D.1 glider: 1907

C. De Pischoff I tractor biplane: 1907

until 1910–11, this machine displayed and pre-visioned its basic characteristics now in 1907. It had no forward elevator, and no side-curtains; there was a tail-unit comprising a cruciform arrangement of tailplane, fin, elevator and rudder, and a wide-track cycle-type under-carriage: there was also no voluntary lateral control. The engine was an air-cooled 3-cylinder fan-type Anzani of 25 h.p.: this was the first time an Anzani engine — to become world famous on the Blériot XI in 1909 — was used in aviation. Also of importance was the propeller — a Chauvière *Integrale* — the first truly sophisticated airscrew to appear in Europe, whose descendant was also to appear on the Blériot XI.

The Year 1907:
BIPLANES — VOISIN-DELAGRANGE I

Before embarking on the first powered Voisin machine, Gabriel Voisin built a modified Chanute-type biplane hang-glider (Fig. A) which was tested at Le Touquet in May 1907. It thus had no forward elevators, and the tail-unit was altered to become a two-cell box-kite, à la the 1905 float-glider: it had no controls other than body swinging. (See Notes.)

When building their first powered aeroplanes, the Voisin brothers returned to the Wrights' front elevator, temporarily abandoned the side-curtains on the wings, but retained the box-kite tail-unit. The first of these machines was built for Henry Kapferer, a distinguished engineer and airshipman, and was completed by March 1907; but it never flew. The appearance and specification of the Voisin-Kapferer were very similar to the Voisin-Delagrange (see below), but it had an 8-cylinder 20–25 h.p. Buchet engine. In such a form it would have been badly under-powered, but for reasons not yet found, this machine was never modified or re-engined, and all trace of it was soon lost.

The main powered biplane tradition in Europe was first displayed in the second Voisin machine, known at the time as the "Delagrange No. 1" following the Voisins' shrewdly flattering custom of naming their aircraft for their clients. It will be referred to here as the Voisin-Delagrange I (Figs. B, C) to avoid the confusion that would otherwise result. Here is the basic Voisin configuration which (with variations) was to persist right into the year 1910. The Voisin-Delagrange I had a forward biplane elevator on the front of the nacelle; biplane wings of 40 sq. m. area; 10 m. span and 2 m. chord, and a wing gap of 1·50 m. A 50 h.p. Antoinette in the back of the nacelle drove direct a two-bladed metal Voisin propeller of 2·10 m. diameter at 1,000 r.p.m. The tail comprised a broad two-cell box-kite unit with twin rudders hinged to the outer side-curtains. There was no voluntary lateral control. The weight was 450 kg. It made 6 take-offs at Bagatelle from March 16th to April 13th, its best hop-flight being 60 m. in 6 sec., piloted by Charles Voisin.

The machine was then fitted with floats and tested on the Lake d'Enghien in the spring of 1907, when it was known as the "Delagrange-Archdeacon", as the latter shared in the experiments and

A. Voisin hang-glider (Chanute type, modified): 1907

B. Voisin-Delagrange I: 1907

C. Voisin-Delagrange I: 1907

[116]

A. Voisin-Farman I, with broad tail-unit: 1907

B. Voisin-Farman I (mod), with smaller tail-unit: 1907

C. Antoinette 50 h.p. 8-cylinder engine

[117]

suggested modifications; but it did not succeed in flying. Then, with one (central) rudder instead of two, it was refitted with a wheeled undercarriage, and made two take-offs at Issy (November 2nd and 3rd, 1907) piloted by Delagrange. It hopped 50 m. on the first date, and 500 m. on the second, when it crash-landed and was destroyed.

An interesting point about all three of the first Voisin machines was their Wright-derived forward elevators which were biplane elevators, not monoplane as in the Wright gliders which had precipitated the European movement. The reason for this was the publication in the Paris *L'Auto* (December 24th, 1905) of the first illustration — a crude drawing — ever to appear of a Wright powered aeroplane, in this case the Wright Flyer III. It was pirated from a Dayton newspaper, which had tried to suppress it, and showed clearly the biplane elevator which the French pioneers copied. We have Ferber's authority for this train of events.

34

The Year 1907:
BIPLANES — VOISIN-FARMAN I

With the Voisin-Farman I (called then "Henri Farman No. 1") we come to the only "biplane man" to imprint his personality strongly on the basic Voisin design by modifying it himself after purchase.

One-time art student, then cycle and automobile racer of renown, Henri Farman was a French-domiciled Englishman — both parents were British — who did not take French nationality until 1937. He ordered a Voisin machine on June 1st, 1907, which was to be the third powered Voisin. This historic machine was to undergo various transformations in its long career, which lasted through into 1909.

In its first form, the Voisin-Farman I closely resembled the Voisin-Delagrange I; but the broad tail-unit was a single cell with a centralised rudder, and the main wing-span was slightly increased from 10 m. to 10·20 m. The weight (due probably to a stronger structure) had risen to 520 kg. After the first tests had got well under way in October, the biplane elevator was exchanged for a monoplane one, and the wings were rigged to form a dihedral angle for lateral stability (Fig. A): then, in November, the broad tail-unit was reduced from a span of 6 m. to 2·10 m. as shown in Fig. B, and the machine may now be called the Voisin-Farman I (mod).

The Voisin-Farman I made some 20 take-offs at Issy from Sept. 30th to November 23rd, 1907, including the following creditable flights during 1907:

October 26th, 771 m. in $52\frac{3}{5}$ sec.
November 8th, (his first turn)
November 9th, 1,030 m. in 1 min. 14 sec. (his first
  unofficial circle).

This last was the first time an aeroplane other than the Wrights' was airborne for a full minute, and the first time a non-Wright machine had made a circle. This flight won him the Archdeacon cup for the first officially recorded flight of 150 m. [for the famous flight of January 13, 1908, see the next section.]

It was now clear to all that, in Henri Farman, an outstanding pilot and potential designer had arrived on the European scene, who was only later to be equalled in achievement and influence by Louis Blériot. Farman was able to learn many of the practical lessons of

[119]

aviation; to see where improvements could be made; and incorporate them effectively. He was a man of considerable originality; he could quickly appreciate technical problems, and then tackle them realistically. He was also a true airman at heart, although still somewhat conditioned at this time by the surrounding "chauffeur" attitude towards flying in Europe: he did not yet appreciate the importance of lateral control. From now until the end of 1908, Farman was to remain the leading European aviator.

In order to underline the vital importance of the aircraft power-plant, I have included here (Fig. C) the best contemporary photograph (late 1907) of the 8-cylinder 50 h.p. Antoinette engine, fitted here in the Gastambide-Mengin I monoplane (to be described in Sect. 39). Leon Levavasseur's Antoinette engines virtually made early European aviation viable.

THE YEAR
1908

35

SURVEY OF THE YEAR 1908

The year 1908 was an *annus mirabilis* in aviation history, for the Wright brothers first flew in public — Wilbur in France in August, and Orville in the United States in September — and revealed in dramatic fashion the true nature of the aeroplane and its control in the air. They revealed a type of flying machine whose every part and feature had grown out of masterly design and experimentation, a machine inspired by a clear vision of the nature of mechanical flight, and of the proper kind of vehicle to accomplish it. This vision and this experimentation were seen to have conditioned and unified the whole aircraft, its aerodynamic qualities, its construction, motor, propellers and — above all — its flight control system.

The Wrights also revealed themselves, not only in their consummate skill as pilots, but in their personal modesty and integrity in the midst of their triumphs. Where the Europeans chauffeured their machines cautiously and doggedly, as if they were steering fractious winged automobiles through the alien air, the Wrights rode their aircraft as if man and machine were one — "je vais faire corps avec la machine" as Françoise Sagan put it — rode them with perfect ease and assurance; rode them with the mastery of born airmen. They were, indeed, the mythical "hommes oiseaux" come to life.

The spectators whom Wilbur Wright faced on August 8th, 1908 — at the small racecourse of Hunaudières, near Le Mans — comprised the most combative audience imaginable; these were the aviators and would-be aviators of France who, in their own uncertain hopes, were the aviators of the world. Their confidence and peace of mind had been severely ruffled, first by rumours of the Wrights, then by more unsettling reports: those who believed the reports, awaited this first performance with resignation, or perhaps hopes of failure; but the confirmed sceptics, with their dogged ostrich attitude, were ready with their derision.

Then Wilbur started flying; briefly at Hunaudières, then for four months on end at Auvours; as he gracefully banked, turned, circled, and made figures of eight, his onlookers saw their world collapsing about them. They were by turns astounded, dismayed and — to give them credit — repentant; repentant of their six years of disbelief, and dismayed at the memory of their six years aeronautical fumbling. With on proper control in their hands, and indeed no image of true

[122]

flight in their minds, they were now experiencing a painful moment of truth. The veteran pioneer Léon Delagrange spoke for all his honest countrymen when he exclaimed, "Well, we are beaten! We just don't exist." ("Eh bien, nous sommes battus! Nous n'existons pas!")

When Wilbur was finally established at Auvours (still near Le Mans) in late August, the Europeans flocked there as the Faithful flock to Mecca. Those who went "to pray", as distinct from those who went "to stare", paid special and sustained attention to two particular features of Wilbur's flying; his mastery of flight control and man-oeuvre, especially the co-ordinated use of warping and rudder, and his sophisticated, efficient propellers, geared-down to produce optimum thrust, as opposed to the primitive direct-drive "paddles" used by the Europeans. The result was a revolution in aviation, which by next year was to result in the powered aeroplane emerging as the world's new practical vehicle.

The men of most significance who now were truly to mark, learn and inwardly digest what the Wrights revealed, and set out to incorporate it in their own machines, were Glenn Curtiss in America: and — in Europe — Levavasseur with his Antoinette monoplanes, Blériot with his No. XI monoplane, and Henri Farman, at first with his already much-modified Voisin biplane, then with his own No. III: but their work was not to mature until next year. In addition, these men also incorporated their own idiom of inherent stability, and so were later to improve on the Wrights.

The impact of the Wrights in 1908 was so vital and so decisive that the modest achievements of all others seem inevitably to be thrown into the shade. These achievements were indeed modest in every respect, but they were — until August — lauded as remarkable, even epoch-making. Henri Farman, the leading European pilot, made the first official circle on January 13th, and was airborne for nearly $1\frac{1}{2}$ min.; by July he had made a flight of just over 12 miles (in 20 min.). Léon Delagrange made similar progress. In the United States, the members of the Aerial Experiment Association were getting under way with their Wright-derived biplanes, and Glenn Curtiss made the first public flight in America (5,090 ft. in 1 min. $42\frac{1}{2}$ sec.). In England, A. V. Roe was experimenting tentatively in June with a Wright-derived biplane. The first "hop-flight" in Europe with a passenger was made by Farman in May.

In the monoplane field, Blériot was developing his No. VIII, which was promising, and Levavasseur, with the Gastambide-Mengin mono-plane he had designed, was feeling his way toward his classic Antoinettes.

[123]

The Wrights, grounded since 1905, first flew again in May in order to regain their skill in pilotage, using their Flyer III of 1905 modified to become a two-seater; they also made the world's first passenger flights. All their new machines were also to be two-seaters.

Wilbur then came to Europe, where he flew continually and spectacularly from August to December, making over 100 flights (some 60 with passengers) and being airborne for some $25\frac{1}{2}$ hours. The best of his many long flights lasted for two hours and twenty minutes and — in passing, so to speak — he created an altitude record of 360 feet. Orville's acceptance trials for the U.S. Army in September got off to a brilliant start, but were tragically cut short on September 17th by a propeller breakage and crash, in which Orville's passenger, Lieut. Selfridge, was killed and Orville himself seriously injured: this was powered aviation's first fatality.

The latter part of the year saw the Europeans taking heart, and trying to put the Wright's revelations of control into practice; but pending the completion of their new aircraft, they could achieve little more than a steady improvement of their previous kind of flying. Farman and Delagrange led in biplanes, Blériot in the monoplane. By the end of the year Farman had made a few long flights (up to 25 miles in some 45 minutes), with Delagrange not far behind, and Blériot bringing the monoplane record up to $16\frac{1}{2}$ miles in 20 minutes. Both Farman and Blériot were now experimenting successfully with ailerons, and Esnault-Pelterie — quietly reversing his previous attitude — fitted warping on his monoplane. By December, Levavasseur had started tests with the first two of his true Antoinette types, both fitted with ailerons. Only the Voisin brothers stubbornly refused to progress, and took no steps to introduce any lateral control.

The world's first two powered triplanes, the Goupy I and the de Caters, also made their first tentative tests from September to December. Cody, still an American citizen, made the first brief powered flight in Britain on October 16th; in December, the first resident Briton — Farman was British, but an ex-patriate — learned to power-fly on a Voisin in France, in the person of the late J. T. C. Moore-Brabazon (Lord Brabazon of Tara). The first tentative powered flights had also been made in Germany and Italy.

The world's first true cross-country flights were made on October 30th and 31st, the first by Farman from Bouy to Reims (27 km.), the other by Blériot, on his VIII-*ter* from Toury, around Artenay, and back, with two landings en route (28 km.).

First Half of 1908:
FARMAN; DELAGRANGE

T he year 1908 opened with what seemed to contemporary Europeans as an outstanding achievement — the first official kilometre circular flight in Europe. This consisted of taking off, flying between two posts, then round a single post 500 metres away, and back to pass airborne between the twin posts again. This "kilomètre bouclé" was performed by Henri Farman in his Voisin-Farman I (mod) at Issy on January 13th, 1908 (Fig. A), and won him the Deutsch-Archdeacon prize of 50,000 francs, with medals going to the Voisins for construction — which in view of Farman's modifications they only just deserved — and to Levavasseur for the Antoinette engine. The London *Times* called the day "epoch-making". Nothing reveals the profound difference in criteria and performance between the Europeans and the Wrights better than this event. The former, having been alerted by Chanute in 1903 — and having abandoned the effort to master glider flight before attempting powered flight — were now at last (in 1908) starting to circle in the air, but with no voluntary lateral control, and treating it as an epoch-making step. The Wrights, having mastered control in the air in gliders, went on to power-flying and to perform circles in their second and third Flyers as one of the essential and matter-of-fact accomplishments of flying.

Farman had to achieve his circle with a wide yawing turn, since he had no warping or ailerons; with the outer wings thus moving faster and the inner moving slower, the machine was in a banked attitude during the whole manoeuvre, but had to be turned in as large a circle as possible to avoid stalling, or rolling into the ground.

After his kilometre circle, during which he actually covered about 1,500 m. in 1 min. 28 sec., Farman made one more flight that day of 500 m.; then, also at Issy, three flights on January 15th, the best being about 1,500 m. Next, he carried out further modifications on his machine (see next section), in which he was to make significant flights. Delagrange, who now becomes Farman's rival, is dealt with here for convenience.

Delagrange, after his crash-landing in November last, had the Voisins build him a second machine — probably using much of the first — which became the Voisin-Delagrange II (called "Léon Delagrange No. 2") (Fig. B). It will be seen how closely it resembled the

[125]

A. Voisin-Farman I (mod) flying the first kilometre circle: 13th January, 1908

B. Voisin-Delagrange II: 1908

C. Voisin-Delagrange III (with two side-curtains): May, 1908

A. Voisin-Farman I-*bis*: 1908 (Henri Farman at right)

Farman, with the latter's modifications of monoplane elevator, dihedral on the wings, and small tail-unit. In May — after a crash-landing on May 3rd — two side-curtains were fitted to promote lateral stability, and the machine was given a new designation, "Léon Delagrange No. 3" which we will call Voisin-Delagrange III (Fig. C).

In late July the machine had its two inner side-curtains removed, and four fitted, which enclosed the outer bay on either side (see Sect. 46).

The machine, in its two first versions, *i.e.* as the Voisin-Delagrange II and III, made some 40 take-offs from January 20th to July 10th, 1908 at Issy, Rome, Milan and Turin, which included many good flights and some circles, the best being as follows:

March 20th	at Issy,	1 km. 500 m. in 2 min. 30 sec.
April 10th	at Issy,	2 km. 500 m. in 3 min.
April 11th	at Issy,	3 km. 925 m. in 6 min. 30 sec.
May 30th	at Issy,	12 km. 750 m. in 15 min. 25 sec.
June 23rd	at Milan,	14 km. 270 m. in 18 min. 30 sec.

These Voisin-Delagrange and Voisin-Farman biplanes (whose further performances in 1908 are noted in Sections 37 and 46), were the only European machines of any kind to make consistently good flights in 1908. No monoplane could be rated as practical until 1909.

First Half of 1908:
FARMAN (contd.)

Farman and Delagrange carried on a friendly rivalry throughout much of the year in their respective modified Voisins. They also paralleled one another till the Autumn in the various alterations made; but in the Autumn, Farman — who was more talented aeronautically — set about incorporating important features in an effort to produce the results which he saw the Wright machine achieve.

The photograph reproduced here (Fig. A) shows the Voisin-Farman I-*bis* (called "Henri Farman No. 1-*bis*") as modified and ready to fly in March 1908: in the course of its long career, this machine was to survive longer, and undergo more transformations, than any other European aircraft, from its first hop-flight on September 30th, 1907 to its last take-off on May 23rd, 1909.

The I-*bis* had wings of 40 sq. m. area. 10 m. span, 2 m. chord, and 1·50 m. gap, with a weight of 530 kg.: the span of the tail-unit was 2·10 m., the chord 2 m., and the gap 1·50 m. There were thus only minor differences in dimensions and weight from the original Voisin which Farman had purchased in September 1907 (*i.e.* 10·20 m. span, same chord, and 520 kg. weight). Farman's own important modifications of incorporating dihedral and a smaller tail-unit had already been made before the end of the year 1907. Now the fabric had been renewed, "Continental" rubberised linen (as used for airships) being substituted for the previous varnished silk. A new engine was installed, an 8-cylinder 50 h.p. air-cooled Renault, which drove direct the same primitive Voisin propeller at 1,100 r.p.m.: but this engine was only used in one take-off (the first on March 14th), and was then replaced by the original 50 h.p. Antoinette. It is not known why the Renault proved unsatisfactory. In May, two inner side-curtains were added between the centre section struts, closely enclosing the pilot.

The I-*bis* made some 38 take-offs from March 14th to August 9th, 1908 — at Issy, at Ghent in Belgium, and in the U.S.A.; but only three significant flights resulted:

March 21st, at Issy, 2 km. 4·80 m. in 3 min. 31 sec.
May 29th, at Ghent, 131 m. in 11 sec., with Archdeacon as passenger.

[129]

FARMAN (contd.)

May 30th,   at Ghent,   1,242 m. with Archdeacon as
passenger.

May 30th,   at Ghent,   a flight (unmeasured) which attained
a height of 12 m.

July 6th,   at Issy,   duration flight of 20 min. 20 sec.

The hop of May 29th was the first tentative passenger-carrying in Europe (see Notes) and the flight of July 6th was a new European record, the first time a European had exceeded a quarter of an hour's flight duration, for which Farman received the Armengaud prize of 10,000 francs for the first quarter hour flight.

After a brief and unsuccessful visit to the United States in July and August (see Notes), Farman was back in Europe in August. His I-*bis* was now due for its next modification (see Sect. 46.)

Before going on to normal monoplane development in the first half of 1908, a word should be said of the machine, given the English title of the *Flying Fish* — with the designation "Henri Farman No. 2" (see Notes) — which the Voisin brothers were building for Farman during February and March 1908, but which was never completed and tested. It was to have been a tractor monoplane with three sets of small main-wings in tandem, and a fixed tailplane in tandem with the elevators; the intention seems to have been to reduce wing-loading, and hence the danger of breakage.

First Half of 1908:
MISCELLANEOUS BIPLANES

Although, in England, Cody's biplane was ready in the early summer of 1908 (see Sect. 47), it was not tested until September-October, and it was A. V. Roe who in England was next after Phillips to test (at Brooklands) a full-size powered machine. After winning the *Daily Mail* prize for his Wright-type biplane model in March 1907, Roe built a full-size Wright-derived machine, minus rudder (Fig. A), with a span of 30 ft., a weight of 600 lbs., and a 9 h.p. J.A.P. engine: this was far too weak, and was exchanged for a 24 h.p. Antoinette. In June 1908, the machine was air-towed behind a car, and also made a few self-propelled take-offs (probably after down-hill runs) covering up to about 150 ft. It never flew in any real sense. Although Roe was later to do outstanding work, this first machine is of little significance historically: it is here designated the Roe I.

Back in France, Ferber came into prominence again — and for the last time — with a tractor biplane which kept his would-be inherently stable "tailed" concept before his contemporaries' eyes, and continued to influence them in that direction. This machine was the Ferber IX (Figs. B, C) which, owing to Ferber's having joined the Antoinette company, confusingly bore also the alternative designation of Antoinette III: it had a span of 10·50 m. chord of 1·60 m., a wing area of 30 sq. m., a 50 h.p. Antoinette engine and a weight of 400 kg. The forward elevator was retained and there was a fixed tailplane and fin. At first, two flimsy triangular rudders were attached to the outer rear struts (Fig. B); then these were exchanged for a rear rudder (Fig C). There was a two-wheel tandem undercarriage. This machine made some 8 take-offs from July 22nd to September 19th, 1908, at Issy, the best result being 256 m. covered on August 19th, and 500 m. on September 19th (with a crash-landing), with Legagneux piloting it on both occasions. Ferber then abandoned this machine and did no more original work. He was killed when his standard Voisin met a ditch at speed after landing, on September 22nd, 1909.

The biplane designed and built by the brothers Ernest and Paul Zens at Gonesse has a certain interest in its extended lower wings, which seem to have consisted of smaller surfaces laid on the main wings and overlapping them, not — as it sometimes appears — raised above them; in the different dihedral angles of the wings, and in the

A. Roe I biplane at the top of the "pull-up" at Brooklands: 1908

B, C (on right.) Ferber IX
(Antoinette III): 1908

D, E (on right). Zens biplane: 1908

F, G. Gasnier biplane: 1908

rocking elevator out front which was also intended for steering (Figs. D, E). There was a fixed tailplane well out behind. It had a 50 h.p. Antoinette. The machine was tested at Gonesse on August 4th; after making a few hops, it was damaged and then abandoned.

The pusher biplane designed and produced by René Gasnier, also powered by a 50 h.p. Antoinette (Figs. F, G) was a somewhat similar machine, and had some limited success. It was an interesting variation on the Voisin theme with main-plane dihedral, a fixed monoplane tail and, as with the Zens, a forward rocking elevator to act also as a rudder (particularly in evidence on the uncovered airframe shown in Fig. F). It had a wing area of 30 sq. m. and a span of 10 m. The machine made some 45 take-offs from August 17th to September 17th, 1908, at Rochefort-sur-Loire, its best performance being 500 m. on September 17th, when it crash-landed and was abandoned.

39

First Half of 1908:
GASTAMBIDE-MENGIN/ANTOINETTE

This is the proper place to introduce formally the figure of Leon Levavasseur, artist turned engineer, who always remained an artist in whatever he did. He was the mainspring of the Antoinette firm ("Société Antoinette"), Antoinette being the name of the daughter of Jules Gastambide, the head of the firm. As already noted, Levavasseur's first successes were with his remarkable series of Antoinette engines, used first in his abortive aeroplane of 1903; then successfully in motor-boats from 1904 onwards. It was Antoinette engines that virtually made early European aviation possible. But Levavasseur was to become just as great an aircraft designer as he was an engine designer.

In 1907, Levavasseur designed a monoplane for two members of the firm — MM. Gastambide (the head of the firm) and Mengin — which emerged in February 1908 as the Gastambide-Mengin I (Fig. A). This machine and its successors provide for the monoplane the same instructive evolutionary series as do Henri Farman's machines for the biplane. It had a wing area of 24 sq. m. and weighed 350 kg.; the wings, which had pronounced camber and dihedral, were of 10·50 m. span, with a chord tapering from 3 m. to 1·70 m. The engine was a 50 h.p. Antoinette driving direct a two-bladed metal propeller at 1,250 r.p.m. (shown close up in Sect. 34, Fig. C): there was a four-wheel undercarriage (the offside rear wheel is hidden in Fig. A). This tentative machine had no control surfaces; but, following Phillips, Levavasseur introduced one feature of outstanding importance in aviation, the first wing of thick aerofoil section in which the upper curvature was greater than the lower. Up till now, attention had been paid to the camber and lifting qualities of the thin double-surface wing, with similar curvatures on top and bottom, especially by the Wrights; but here we have the practical beginnings of the efficient modern aerofoil with a high lift/drag ratio. Also seen in this machine is the start of the next practical stage — following Ferber in his biplanes and the REP. No. 1 — of incorporating a "floating tail", rather than a "lifting tail", for monoplanes. The Gastambide-Mengin I made some 4 take-offs at Bagatelle (piloted by the mechanic Boyer) from February 8th to 14th, 1908, its best hop being 150 m. on the 13th. It is uncertain whether there were any tests after the 14th, when it crash-landed; probably not.

[134]

A. Gastambide-Mengin I: 1908

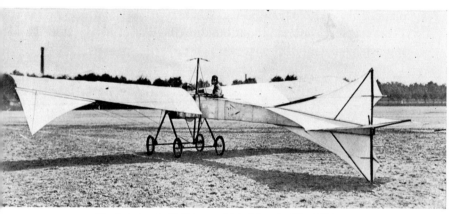

B. Antoinette II (Gastambide-Mengin II): 1908

C. Antoinette II (Gastambide-Mengin II): 1908

GASTAMBIDE-MENGIN/ANTOINETTE

The machine was rebuilt by July 1908, when it was sometimes referred to as the Gastambide-Mengin II, but also — and more correctly as we now know — as the Antoinette II (Figs. B, C). It made its first take-off on July 22nd, and was extensively tested during July and August at Issy, piloted by Welferinger (of the Antoinette firm); it also appears to have been slightly modified in its stabilising and control surfaces along the way. Unfortunately, the specification of this new monoplane has not yet been found: but it has now taken on something of the true Antoinette "look" of the later developed machines: it had triangular ailerons (invisible against the sky in Fig. C), twin rudders, and an elevator. On August 20th, Welferinger carried Robert Gastambide for two short hops (the best was 100 m.); and on August 21st the machine made a creditable flight of 1 min. 36 sec., during which it performed a complete circle — the first by a monoplane. This seems to have been its last test.

Levavasseur then set about building the first of his developed and sophisticated Antoinettes (see Sect. 49).

First Half of 1908:
ELLEHAMMER; THE A.E.A.

In Denmark, Ellehammer persevered, but did not advance aviation technically, with his No. IV (Fig. A) which was a tractor biplane with the same engine as the triplane, and the same pendulum control system. It started making take-offs on January 14th, 1908, and at Kiel on June 28th made the first official hop-flights in Germany: there were two of 11 sec. each, which could have been exceeded had the ground allowed. Then the machine, which was not practical, was abandoned.

It was the founding in the U.S.A. of the Aerial Experiment Association by Mrs. (the prime mover and provider of the money) and Dr. Graham Bell (the leader), Glenn Curtiss and others at Hammondsport on Lake Keuka in September 1907, that was later to lead to the only American rival of the Wrights in the person of Glenn Curtiss. The Association produced four pusher biplanes in 1908–09 called "Aerodromes" — following Langley's misnomer — which derived initially from the Wrights, with some Voisin influence. Each of the first three machines had a forward elevator, wings curving towards one another from the centre section, a rear rudder, and a tailplane for longitudinal stability: the first three had the excellent Curtiss air-cooled V-8 engine of 30–40 h.p. The object of the combined dihedral and anhedral seems to have been to obtain lateral stability with the lower wings, and minimise the disturbing forces of side gusts with the upper.

The first A.E.A. machine was the *Red Wing* (Fig. B) designed by another member, Lieut. T. E. Selfridge, who was to meet his death as powered aviation's first fatality in September 1908. It had a wing area of 385·7 sq. ft., a span of 43 ft. and a weight of 385 lbs. It had no lateral control, and was fitted with a skid undercarriage for taking off from the ice-covered lake. It was only tested twice, both times on Lake Keuka on March 12th, 1908, piloted (in Selfridge's absence) by another member, the Canadian F. W. Baldwin: the best of the two hops made was the first, of 319 ft.; but the machine was abandoned after crash landing at the second.

The second A.E.A. biplane was the *White Wing*, designed by Baldwin, with small ailerons and a wheeled undercarriage (Fig. C). This machine made 5 take-offs from May 18th to 23rd, 1908, piloted

A. Ellehammer IV: 1908

B. A.E.A. *Red Wing*: 1908

C. A.E.A. *White Wing*: 1908

D. A.E.A. *June Bug*, Curtiss piloting: 1908

by various members. Its best performance was on May 22nd, when it covered 1,017 ft. in 19 sec. It, too, was abandoned after a crash-landing.

The third A.E.A machine, the *June Bug*, was designed by Curtiss and was a more sophisticated aircraft, with four triangular wing-tip ailerons and a biplane tail-unit (Fig. D): it made over 30 take-offs from June 21st to August 31st, 1908, piloted mostly by Curtiss and the Canadian J. A. D. McCurdy, another member; its best performances were 1 mile (July 10th), $1\frac{1}{2}$ miles (July 29th) and 2 miles (August 29th): on July 4th, 1908 Curtiss won the *Scientific American* magazine's trophy for the first officially recorded flight of over a kilometre in the U.S.A., with a flight of 5,090 ft. in 1 min. $42\frac{1}{2}$ sec. This machine — which also made one circle — was still little more than a primitive affair; but Curtiss was, in his next biplane the *Gold Bug* (see Sect. 62) to produce an excellent aeroplane.

The fourth A.E.A machine, *Silver Dart*, which McCurdy flew in Canada in 1909, is described in Sect. 59.

41

The Year 1908:
REP. 2; BLÉRIOT VIII

The lone figure of Esnault-Pelterie produced the second version of his monoplane in 1908, the REP. No. 2 (Figs. A and B). It was now "cleaned up" all round, and a great improvement on the first, with a wing area of 17 sq. m., a span of 8·6 m., and a weight of 350 kg. There was the same 7-cylinder air-cooled REP. engine of 30 h.p. driving direct a four-bladed propeller. The wing anhedral, with downward warping control, had been retained; but a large expanse of fin area (somewhat lost against the sky in Fig. A) was added to improve directional and lateral stability, along with a larger tailplane, a rear rudder, and twin auxiliary elevators on the fuselage just behind and below the engine, which were later removed (Fig. B). The tandem undercarriage and wing wheels were as before, but efficient hydraulic brakes were fitted — history's first. This machine made an unknown number of tests at Buc, from June 8th, 1908 to the end of November, which included a flight on June 8th of 1,200 m. at an unconfirmed speed of some 50–55 m.p.h. ("une vitesse vertigineuse"), an extraordinary achievement at that time: it also attained an unofficial height record of 30 m. on that day. Esnault-Pelterie's machines, although growingly successful, did not appeal to his contemporaries as worthy of imitation, probably owing to their low degree of inherent stability.

Meanwhile, Blériot had come near to his finalised monoplane configuration in his No. VIII, except in lateral control, which first flew on June 17th, 1908; between then and October 31st it made — in its three versions — over 30 take-offs at Issy and Toury. It was a tractor monoplane with a long "trellis" fuselage, a wing area of 22 sq. m., an initial span of 11 m. later reduced to 8·5 m., and a 50 h.p. Antoinette engine driving direct a four-blade metal propeller (badly retouched on one blade in Fig. D). When first completed, it was an enclosed fuselage type (reminiscent of the VII), but did not fly in this form. In its first tested form (Fig. C) two inadequate triangular ailerons were fitted at the wing-tips, a lifting tailplane flanked by twin elevators, and a rudder. It was tested from June 17th to June 29th at Issy; and of its half-dozen take-offs, the best achievement was 700 m. on June 29th.

Either during these tests, or immediately after, large flap-type ailerons (down-moving only) were fitted — the first of their type in history — and the machine was re-designated the Blériot VIII-*bis*

[140]

A. REP. 2: 1908 (fin invisible against sky)

B. REP. 2: 1908

C. Blériot VIII: 1908

D. Blériot VIII-*bis*: 1908

E. Blériot VIII-*ter*: 1908

(Fig. D): in this form it made some fair flights, incuding several turns, among its more than 20 take-offs at Issy during July and September; the best was of 8 min. 24 sec. duration, on July 6th.

The Blériot VIII was modified in September 1908 to become the Blériot VIII-*ter* by having pivoted wing-tip elevons substituted for the flap-type ailerons — thus returning to his practice with the *Libellule* of 1907 — and the fixed tailplane placed on top of the fuselage slightly forward of the rear elevators (Fig. E). In this form, the machine made some half-dozen take-offs from October 2nd to 31st, 1908, when its best flights were one of 4·5 km. (2¾ miles) at Issy on October 2nd, and a celebrated cross-country journey from Toury around Artenay and back (October 31st) a distance of about 28 km. (17⅜ miles) which it made, with two landings en route, in about 22 minutes flying time.

It should be noted that the VIII-*ter* was not flying until the Autumn of 1908, and is only included here to show it along with its earlier versions: its performance should be compared with those aircraft dealt with after the sections on the Wrights in 1908.

The Year 1908:
THE STANDARD WRIGHT MODEL A

The Wrights had not once left the ground between October 16th, 1905 and May 6th, 1908 — a period of $2\frac{1}{2}$ years — nor did they allow anyone to view their machine. This interregnum, as noted before, was due basically to the continued thwarting of the Wrights' legitimate demand that any client must guarantee to purchase their machine provided they (the clients) agreed the desired performance, and provided that the machine performed as agreed. But the clients, particularly the U.S. Government, insisted on viewing the machine (or drawings of it) before signing a contract, an unreasonable and totally unacceptable condition to the Wrights, especially in view of the many would-be spies who had heard reports of the 1904 and 1905 flying, and were out to learn all they could.

During this lamentable $2\frac{1}{2}$ years' interregnum the brothers built some half-dozen improved engines, and two or three new Flyers, pending a satisfactory agreement with their own or a foreign Government; or — failing that — some commercial firm. These machines may now be described (see Appendix on Nomenclature) as the Wright Flyer Model A, or simply Wright A: they were the more or less standard type being built from 1907 to 1910 (see Figs. in Sects. 42, 43, 44, 45, 57, and 67). The Wrights themselves built some ten of these type A machines during the period 1907–09, apart from the somewhat modified one built for the U.S. military trials in 1909 (see Sect. 57); six were built under licence by Shorts in England, but the numbers built on the Continent are not yet known. All the machines were similar, with only minor differences such as the three differing mechanisms for operating the warp and rudder control (see Appendix VI): they represent not only the culmination of the Wrights' achievement, but the type of Wright machine which was first seen in public, and which directly inspired the last and triumphant phase of world aviation in which the powered aeroplane was established as a new and practical vehicle in the year 1909.

The approximate specification of the standard Model A was:

Wing area: 510 sq. ft.	Span: 41 ft.
Chord: 6·5 ft.	Wing Gap: 6 ft.
Elevator area: 70 sq. ft.	Rudder area: 23 sq. ft.

[143]

THE STANDARD WRIGHT MODEL A

Length: 29 ft.   Engine: 4-cyl., 30 h.p.
Weight (empty): 800 lbs.   Propellers (2) of 8·5 ft. diam.
                                                    geared-down to revolve at
                                                    420 r.p.m.
Weight (loaded): 1,000 lbs.   Speed: 35–40 m.p.h.

This type — similar in general configuration to the 1905 Flyer — was now also a two-seater, with upright seating: it still retained the skid undercarriage and derrick-and-rail launching, although it could (and occasionally did) take off from the rail on engine power alone. Also, as before, it was inherently unstable, and it was this feature — along with the rail launching — which rightly struck the Europeans as undesirable in an ordinary "workaday" aeroplane.

A. The first standard Wright Flyer, the Wright A (France) being flown by Wilbur Wright at Hunaudières: August 1908

The Year 1908:
WILBUR WRIGHT IN FRANCE

At last, after interminable negotiations, the Wrights signed contracts with the U.S. Army in February 1908, and with a French company in March. It was decided that Orville would conduct the Army tests, and Wilbur demonstrate in Europe, where (at Le Havre) a Flyer already lay crated, having been sent over to France in July of 1907.

To regain their skill, the brothers took their Flyer III (of 1905) and adapted it to take two men, who were now seated upright for the first time: this machine may be called the Wright Flyer III (mod). They returned to the Kill Devil Hills, and practised there from May 6th to 14th, 1908, incidentally making the world's first two passenger flights, when each brother took up C. W. Furnas on 14th May.

Wilbur went to France late in the same month and, after various delays, completed the assembly of the 1907-built Flyer in his friend Leon Bollée's factory at Le Mans. We may call this machine the Wright A (France). Intense and widespread interest, suspicion, and scepticism, was focused on Wilbur by both the French aviators and the Press, following the reports of the Wrights' power-flying in 1904 and 1905. Therefore, when Wilbur announced his first flight in public — he had so much confidence in the machine that he made no secret flight tests — the most critical of technical audiences assembled on August 8th, 1908 at the small local racecourse at Hunaudières (5 miles south of Le Mans).

On that memorable day, Wilbur took off, made two graceful circles and landed smoothly: he was in the air for only 1 min. 45 sec., but he had revolutionised European aviation.

European flying, despite its devotees, was still in a parlous condition, its worst features being the lack of lateral control and of proper manoeuvrability in general — the first European circle had only been made that January — and the inefficient propellers. It is hard for us today to realise the shock, and almost stunned amazement, which greeted Wilbur's effortless mastery of control, his graceful banks and turns. "No one can estimate", said one French spokesman, "the consequences which will result from this new method of locomotion, the dazzling beginnings of which we salute today." "For us in France," exclaimed Blériot, "and everywhere, a new era in mechanical flight has commenced . . . it is marvellous". "It is a revelation in aeroplane work," said René Gasnier, "who can now doubt that the Wrights have done all they claimed? . . . We are as children compared with the Wrights." "Mr. Wright has us all in his hands," said Paul Zens. The French aviation press was equally repentant, and enthusiastic; "One of the most exciting spectacles ever presented in the history of applied science." And finally, here is the great French pioneer, Leon Delagrange: "Well, we are beaten! We just don't exist!" (Eh bien, nous sommes battus! Nous n'existons pas!").

Between August 8th and 13th Wilbur made nine flights, the longest lasting just over 8 minutes. Then he received permission to use the Camp d'Auvours, the great military ground 7 miles east of Le Mans. Here, from August 21st to the last day of December 1908, he made 104 flights, and was airborne for about $25\frac{1}{2}$ hours, thus making some 26 hours for the combined French locations that year. [Continued in next section].

· · · · ·

Certain writers (referred to before) seek to diminish not only the influence of the Wrights in reviving European aviation in 1902–05, but the decisive revolution which Wilbur brought about in Europe in 1908 when he first flew in France. This was due almost entirely to his mastery of control and manoeuvre. On August 10th, 1908, *The Times*, reporting Wilbur's first flights, said: "All accounts . . . published in this morning's papers from the correspondents on the spot, attest the complete triumph of the American inventor . . . the enthusiasm was indescribable . . . all accounts agree that the most admirable characteristic of yesterday's flight was the steady mastery displayed by Mr Wright over his machine." The Europeans, until this moment, had virtually no notion of flight control: now they acquired that notion properly for the first time, and it effected the revolution necessary to bring about the final conquest of the air.

A. Wright A (France) at Hunaudières: August 1908

B. Close-up of Wright A (France) showing early-type propellers: 1908

C. Wilbur Wright about to take up Mme. Hart O. Berg at Auvours:
October 7th, 1908

A. Wright A (France) about to be launched: 1908

B. Wright A (France) leaving the launching rail: 1908

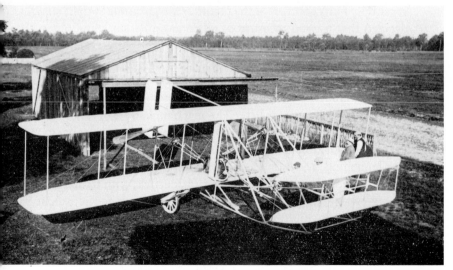

C. Wright A (France) on its handling dollies: 1908

The Year 1908:
WILBUR WRIGHT IN FRANCE (contd.)

Wilbur's astonishing 1908 "season" at Auvours included the following: taking up passengers on some sixty occasions; 14 flights of between $\frac{1}{4}$ and $\frac{1}{2}$ hr. duration; 6 of between $\frac{1}{2}$ and $\frac{3}{4}$ hr.; 6 of between 1 and 2 hr.; and his record (on December 31st) of 2 hr. 20 min. 23 sec. Also one flight to gain the altitude record of 360 ft. (on December 18th).

The world — not only of aviation but of politics and power — soon endorsed the now famous statement of Major B. F. S. Baden-Powell, the Secretary of the (later Royal) Aeronautical Society: "that Wilbur Wright is in possession of a power which controls the fate of nations, is beyond dispute."

Auvours soon became a Mecca for all those seriously interested in aviation. As Wilbur went from strength to strength, his achievements — as well as his compellingly modest personality — won him world renown. One of the first admissions to be made by even the most sceptical of Frenchmen was that, to have advanced so far, the Wrights' claims to having flown in 1903 were undoubtedly true.

The Wright machine was analysed in minute detail by the French and British visitors; the accent was always on the Wrights' superb mastery of control — especially lateral control — and its lamentable lack in Europe. But the Europeans, although they quickly realised the sensitivity to its controls of the intentionally unstable Wright machine, decided that a good measure of all round inherent stability must be built into their own future aircraft. They also rightly came to criticise the Wrights' rail-and-derrick take-off technique, when aerodromes were rapidly being prepared all over Europe.

As this launching technique is of considerable historical interest, a description of it is given here. The machine had to be wheeled about the aerodrome on two handling dollies lashed to the lower wings: they are seen in position in Fig. C, and — removed — on the left of Fig. A. For launching, a sectioned wooden rail ("monorail") of up to 100 ft. long, was laid down into wind; and the derrick, with its weight of up to $15\frac{3}{4}$ cwt. (800 kg.), was set up behind it (Fig. A). The weight was raised, either by multiple man-power, or by an automobile. The $\frac{1}{2}$ in. rope ran from the weight up to, and over, pulleys in the top of the derrick; down to the base of the derrick, and round up another pulley;

[150]

along beside the rail; up and around a final pulley at the rail end; and then back to the aircraft: here, a metal eye in the rope's end was slipped over a pin projecting downwards from the launch tow-rod of the aircraft, which was hinged to the lower wing. The aircraft's skids rested freely on a yoke ("truck") running on tandem rollers. When the weight was released by a lever on the aircraft, the machine was pulled rapidly along the rail: as it was nearing the end, the pilot raised the forward elevator, whereupon a cross-bar of the elevator-outrigger met and held the tow-rod, causing the eye of the rope to slide off the pin, and allowing the machine to take off (Fig. B). It was a laborious, but extremely reliable, technique of launching an aeroplane, and never failed in thousands of Wright take-offs. An interesting detail was still the spring device which allowed the rudder-outrigger to hinge up-wards if the rudder hit the ground on take-off or landing. Despite the obvious advantages of the wheeled undercarriage, the Wrights did not adopt wheels until 1910, although some individual owners were to add wheels to the skids of their standard Wright machines in 1909.

PS. Those writers who were curiously bent on denigrating the Wrights, point to the difficulty (and length of time taken) in 1909–10 of being taught to fly a Wright machine, and to the way in which one could learn to fly a Voisin in a matter of minutes. The truth was, of course, that becoming airborne in a Voisin — with no lateral control — was not flying in the true sense; one need only ask a pilot today what he would do without ailerons, in order to appreciate the difference.

A. Wright A (Fort Myer), Orville pil
in flight at Fort Myer: September 12th,

B. Close-up of the Wright A (Fort M
showing the "bent end" propellers: 1

C. The fatal crash at Fort Myer,
when Lieut. Selfridge was killed and
Orville injured: September 17th, 1908

45

The Year 1908:
ORVILLE WRIGHT IN AMERICA

When Orville Wright embarked on his acceptance tests for the U.S. Army in September 1908, he flew as spectacularly as his brother was doing in France: the tragedy that ended these trials did nothing to diminish his triumph. Wilbur wrote to their sister: "Tell Bubbo (Orville) that his flights have revolutionised the world's beliefs regarding the practicability of flight. Even such conservative papers as the London *Times* devote leading editorials to his work and accept human flight as a thing to be regarded as a normal feature of the world's future life."

Orville's machine, which may be called the Wright A (Fort Myer), was the second of the standard Model A type, with "Orville" controls. Supervised by officers of the U.S. Signal Corps, Orville started the tests at Fort Myer (at Washington, D.C.) on September 3rd, 1908, and crashed — killing his passenger Lieut. T. E. Selfridge — on September 17th. But, during those few days, although he made only ten flights, he was airborne for nearly six hours: the flights included one of 57 min. 25 sec., four of over an hour each (1 hr. 2 min. 15 sec.; 1 hr. 5 min. 52 sec.; 1 hr. 10 min. 24 sec.; 1 hr. 15 min.) and three passenger flights. During two flights he created altitude records of 200, then 310, ft. surpassed only by Wilbur on December 18th, 1908.

Although the first official flight in public in the United States had been made on July 4th, 1908, when Glenn Curtiss flew some 5,090 ft. in 1 min. 42$\frac{1}{2}$ sec. (see Sect. 40) this was a primitive achievement, ranking with similar flights in Europe; it was Orville's flying in September that brought home to the American public that the air had really been conquered.

The fatal crash — the first in powered aviation — happened at 5 p.m. on September 17th (Fig. C). Orville had taken up Lieut. Selfridge as an official passenger, and was making the fourth round of the field when the trouble struck. A blade of the starboard propeller developed a longitudinal crack which caused it to flatten and lose its thrust, thereby setting up an imbalance with the good blade: the consequent violent vibration loosened the supports of the propeller's long shaft, causing the latter to "wave" to and fro, and thus enlarge the propeller disc: the good blade then hit, and tore loose, one of the four wires bracing the rudder-outrigger to the wings, the wire winding itself round the blade and breaking it (the blade) off. Orville cut the motor, and tried to land; but the rudder canted over and sent the machine out of control: even then, in the ensuing nose-dive, Orville was succeeding in bringing up the nose with the elevator; but it was too slow, and the Flyer crashed, killing Selfridge. Orville was seriously injured, but made a good recovery.

From the death of Lilienthal to the end of 1908 — that is to say, during the birth years of the practical aeroplane — only four men had been killed, Lilienthal (1896), Pilcher (1899), Maloney (1905) — all on gliders — and Selfridge (1908); a very small total considering the risks.

The death of Selfridge did nothing to deter the United States Army's interest in the Wright aircraft: having seen the outstanding performances Orville had already put up, they were determined to go ahead as soon as he recovered.

46

Later in 1908:
FARMAN; DELAGRANGE

From September 1908 to the end of the year, and on into 1909, the two most famous European aviators were Farman and Delagrange, with Blériot also coming more and more into prominence. Farman and Delagrange were looked upon as the two chief rivals, but Farman was far and away ahead, both in his actual performances and in his efforts to improve his aircraft. When he returned from his fruitless visit to America in mid-August, he had his machine fitted with four side-curtains instead of the previous two, spaced to give a cell in each pair of wings and leaving the large inner area free (Fig. A). This modification — possibly suggested by the Voisins and Colliex — was to try and provide better lateral and directional stability, the aircraft still having no lateral control.

The designation was still "Henri Farman No. 1-*bis*", which we will now call the Voisin-Farman I-*bis* (mod). In this form it made some half-dozen take-offs at the Camp de Châlons (near Bouy) from September 26th to October 2nd, 1908, including the following good flights:

September 29th   42 km. (26 miles) in 43 min.
September 30th   34 km. (21 miles) in 35 min. 36 sec.
October   2nd   40 km. (25 miles) in 44 min. 31 sec.

Meanwhile, Wilbur Wright had been stealing most of the aviation thunder at Hunaudières and Auvours, but Farman at last became fully aware that much of the Wrights' success was due to their lateral control: he had previously considered aileron control — he would have been well aware of Blériot's ailerons — and now decided to fit them to his I-*bis* (mod). Four large, downward-moving, ailerons were accordingly fitted between October 2nd and October 20th (Fig. B): these were the world's first properly practical ailerons, and marked the beginning of effective aileron usage. The I-*bis* (2nd mod) — as this may be called — then made some six or more take-offs from October 20th to November 3rd, including his most famous flight, on October 30th, from Bouy to Reims — the world's first proper cross-country flight — 27 km. in 20 min. Next day (October 31st) he won the French Aéro-Club's altitude prize for attaining 25 m. Then, restless to improve his flying, Farman set about converting the I-*bis* (2nd mod) to a semi-triplane (see next section).

[155]

A. Voisin-Farman I-*bis* (mod), with four side-curtains: 1908

B. Voisin-Farman I-*bis* (2nd mod), with ailerons: 1908

C. Voisin-Delagrange III (mod), with four side-curtains: 1908   (*Note: The lower ou* *booms do not show in this contemporary photograph*)

FARMAN; DELAGRANGE

Meanwhile, Delagrange — in July or August — had also equipped his machine with four side-curtains; and, although the records do not mention it, the wing-gap was increased, as is clearly seen from photographs (Fig. C): the machine may now therefore be called the Voisin-Delagrange III (mod). From September 3rd to November 29th, it made some 12 take-offs at Issy and at Juvisy (Port-Aviation), which included the following good flights (at Issy):

September 6th   24 km. 727 m. in 29 min. $53\frac{1}{5}$ sec.
September 7th   (unrecorded distance) in 28 min. $1\frac{1}{5}$ sec.
September 17th   (unrecorded distance) in 30 min. 27 sec.

Delagrange continued to fly at Juvisy and Argentan from February 4th to the end of June 1909, but most of his flights were insignificant.

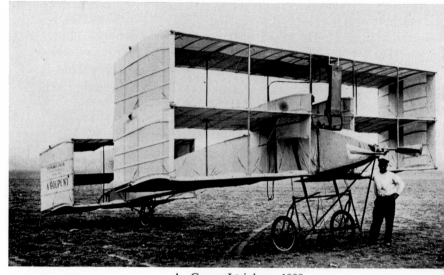

A. Goupy I triplane: 1908

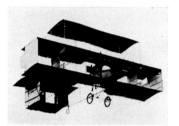

B. Voisin-Farman I-*bis* (triplane): 1908

C. Grade I triplane: 1908

D. Vanniman triplane: 1908 ("faked" photograph)

E. Cody 1–B biplane: October 190[

47

Later in 1908:
TRIPLANES; ALSO CODY

The idea of the triplane, in providing the necessary lift in a small-span and robust structure, had been in the minds of inventors ever since Cayley suggested the idea in 1843. He built and tested one in 1849. Then Stringfellow publicised the configuration in his model of 1868, which was much illustrated thereafter.

The first man to realise a full-size powered triplane was Ambroise Goupy who had it — the Goupy I — built by the Voisins at Billancourt in the summer of 1908, and tested it without success in some four take-offs from September 5th to December 7th, 1908 at Issy (Fig. A), its best hop being only 150 m. It had a wing area of 43 sq. m., and a weight of 500 kg.: the span was 7·50 m., and the chord 1·60 m., with a gap of 1·60 m., there being enclosing side-curtains at the wing-ends: there was a biplane box-kite tail enclosing the elevator, and a rudder out back: it was powered by an 8-cylinder 50 h.p. Renault driving a tractor propeller. The importance of this triplane is mostly in the influence it was to have later in inspiring A. V. Roe and others (see Sect. 61). Goupy himself went on to make an even more influential biplane (see Sect. 60).

Curiously enough, Baron de Caters had the Voisins build him a triplane closely similar to the Goupy, which made better hops — the best was 800 m. — than the Goupy, in its few take-offs at Issy and Brecht (Belgium) during October-December 1908: but it was not *en évidence* like the Goupy, and had no influence.

Of the other three triplanes to be considered here, the semi-triplane into which Farman converted his historic machine — now the I-*bis* (triplane) — made the only significant flights; but it was a bastard and sterile configuration (Fig. B). Apart from a day or two in late November 1908, when Farman re-converted it to a biplane, this semi-triplane made over 25 take-offs from November 16th, 1908 to May 23rd, 1909, its best flights being two each of 10 km. on November 17th and January 16th at Châlons. This fine old machine was finally sold to a Viennese syndicate in February 1909, and disappeared from view after its last flight there in May.

Hans Grade was the first native German pilot, and he chose to build a primitive triplane as his first aircraft, the Grade I (Fig. C): it made a few take-offs at Magdeburg from October 28th, 1908 to mid-February 1909, its best performance being 400 m. in February.

[159]

The photograph of Melvin Vanniman's triplane in France (Fig. D) is faked, as it never flew. It was an ambitious machine of 72 sq. m. area, with a forward rudder, stabilising tail-unit, and pivoting wing-tip ailerons: it was completed at Gennevilliers in France about October 1908, but could not fly.

The parlous condition of aviation in Great Britain since the death of Pilcher in 1899 has been described elsewhere by the present writer. The first powered flight in Britain was made by S. F. Cody (an expatriate American) at Farnborough on October 16th, 1908, and covered 1,390 ft. in 27 sec.: the machine, "British Army Aeroplane No. 1" (Cody 1-B) was Wright-derived, with a forward elevator, rear rudder, and an auxiliary rudder on the upper wing (Fig. E): a 50 h.p. Antoinette drove two pusher propellers. It originally had between wing ailerons (Cody 1-A), but these were removed before the first flight, which was made with the machine in the form now called the Cody 1-B. Cody was an ingenious and indefatigable pioneer, but he only influenced aviation indirectly, by helping to make Britain airminded and thus produce her own designers. Cody was naturalised in October 1909.

Later in 1908:
MISCELLANEOUS MONOPLANES, ETC.

Before considering the emergence of the two "classic" early monoplanes — the Antoinette and the Blériot XI — there are three machines which deserve mention.

First is the Koechlin-de Pischoff tractor tandem monoplane (Fig. A) which seems only to have made one hop-flight of 500 m. on October 29th, 1908 at Villacoublay, and was then abandoned. It had three sets of wings, of diminishing spans, set in tandem, with a combined lifting area of 25 sq. m. and weighed 242 kg. The span of the first pair was 6·3 m., the second 5·3 m. and the third 3 m.: there was only a fin at the rear, with twin elevators up front, where the rudder was also said to have been positioned (it is not visible in the photographs). The engine was a horizontally opposed 2-cylinder Dutheil-Chalmers of 20 h.p. This machine (ultimately deriving from Langley) seems to have been another attempt both to compact the lifting surfaces and to achieve inherent longitudinal stability. The success of the Blériot and Antoinette monoplanes was soon to consign most of these *outré* machines to oblivion.

Santos-Dumont, whose concern with his latest and last type of aeroplane was diverted first by other interests, then by illness, returned to modify his No. 19 (*Demoiselle* type) by placing a 24 h.p. Antoinette engine between the wheels, driving (via a belt) a primitive two-bladed propeller (Fig. B) the intention being presumably to achieve pendulum stability: this machine, which was known as the "19-*bis*" was completed in November 1908: it was, however, a failure, and — so far as we know — never even took off. Santos was soon to produce the next and successful version of the "*Demoiselle*-type" (see Sect. 53).

Among the stranger products of the year — and included here to show the still persisting vagaries of European inventors — was the Henri Robart semi-biplane (Fig. C) completed and tested at Amiens at the end of December 1908: it apparently just left the ground on December 21st, and was never heard of again. Its dihedrally curving wings had a span of 12·75 m. and the total wing area was 50 sq. m. A 50 h.p. Antoinette drove two tractor propellers via a chain transmission.

In the latter part of 1908, the lessons to be learnt from the Wright machines concerning dynamic flight control had been absorbed by all

A. Koechlin-de Pischoff tandem monoplane: 1908

B. Santos-Dumont 19-*bis*: 1908

C. Robart monoplane: 1908

except the Voisin brothers and their clientele. From now on, flight control and efficient propellers were to become the major preoccupations among all forward-looking designers.

The second Breguet helicopter — the Breguet-Richet II — was a gyroplane designed to rise vertically and then fly horizontally, using its two rotors for both functions. It lifted briefly off the ground twice at Douai, first on July 22nd and then on September 18th. It was then transformed into the Breguet-Richet II-*bis* and exhibited at Paris in December: this machine was tested tentatively in April 1909, but was completely destroyed when the Breguet hanger at Douai was wrecked by a hurricane in May 1909.

PS. Dollfus tells me that the Koechlin-de Pischoff tandem monoplane was later modified into a conventional monoplane and made two hops of some 500 m. each.

A. Antoinette IV: 1908 (ailerons indistinct)

B. Antoinette V, showing the between-fin rudder: 1908–9

C. Antoinette V: 1908–9

49

Winter of 1908–09:
ANTOINETTE IV AND V

Leon Levavasseur, upon whose engines nearly every European pioneer had depended since the beginning, at last came into his own as an aircraft designer: the artist in him blended admirably with the engineer, and his machines had an inherent gracefulness that prompts one to compare him with Geoffrey de Havilland who, at about this time (October 1908), was deciding to abandon the automobile industry for aviation, having been — as he records — inspired to action by Wilbur Wright's flying in France.

Levavasseur had completed his Antoinette IV by October 1908 (it will be recalled that the Antoinette III had been the Ferber biplane); this machine was to become one of the classic aeroplanes of history, and in its long life was even to fall into the English Channel! It was a tractor monoplane (Fig. A) with slightly tapering, dihedrally set, wings of thick cambered section, fitted with tapering ailerons (indistinct in the photograph), a long fuselage of triangular section, and an elaborate "floating" tail-unit of tailplane, elevator, fin, and rudder: the IV seems to have been the only Antoinette to have the small wings, of 30 sq. m. area, and 12·80 m. span: the engine was a 50 h.p. Antoinette driving direct a two-bladed metal propeller of 2·20 m. diameter at 1,000 r.p.m.: the weight was 460 kg. This machine, like its immediate successor the V, underwent various modifications to its undercarriage and tail-unit; but for some reason now lost to us, almost all the contemporary publicity, photographs, and descriptions were concentrated on the V; we do not yet know exactly what the IV looked like when it made its first take-off on October 9th, 1908 at Issy, piloted by Welferinger. (Fig. A certainly does not show its first form, which had a curious tandem-wheel-cum-skid undercarriage.) By the end of November, the IV had made only a few hop-flights, the best being 900 m. on November 18th. Between November and March it seems to have been altered — but as yet we do not know how — at the Antoinette factory at Mourmelon (Camp de Châlons) where all its tests were made from February to July 1909: it is quite likely that the larger (50 sq. m.) wings were fitted. On February 19th, 1909 it flew for 5 km: then, after the Anglo-French sportsman Hubert Latham took over as its pilot on March 26th, the performances went from strength to strength (see Sect. 55).

[165]

ANTOINETTE IV AND V

The much publicised Antoinette V (Figs. B and C) was completed in December 1908, and first flew at Issy on the 20th of that month, piloted also by Welferinger. It had larger wings than the IV, and was to set the standard for the dimensions of many — but not all — subsequent Antoinettes:* the wing area was 50 sq. m., the chord 2·80 m. at the roots and 1·90 m. at the tips: it had a weight of 520 kg.: it, too, had ailerons, but of triangular form — they were only downward acting in both Antoinettes — and in its first form a rudder curiously placed between the two-part tail-fin. It had the same type of engine and propeller as the IV. The V was built for René Demanest, a senior member of the Antoinette firm. Oddly enough, it did not perform too well until April of 1909, and its best flight of the summer was on July 9th, when it flew, piloted by Demanest, for 15 minutes at Mourmelon.

These two Antoinettes together established one of the classic monoplane-types of history.

* The dimensions and wing-area of even the standard 1909–10 type of Antoinette is given with bewildering variations in the contemporary documents, but a 50 sq. m. area seems to be the most probable.

THE YEAR
1909

50

SURVEY OF THE YEAR 1909

During 1909 the aeroplane came of age, and became accepted as the world's new practical vehicle. This acceptance was particularly signalised by two events, Louis Blériot's Channel crossing on July 25th, and the first great air meeting at Reims in August. The former was a splendid feat of daring, aided by luck, performed in a totally unsuitable machine; it fired the public's admiration — and imagination: it shook the confidence of governments in the invincibility of navies; and it cast a long and ominous shadow across the minds of many sober men, filling them with dread and apprehension for the future of mankind.

The Reims meeting, with its prizes for distance, speed, altitude and passenger-carrying, was an outstanding success; socially, officially, and above all, technically. It reinforced the message of the Channel crossing by bringing together the best in machines and pilots in an effective concentration, and exhibiting the variety and possibilities of the new vehicle: the impact on public and governments alike was formidable.

It was inevitable that the eyes of the world would remain fixed on the Wrights for much of 1909; for the brothers continued to make spectacular flights in France (at Pau), Italy, Germany and the United States, and at last received the universal honour and acclaim they deserved.

But significant developments in Europe were soon attracting attention. Having been put firmly on the right "control" road by the Wrights' example, European aviation — and Curtiss in America — developed and blossomed into mature success during 1909. Two general achievements soon emerged as dominant in aviation, and came to condition all future flying. The first was effective control in the air, control in three dimensions. This stemmed direct from the Wrights, and involved the understanding of lateral control and its co-ordination with both directional and longitudinal control, not only to preserve equilibrium, but, equally important, the dynamic employment of this co-ordinated control to *initiate* manoeuvres. Until Wilbur Wright flew in France in 1908, the Europeans had looked upon flight control in a spirit of passivity; as a technique of simply remaining intact in the air by corrective action.

It had been the chauffeur's attitude, so often noted before, in which the pilots saw themselves as driving their winged automobiles off the ground and keeping them in equilibrium on the aerial highway; and only steering them cautiously to right or left when necessary. Then, in 1908, they saw Wilbur using his flying controls actively and dynamically as an airman. Translated into the sphere of equitation — an analogy which Wilbur himself had favoured — it meant the difference between a rider whose whole effort is devoted passively to staying on the horse's back, and one who actively rides and commands the horse, and bends it to his will.

The second achievement was the successful marriage of control-cum-manoeuvrability with the inherent stability which had been a concept fostered by the Europeans (in models and full-size attempts) ever since Cayley advocated it in 1809: with this union, having now matched their mentors in control, the Europeans were now to make their own major contribution to aeronautical history.

Deliberate inherent instability, which the Wrights had seen as an essential factor in their development and mastery of flight control, meant that the aircraft had to be actively pilot-controlled during every second in the air: hence Wright pupils had to acquire considerable skill before they felt confident to fly successfully. This was not only a short-sighted flight philosophy, but was highly discouraging to the average would-be pilot, who rightly demanded a reasonable amount of repose and security when airborne. The stable aeroplane — not to appear in its fully-fledged form until the British B.E.2c of 1913 — increased safety, and reduced the measure of skill necessary to fly an aeroplane, thus increasing the number of potential pilots, and allowing the skilful a wider margin of safety in their pilotage; and all this without sacrificing controllability.

The next important feature of the first half of the year was the rise of the monoplane, a class of flying machine till now regarded as a tentative and doubtful proposition. It was the successful emergence, with steadily improving performances, of Levavasseur's two graceful Antoinettes (the IV and V), and of Blériot's small No. XI, that put the monoplane squarely in the public eye, a position of prominence greatly enhanced by these aircraft being the only protagonists in the "battle of the Channel".

Despite the growing success of the monoplane, it was the biplane which in the eyes of professional and amateur alike, still represented the only fully tried and reliable species of aeroplane during the first six months of the year; but even here, only two makes were fully established, the manoeuvrable two-seat Wright, with its rightful aura of fame; and the limited but reliable single-seat Voisin, already obsolescent, on which almost anyone in their right mind could become safely airborne in straight hop-flights in calm weather, after the briefest of briefings on the ground.

But, by the close of the Reims meeting, a newcomer, the Henry Farman biplane (basically the Henry Farman III), had blazed its way into acceptance as the leading biplane of the day — and the morrow — with a highly attractive compromise between Wright-like manoeuvrability and Voisin-like stability, and an overall air of flyability and reliability. Close runner-up in this class of biplane, and superior in speed, was the Glenn Curtiss *Golden Flyer*, which was soon to become, so to say, the Farman of the U.S.A.

There also appeared two tentative tractor biplanes, which were later to condition the form of the modern biplane: these were the Goupy II, with its staggered wings, and the Breguet I, both of which had eschewed the Wright-derived forward elevator.

A passing tribute — perhaps coupled with a retrospective sigh — should be paid to the many inventors on both sides of the Atlantic who designed, and often constructed, a strange variety of flying-machines during 1909. Few of them ever left the ground, few possessed true originality, and fewer still combined originality with any degree of practicality. In short, there was in 1909 — along with the few successful aeroplanes — a prodigious amount of wasted aeronautical energy.

In the sphere of propellers, the year saw at last one European product, the Chauvière, to rival the Wrights; and it appropriately came to power the Farman and Blériot machines. In the matter of engines, the aviators of the day had little difficulty in agreeing that it was in these prime movers that the chief weakness of aviation now lay: it was not heaviness, but the unreliability of the engines, which was the bugbear of early flying, despite the many excellent qualities of the ubiquitous Antoinette, the Vivinus, the Anzani, the REP., and the revolutionary rotary Gnome. But still the most reliable of all was the 30 h.p. Wright motor, now also being built under licence in France.

The collective identity of the aeroplane as revealed at Reims showed the world's new vehicle as capable of conveying two men through the air in comparative safety at some forty miles per hour; of being kept in satisfactory aerial equilibrium; of being adequately controlled and manoeuvred; and of being able to fly reliably for two or more hours at a time. It was now evident to one and all that the flying-machine had truly "arrived", and that the way was open to rapid progress in both biplanes and monoplanes.

[170]

51

The Year 1909:
BLÉRIOT IX AND XI

By December of 1908 Blériot had virtually completed two new monoplanes, (the IX and XI) and a biplane (the X): all were on show at the world's first full-dress "Salon de l'Aéronautique", which actually comprised Section 21 ("Aérostation et Aviation") of the annual "Salon de l'Automobile" at the Grand Palais in Paris, from December 24th to 30th, 1908.

The biplane, which was probably never quite completed, and certainly never tested, and which had no influence on aviation, was a large three-seater derived — with curious deviations — from the Wright machines.

The No. IX was a long (12 m.) monoplane of 26 sq. m. area, a fuselage of V-section (with an "armature de renforcement" to protect the pilot), wing-tip elevons, a tailplane with the main elevator above it, and a balanced rudder (Fig. A). The engine was the new 100 h.p. 16-cylinder Antoinette, driving a primitive four-bladed propeller. But the IX could only make "galops d'essais" across the aerodrome in January and February; it never flew. It is not clear what particular qualities Blériot was aiming at with this non-starter of his.

But in the No. XI (Figs. C to E) Blériot had what was to become — after modification — the second of the two "classic" monoplanes of early aviation, and the first fully successful example of wing-warping after the Wrights. Figs. C and D show it in its first form (the rudder has not been fitted in Fig. C). The pronouncedly cambered wings were of only 12 sq. m. area, with a span of 7·20 m. The length of the machine was only 8 m. Lateral control was by wing-warping in concert with two rear elevons set on either side of the tailplane; there was a balanced rudder, and a small fixed fin above the centre section to improve the longitudinal stability by providing more keel area. The engine was, in this first form, a 30 h.p. 7-cylinder air-cooled REP., driving a primitive four-bladed propeller.

The XI made its first take-off at Issy on January 23rd, 1909, and was flown at Issy and Buc through February and March without the success Blériot had hoped for it. After a two minute flight at Buc on April 5th, he withdrew it for modification.

By the end of May 1909, the XI had a new engine, a 3-cylinder 25 h.p. Anzani driving direct an excellent Chauvière propeller at

[171]

A, B. Blériot IX: 1909

C. Blériot XI, first form, minus rudder: 1909

D. Blériot XI, first form: 1909

E. Blériot XI (mod): 1909

1,400 r.p.m. The centre section fin was removed; the rudder was enlarged and made much higher; and the elevons were rigged to work only as elevators, with all lateral control being effected by the wing-warping (Figs. E and 67E). In this radically revised form it may be called the XI (mod).

Blériot was the first European to make the Wrights' wing-warping system work effectively, with Esnault-Pelterie the runner-up. The XI (mod) soon became an outstanding machine, and from May 27th until its cross-Channel triumph on July 25th, 1909, Blériot made some excellent flights at Issy and Toury, the best being:

May 31st, 1909 at Toury, about 14 km. (8½ miles.)
June 25th, 1909 at Issy, a flight of 15 min. 31 sec.
June 26th, 1909 at Issy, a flight of 36 min. 55⅖ sec.
July 4th, 1909 at Port Aviation, a flight of 50 min. 8 sec.
July 13th, 1909 from Mondésir (Étampes) to Chevilly (Orléans) with one stop, 41·2 km. (25½ miles) in 44 min.

After the Channel crossing, the XI (mod) became an honoured museum piece, and is today preserved in the Paris Conservatoire des Arts et Metiers. It did not therefore fly at Reims; but a number of "type XI" machines were completed by the end of the summer, two of which flew at Reims.

PS. Charles Dollfus tells me he has discovered definite evidence that the famous No. XI was "mainly designed by Raymond Saulnier". Doubt has often arisen over the amount of credit due to Blériot for the designs of his machines, and this new discovery is of great historical interest.

P.PS. The span of the XI (mod) was 7·8 m., and wing area 14 sq. m.

The Year 1909:
MISCELLANEOUS MONOPLANES, ETC.

This section includes only one significant aircraft, the REP. No. 2-*bis;* otherwise it presents a group of ingenious but unsuccessful machines to remind us that amid the now "full-tilt" development of the aeroplane, many inventors were still bent on exploring paths other than the central one.

The Raoul Vendome, called at the time the No. II — the I of 1907–8 having never flown — was a slender tractor monoplane clearly inspired by Blériot (Fig. A), whose most interesting feature was the independent swivelling of each whole wing in lieu of warping; they could also be operated together with varying angles of incidence. There was no rudder, and steering was to be aided by the movement of two small surfaces lying on top of the wing-ends: there was also a large rear elevator. Powered by a 50 h.p. Anzani, the Raoul Vendome II managed to make a few brief hops at Bagatelle, and was then abandoned.

The tandem idea had always had its devotees: the Astra tractor tandem monoplane (Fig. B) was clearly derived from Langley via the Blériot VI (*Libellule*); it was tested without success at Buc about January 1909, and then abandoned.

Another tractor tandem monoplane, with birds added to the Astra's ancestry, was that made by a Mons. Guillebaud (Fig. C); it was an oddly graceful monster with curving dihedral and a cruciform tail-unit, which was completed at Rouen about February 1909, but never flew.

Of more interest was the multicellular tractor tandem machine designed by Mons. Givaudan, and completed at the Vermorel factory at Villefranche (Rhône) about May 1909 (Fig. D), which also never flew: it derived from a form of box-kite comprising cylindrical aerofoils (invented by Hargrave) in which Givaudan had amalgamated one of these Hargrave cylindrical box-kite forms: all control was to be carried out by movements of the front wing, which could be moved at will about a universal joint.

In Scotland, Preston A. Watson — after reading of the Wright's warping system in 1908 — built late in 1908 or early 1909 (and patented in 1909) a rocking aerofoil above the wings to provide lateral control (Fig. E): there were three versions — this first, the II of 1910, and the III of 1913: the idea was ingenious, but not practical. It is not known whether the first version took off (it later was made into a glider): but the II and III flew with some small success.

The lone figure of Robert Esnault-Pelterie now appeared in 1909 with an improved version of his earlier machine, the REP. No. 2-*bis* (Fig. F). Its general configuration was similar to the No. 2, but the wing area was reduced from 17 sq. m. to 15·75 sq. m.: the main difference was the placing of the elevator well out at the rear to obtain better longitudinal control (the balanced rudder may also be noted). This machine made its first take-off on February 15th, 1909 (not November 21st, 1908, as is sometimes given), and made many flights between then and August, the best being 8 km. at Buc, on May 22nd. Esnault-Pelterie, after his reprehensible actions concerning the Wrights, was developing into a talented designer of engines and aircraft, and an excellent pilot; but he was always to remain outside the main stream of aviation, and did not influence it. Four REP.'s were entered for the great Reims meeting, but only the original 2-*bis* seems to have taken off. But some weeks before the meeting, the machine — along with those which did not fly — had been drastically modified: the rear elevator was rigidified into a fixed tailplane, and the wings were converted into giant elevons, an alteration which contemporaries believed caused the machine to force-land after its first take-off at the Reims meeting on August 22nd, 1909.

A. Raoul Vendome II: 1909

B. Astra tandem monoplane: 1909

C. Guillebaud tandem monoplane:

D. Givaudan multicellular machine: 1909

E. Watson rocking-wing machine:

F. Esnault-Pelterie REP. No. 2-*bis*: 1909

[176]

53. THE YEAR 1909: SANTOS-DUMONT 20 (*Demoiselle*)

A. Santos-Dumont 20 (*Demoiselle*): 1909

B. Close-up of the Santos-Dumont 20: 1909

C. Santos-Dumont 20 in flight: 1909

53

The Year 1909:
SANTOS-DUMONT 20 (*Demoiselle*)

Santos-Dumont's last aeronautical creation before a tragic illness overtook him, was his No. 20, the developed *Demoiselle* (Figs. A to C). This had a more robust bamboo fuselage of triangular section, slightly larger wing area (10 sq. m.), with a small Darracq, Dutheil-Chalmers or one of several other engines, driving an excellent Chauvière propeller (Fig. B) at 1,800 r.p.m. The engine was again placed on the wings; there was the same cruciform tail-unit on a universal joint, acting as both rudder and elevator, and hand-lever operated; the same under-wing pilot position; but now with wing-warping by means of rocking the body from side to side, operated by a vertical lever strapped to the pilot's waist. It had a weight of 290 kg.; its speed was claimed to be about 90 km.p.h. (56 m.p.h.), and its best flight duration was about 10 min.

The No. 20 made its first take-off at Issy on March 6th, 1909, and soon became accepted as the world's first viable light aeroplane; it was very popular with the public, and with a few pilots. Not being much of a vehicle, in the more serious aeronautical sense, the machine was looked upon as a sportsman's "mount", and had a limited career through 1909 and 1910. It was offered for sale in France for 5,000 francs, and in England for £300.

The No. 20 *Demoiselle* was in its way a *tour de force* in design, considering no other designer or manufacturer was willing to embark on light aircraft, and a great credit to Santos' ingenuity and enthusiasm; it certainly paved the way for future enthusiasts wishing to fly a small sporting machine. Contemporary pilots were apparently not over enthusiastic about the flying qualities of the *Demoiselle*, and found it ticklish to handle in any weather conditions much beyond a dead calm.

The Year 1909:
BLÉRIOT XII

Passenger-carrying in Europe had been little more than a stunt, and no European aeroplanes were built specially to take more than one person until well on into 1909. The indefatigable Blériot was determined to build the first of such machines. This was the Blériot XII (Figs. A to D) which first took off in May: it was a tractor monoplane with a wing area of 22 sq. m., a span of 10 m., and a weight of 620 kg. The engine was an 8-cylinder E.N.V. of 35 h.p. (later a 60 h.p. E.N.V.) driving a Chauvière propeller geared down to 500 r.p.m. The pilot and one passenger (two when Blériot won a prize at Reims in August) sat beneath the wing. Its speed was about 70 km.p.h. (43½ m.p.h.).

An important feature of the XII was its rigid wings, with lateral control exercised through two ailerons attached to the lower longerons of the fuselage abreast of the pilot (see Fig. D). Blériot felt that the pendulum stability of this machine was so effective that only small close-set ailerons were necessary.

The progress of directional control and stability in the XII is clearly shown in this series of four photographs. The lifting tailplane on top of the fuselage, and the elevator (below and aft of it) were retained throughout; but the fin surfaces and rudder seem to have given a lot of trouble.

From the first take-off and hops at Issy on May 21st, to about June 2nd, 1909, the machine appeared in two forms. The first (Fig. A) had two small rudders at the end of the fuselage, and a similar-sized fixed fin between, (which also extended forward on top of the fuselage): the paucity of directional stability must soon have become evident.

Blériot then placed a single large square rudder (balanced) on top of the fuselage, just forward of the tailplane, and two large sidecurtains up front (Fig. B). He must now have realised both the lack of length in the fin area, and the lack of keel area forward of it.

So by June 7th he had greatly reduced the size of the forward sidecurtains, and fitted a large and tapering dorsal fin (Fig. C). The photograph shows him making the third of his passenger flights, this time with his mechanic on board, on June 8th, 1909.

By the time Blériot started to fly at Douai on June 28th, he had finalised the machine by slightly lowering and lengthening the fin to meet the rudder; reducing the size of the rudder; removing the for-

A. Blériot XII (first form): 1909

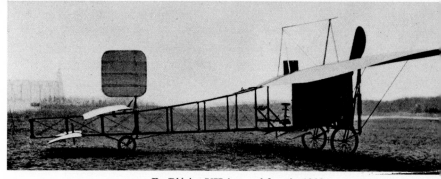

B. Blériot XII (second form): 1909

C. Blériot XII (third form): 1909

D. Blériot XII (fourth form): 1909

ward side-curtains; and covering part of the fuselage-top aft of the wings (Fig. D).

The best flight made by the XII up to August 1909 was 47·27 km. in 47 min. 17 sec. at Douai on July 3rd: the machine flew at Reims (race No. 22) but crashed on landing and was burnt (on August 29th). Blériot escaping with only slight injuries. The XII was the first to carry the pilot and two passengers, when Blériot took up Santos-Dumont and Fournier on June 12th, 1909.

The Blériot XIII was virtually a replica of the XII, but with a 40 h.p. Anzani: Blériot flew it four times at Reims (race No. 21), on three of these occasions with a passenger: its best flight there was one of 5 min. with Alfred Leblanc as passenger. It is not known how many of the XII/XIII type were built, but the number was small.

The Year 1909:
ANTOINETTE MONOPLANES

Levavasseur's robust and graceful Antoinette monoplanes are among the classic aeroplanes of history (Figs. A to C). By August of 1909 there were five Antoinettes flying (see below), two of them rebuilt after falling in the Channel in Latham's two efforts to cross it (on July 19th and 27th). It is still impossible to determine the precise details of these machines, as both French and English contemporary figures disagree among themselves and between each other. But the first of the classic type, the IV, was probably the only version with the small wing area of 30 sq. m. each of the other four having an area of 50 sq. m. But, as noted in section 50, it was modified before the end of March 1909, when it was probably given the standard larger wings of 50 sq. m. All had the 50 h.p. Antoinette engine, but one or two may have had an improved version of that engine.

The most significant features of the Antoinettes were the excellent thick wing-section, the dihedral angle of the wings, and the use first of ailerons, then of warping, for lateral control; and last, but not perhaps least, their great elegance of design.

It is a little strange that Levavasseur decided that wing-warping was to be preferred to ailerons; and all the Antoinettes from (and including) the VI onwards had wing-warping. The aileroned IV and V had their ailerons improved from the downward-moving (only) type, and made contra-acting. The warping was not entirely in the twisting of the wings, as the rear spars had some inches of down-play in their fixtures to the fuselage, which gave the whole wing a greater angle of incidence, with the twisting added to the outer rear portions. (See pages 314, 315.)

It was the brilliant flying of the Anglo-French Hubert Latham (a French citizen) which did so much to bring fame to the Antoinettes, and it was he in his two machines, the IV and the VII, who made the great majority of the best Antoinette flights.

The first five classic Antoinettes (dates are those of first take-offs) were as follows:

Antoinette IV. With ailerons. (October 9th, 1908) The first standard machine, with wing area of 30 sq. m. Flown by Latham. Crashed into the Channel, July 19th. Was rebuilt and flew

A. Antoinette IV, before the Channel attempt: 1909

B. Antoinette VII: 1909

C. Antoinette VII at Reims: 1909

at Reims as No. 13, where it won 2nd prize in the Grand Prix. (Fig. 67-F).

Antoinette V. With ailerons. Built for R. Demanest. (December 20th, 1908) Wing area was 50 sq. m. Did not fly at Reims.

Antoinette VI. With warping. Built for Captain Burgeat. (April 17th, 1909) Did not fly at Reims.

Antoinette VII. With warping. Built for Latham. (July 27th, 1909) Crashed into the Channel on its first flight, on July 27th. Rebuilt, and flew at Reims as No. 29, where it won the "Prix de l'Altitude" (Figs. B and C).

Antoinette VIII. With warping. Built for the Antoinette firm. (August 15th, 1909) Made one brief (2 min.) flight at Reims as No. 11, piloted by Ruchonnet.

The best performances by Antoinettes were: (*a*) the IV, 154·6 km. in 2 hr. 17 min. $21\frac{2}{5}$ sec. on August 26th at Reims: (*b*) the VII, altitude of 155 m. at Reims on August 29th: both Antoinettes won prizes at Reims (see above).

56

The Year 1909:
VOISIN BIPLANES

Although in the autumn of 1909 the Voisin brothers were to produce a tractor adaptation of their standard Voisin machine, this was not successful; and until well into 1910 the standard type of machine was the mainstay of the firm, and a highly unprogressive mainstay at that. But these aircraft represented the safe and steady aerial automobile to many would-be aviators, and were ordered accordingly. By August 1909 there were sixteen standard Voisins flying, apart from Delagrange's famous machine, Henri Farman's much altered one, and the Zipfel biplane; and many more were in course of construction. Seven were entered for the Reims meeting. There were minor differences in the standard Voisins — some, for example, had nose wheels — but they were basically similar. They were cellular pusher biplanes with a lifting biplane tail, equipped with front elevator and rear rudder, but no lateral control: the total lifting surface — wings and tail-unit — was 48 sq. m., of which the wings accounted for 40 sq. m. and the tail-unit 8·4 sq. m. The weight was about 530 kg.; angle of attack 6°; speed about 30 m.p.h. By August 1909, six different types of engine had been fitted to Voisins; the 50 h.p. Antoinette, the 50 h.p. rotary Gnome, the 50 h.p. Renault, the 50 h.p. E.N.V., the 55 h.p. Gobron, and the 50 h.p. Itala.

The following 16 standard Voisins had flown by August 1909: these do not include the machines built for Kapferer, Delagrange, and Farman. The modern designation (see Appendix) is given first; next the client's (or other) name placed on the tail-unit; then the date and location of the first flight:

Voisin (Moore-Brabazon): "J. T. C. Moore-Brabazon No. 3." December 1st, 1908, at Issy. The late Lord Brabazon's first Voisin. The "3" referred to Lord Brabazon's earlier attempts to build aircraft.

Voisin (Études): "Biplan d'Études." February 16th or 17th, 1909, at Issy. Built by the firm for the convenience of clients, and first used by Lord Brabazon to try out the E.N.V. engine he was to fit to his second Voisin. (Fig. C).

Voisin ("Bird of Passage"). "Henri Farman No. 2." March 7th, 1909, at the Camp de Châlons. Commissioned by, and built for,

Farman with special modifications ordered by him; sold by the Voisins to the late J. T. C. Moore-Brabazon (Lord Brabazon) without Farman's knowledge or approval, and without Lord Brabazon knowing it was Farman's. Later christened "J. T. C. Moore-Brabazon No. 4, Bird of Passage" and brought to England, where he made the first flights in Britain by a Briton (April-May 1909). Lord Brabazon could not recollect what happened to his first Voisin.

Voisin (Alsace). "Alsace." Bought by the Ligue Nationale Aérienne, April 7th, at Juvisy. The first aeroplane ever to be officially blessed (by the Archbishop of Paris) on April 1st. This was the first Voisin to have small skids under the front elevator, probably changed to a wheel *à la* Rougier (see below).

Voisin (Rougier). "Henry Rougier." (Fig. B). April 18th, at Issy. No. 28 at Reims. This was the first to be fitted with a nosewheel, which most Voisins included thereafter (not fitted when Fig. B was taken; but shown in Fig. A). (50 h.p. Renault)

Voisin (de Caters). "Baron de Caters." April 18th at Châlons. (60 h.p. Gobron)

Voisin (Gobron). "Jean Gobron." May 12th, at Mourmelon. No. 5 at Reims. (60 h.p. Gobron)

Voisin (Hansen). "Hansen." Built for a Swedish owner. May 14th, at Issy. (50 h.p. Vivinus)

Voisin (Paulhan). "Octavie No. 3." Built for Louis Paulhan. June 7th, at Bar-sur-Aube. The significance of the name cannot yet be traced. No. 20 at Reims. (50 h.p. Gnome)

Voisin (Legagneux). "Georges Legagneux." June 20th, at Copenhagen. No. 38 at Reims.

Voisin (de Rue). "F. de Rue" (Captain Ferber's pseudonym). July 9th at Douai. No. 17 at Reims.

Voisin (Fournier). "Henry Fournier." July 21st, at Mourmelon. No. 33 at Reims. (50 h.p. Itala)

Voisin (Odessa). "Aéro-Club d'Odessa." July 25th, at Odessa.

Voisin (Daumont). "Daumont No. 1." The Comte de Beauregard. August 3rd, at Issy. (50 h.p.Gnome)

Voisin (Bunau-Varilla). "Étienne Bunau-Varilla." (Fig. A). August 23rd, at Reims. No. 27 at Reims, where it won the "Prix des Mécaniciens" on August 29th. (50 h.p. Gnome)

Voisin (Sanchez-Besa). "Sanchez-Besa" (a citizen of Chile). August 23rd, at Reims. No. 37 at Reims. (60 h.p. E.N.V.)

N.B. Where no engine is given above, it was a 50 h.p. Antoinette.

A. Voisin (Bunau-Varilla): 1909

B. Voisin (Rougier): 1909

C. Voisin (Études): 1909

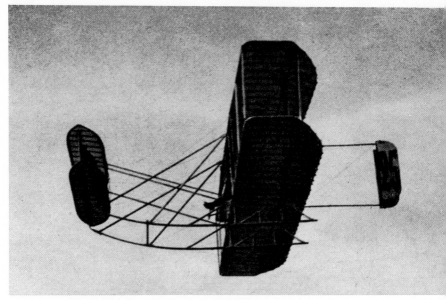

A. Wright A (Lefebvre) at Reims: 1909

B. Wright A (Signal-Corps) machine at Fort Myer: 1909

C. Wright A (Signal Corps) machine at Fort Myer: 1909

The Year 1909:
WRIGHT BIPLANES

In 1909 the Wright brothers reaped the universal honour and glory — official and popular — which was their due. This year also saw the culmination of their own pioneer flying, which had directly brought about the air age.

In January 1909 Wilbur Wright moved to the warmer climate of Pau (in south-west France) where he flew from February 3rd to March 20th, his chief concern being the completion of the training — started at Auvours — of the three French pilots called for in his contract. He was joined there in April by the convalescing Orville and their sister Katharine.

On April 1st the brothers arrived in Rome, and from April 15th to 25th Wilbur gave demonstrations and passenger flights, to great acclaim, at Centocelle (near Rome); started the training of two Italian lieutenants; and took up a cinematographer. His aircraft was a new, but still standard A machine recently assembled at Pau, the parts having been shipped from Dayton. It may be called the Wright A (Rome).

At the end of April the Wrights started their slow triumphal return home to Dayton, being honoured and fêted en route at Paris, Le Mans, London, New York and Washington.

During the period May to July, the next three "European" Wright biplanes started flying; those owned by the Comte de Lambert (May 15th), Paul Tissandier (May 18th), and Eugène Lefebvre (July 18th) (Fig. A): but all three had been made in Dayton and assembled in Europe.

On June 28th Orville made the first of his "warming up" flights at Fort Myer, Washington, D.C., in preparation for his new Army trials. The aircraft was a "one-off" modification of the Model A type, specially built for the trials, with a reduced wing area (415 sq. ft.), higher speed (about 45 m.p.h.), a higher skid undercarriage, and with no spring device on the rudder outrigger (Figs. B, C). By July 30th, after some typically excellent flying, the official tests were successfully completed, and the machine was bought by the Army. It is now preserved in the National Air Museum, Washington D.C., and often known as the "Signal Corps" machine: it is now called here the Wright A (Signal Corps).

WRIGHT BIPLANES

In France, the first great aviation meeting was held at Reims (August 22nd to 29th) in which three Wright machines flew, one of the most popular Wright pilots being Eugène Lefebvre (Figs. A and 67-A).

In August, Orville went to Germany, and between August 29th and October 15th made many successful exhibition and training flights at Tempelhof (near Berlin) and Potsdam. His machine (built in America) is now preserved in the Deutsches Museum at Munich, and is the only standard 1907–09 type Wright aircraft to survive: it may be called the Wright A (Berlin).

Meanwhile, back in America, Wilbur was making demonstration flights in September and October, and from October 8th to November 5th he instructed the first three Army pilots at College Park, Maryland, where he also took up America's first woman passenger (Mrs. Vanderman) on October 27th.

The first Wright pilot, after the brothers, was Wilbur's pupil, the ex-patriate Russian — of French descent — Count Charles de Lambert. The first Wright pilot to be killed was Lefebvre, who crashed (cause unknown) at Juvisy on September 7th, 1909, when testing a new — not his own — French-built Wright.

The English contract to build standard Wright biplanes was granted to Messrs. Short Brothers. Six machines were built, the first of which (commissioned by the Hon. C. S. Rolls) flew in October 1909, and comes outside the present survey.

58

The Year 1909:
HENRY FARMAN BIPLANES

The Henry Farman III is one of the classic aeroplanes of history; its production model became the most popular biplane in the world in the autumn of 1909, and remained so through 1911 (Figs. A to C and 67-C). It came into the world rapidly and fortuitously: as noted in Section 56, the Voisins sold the machine commissioned by Farman (Henry Farman No. 2) to the late Lord Brabazon without the knowledge or permission of Farman. This action so angered Farman that he promptly set up his own small factory to build a completely new aeroplane of his own design.

Farman had learnt from the Wrights the importance of proper lateral control, and he now finally abandoned the Voisin concept of inherent lateral stability in favour of aileron control, although he retained — along with most of the Europeans — a longitudinally stabilising tailplane, as well as the Wright-derived forward elevator. As will be seen from the photographs, Farman also introduced an overall look of lightness, "flyability", and efficiency. The new machine came to have a wing area of 40 sq. m. and a weight of 550 kg.; a span of 10 m. and the engine was at first a 4-cylinder 50 h.p. Vivinus driving a primitive Voisin propeller.

This new machine in its first form is seen in Fig. A: the cumbersome cellular tail-unit (not visible here) is the only obsolete feature, soon to disappear: the elevator is mounted well forward on a light outrigger, and there are four huge down-moving ailerons: the light four-wheel undercarriage, with its curving skids, is also a striking feature. This machine made its first take-offs on April 6th and 10th at the Camp de Châlons. It was then modified by having its lower ailerons disconnected and made into a rigid extension of the lower wing. Shortly after, four smaller ailerons were substituted (Fig. 67-F); and by August the "box" tail had given place to an "open" biplane unit — still a lifting tail — with twin "trailing" rudders (Fig. B). Meanwhile, the machine had been making creditable flights, the best (on July 19th) lasting 1 hr. 23 min. It was in this form that the No. III made its first two flights at Reims on August 23rd. The Vivinus was not behaving well, so Farman received permission to substitute a 7-cylinder 50 h.p. rotary Gnome during the meeting. This change of engine kept him from flying until the 27th; but from then on Farman became the

A. Original Henry Farman III: 1909

B. Original Henry Farman III (mod): 1909

C. Henry Farman III (Sommer): 1909

"lion" of the meeting (see Sect. 66), winning the Grand Prix (for distance) with 180 km. in 3 hr. 4 min. 56 sec. on August 27th; the Prix des Passagers (with 2 passengers), and the second prize in the altitude contest. The Reims competition number of the original III was No. 30, and this Gnome-engined version — changed at Reims — may be called the Henry Farman III (mod).

Two type III Henry Farmans were also flying by August, and both flew at Reims, making three Farmans in all to fly there. The second Farman — which may be called the Henry Farman III (Sommer) — was built for, and piloted by, Roger Sommer (Fig. C) and flew at Châlons from July 4th, 1909; then at Reims (Competition No. 6): it had a Vivinus motor. The third was built for, and piloted by, the Englishman George Cockburn — Henry Farman III (Cockburn) — and flew at the Camp de Châlons from July 20th; then at Reims (No. 32): it had a 50 h.p. Gnome.

The Year 1909:
MAURICE FARMAN; McCURDY

There are a number of miscellaneous biplanes etc., to be considered after the important machines of 1909 already dealt with. The first aircraft has little significance in 1909, but was later to grow into an important type: it may now be called the Maurice Farman I, but was sometimes called the "Maurice Farman-Neubauer", but the name of Maurice Farman's associate was soon dropped and forgotten. Maurice was Henry's brother, and already a well-known cyclist and "automobiliste". He and Neubauer designed this pusher biplane, and had it built at the Mallet factory (Henry's factory had not yet been started); it was intended to combine the advantages of the Wright and Voisin machines, but was not at first satisfactory. The wing area was 40 sq. m. and the weight 528 kg. As first built, it had no side-curtains on either wings or tail-unit: there was at first a 40 h.p. REP. engine; this was changed before the first take-off for a 60 h.p. Renault driving a Chauvière propeller geared-down to 800 r.p.m. It first took off on February 1st, 1909 at Buc and made a bad landing after a hop of 300 m.; it made a similar hop on April 26th. Then the machine was modified as seen in Fig. A, with two side-curtains on the wings and two on the tail-unit: it was not tested again until September 23rd or 24th, when it made a good cross-country flight lasting 15 min.; but this, and its later flights, fall outside the present survey.

The fourth machine produced by the Aerial Experiment Association in the U.S.A. was designed (and piloted) by a Canadian member J. A. D. McCurdy, and named *Silver Dart* (Fig. B): it was somewhat similar to the *June Bug*, but had a considerably larger wing area (420 sq. ft. as against 370 sq. ft.): there were four similar wing-tip ailerons, but a biplane forward elevator — reverting to the Wrights' practice — and a rear rudder with no other tail surfaces: it had a Curtiss engine (50 h.p. as against 30–40 h.p.). The *Siver Dart* was built at Hammondsport, but its first flight took place on the ice-covered Baddeck Bay, Nova Scotia, on February 23rd, 1909, and covered half a mile. This was the first flight in Canada, and the first in the British Commonwealth by a Commonwealth subject (Cody was not to become a naturalised Briton until October 1909); but McCurdy was not — as is often said — the first pilot in the British Commonwealth, who

[194]

A. Maurice Farman I biplane: 1909

B. A.E.A. *Silver Dart*, McCurdy piloting: 1909

was of course Henry Farman. The first Canadian to fly was F. W. Baldwin (see Sect. 40).

The *Silver Dart* made numerous flights thereafter, including one of $4\frac{1}{2}$ miles next day (February 24th), and probably one of 12 miles in March, the date being in doubt: but the machine stood far away from the main stream of flying, and only Curtiss — alone of the A.E.A. — was to influence history.

The Year 1909:
GOUPY; ODIER-VENDOME; CODY

Among the aircraft which were to appear only fleetingly during the year, but which were later to succeed and have a far-reaching influence on the development of aviation, was the Goupy II which — with the Breguet (see Sect. 61) — prefigured and helped to condition the standard biplane configuration of both the pre- and post-war periods (Fig. A). The naval lieutenant Mario Calderara (one of Wilbur Wright's first two Italian pupils) is said to have collaborated with Goupy in the design, the machine being built in the Blériot works. It was a remarkably prophetic tractor biplane, with staggered wings of 26 sq. m., a span of 6 m., and a weight of 290 kg.: there was a biplane tail-unit with elevators pivoted from the lower plane — derived from Blériot practice — and a rudder trailing aft; forward of the wings in low mid-wing position were two elevons; it had a Blériot "cloche" control column, and the engine was a 24 h.p. REP.: the castoring undercarriage and fuselage structure were also Blériot features. The Goupy II made only two take-offs, both on March 9th, and covered 200 m. and 100 m., piloted first by Goupy and then by the Lieutenant: it is not yet clear from the records why this promising machine was not immediately proceeded with, and why it was not until the end of the year that — in improved form with pivoting wing-tip elevons — it started a successful career.

The Odier-Vendôme was a tractor biplane with canopy-type wings and a biplane tail-unit, with wings of 35 sq. m., with a weight of 400 kg.: the engine was a Turcat-Méry of 18 h.p. (Fig. B). It made some 10 take-offs from June 1st to July 25th, 1909; then many afterwards, including some promising flights, of which the best was of 4 min. duration on July 25th at Issy: it also carried one and even two passengers on a number of occasions. The lateral stability — there seems to have been no lateral control — was apparently good; but the machine, although ingenious, did not advance aviation.

Cody in England had reconstructed his "British Army Aeroplane No. 1" by the end of 1908, and from the beginning of 1909 till the autumn, he continued to modify it, and made ever improving flights: he had achieved his first flight of a mile (in 1 min. 50 sec.) on May 14th, 1909. This machine is now called the Cody 2-A, and its subsequent modifications as Cody 2-B to 2-E. Unfortunately, his work was so

A. Goupy II biplane : 1909

B. Odier-Vendome biplane: 1909

C. Cody 3 at Laffan's Plain: 1909

[198]

A. Breguet I biplane (uncompleted): March 1909

B. Breguet I biplane: July 1909

C. Roe II, his first triplane: 1909

far behind the other successful pioneers, that it served chiefly to create air-mindedness among the still tardy English, rather than advance aviation technically. The illustration given here (Fig. C) shows the machine's configuration in June 1909, with large forward elevators, forward rudder, between-wing ailerons, and rear rudder.

61

The Year 1909:
BREGUET; ROE

The second of the two tractor biplanes destined to condition future development was the Breguet I (Figs. A, B, and 67-G). Louis Breguet had collaborated with his brother Jacques and with Charles Richet to produce an ambitious helicopter in 1907 (see Sect. 31): Louis Breguet had now turned to biplanes, and this first machine — the Breguet I — was to prove even more influential in the immediate post-Reims period than the Goupy II, because it (the Breguet) was to fly briefly at Reims and receive much attention. It was a tractor biplane of unequal span, with wing area of 50 sq. m., and with a weight of 600 kg.; the span was 12 m., and the engine a 60 h.p. Renault driving a three-bladed propeller. Control was by twin rear rudders, and by wing-warping for both lateral control and as a combined elevator: this is the first example of warping being used as elevons: it is not clear if there was later a conventional rear elevator on this machine. The Breguet I made its first take-off at Douai on June 28th, and made three short flights (100 m., 500 m., and 300 m.) at the Reims meeting, the last ending in a crash-landing. In 1910, as with the Goupy II, there flew a highly sophisticated development of the 1909 Breguet.

Aviation development in Britain had, as already noted, been virtually moribund from the death of Pilcher in 1899, to October of 1908 when Cody made the first powered flight in the country. Then A. V. Roe made a tentative biplane in 1908. Next, clearly inspired by the Goupy I triplane (which became known in England through illustrations), Roe constructed a small triplane with a lifting triplane tail, powered first by a 6 h.p. J.A.P. and then by a 9 h.p. J.A.P. driving a geared-down four-bladed propeller (Fig. C). This little machine made brief hops during May and June of 1909 at Lea Marshes, Hackney; on July 13th he succeeded in covering a distance of about 100 ft., and on July 23rd some 900 ft. This first Roe triplane — which we may call the Roe II — and named by Roe *The Bullseye*, had a wing area of $217\frac{1}{2}$ sq. ft., a tail area of $108\frac{3}{4}$ sq. ft. and a span of 20 ft. Control was by an elevon system of varying the incidence of the main wings to act as an elevator, and warping them for lateral control. Roe, who was later to build outstanding biplanes, re-engined this triplane in the autumn of 1909, and during 1909–10 built three other triplanes.

The Year 1909:
CURTISS BIPLANES

Glenn Hammond Curtiss was one of the great American pioneers, and it is a great pity that he later tarnished his otherwise fine name by an inexcusable campaign against the Wrights. He started, as the Wrights had done, as a seller, repairer and maker of cycles: to this he added cycle racing. Then he entered the engine and motor-cycle field, designing and building excellent motors — large and small — and machines, and himself becoming a world champion rider on them. On January 23rd, 1907 he covered a measured mile at 136·3 m.p.h. and became the fastest man in the world, his speed on the ground not being beaten until 1911, and in the air, until 1917.

As noted in Section 40, he joined Graham Bell's Aerial Experiment Association in 1907, but continued to run his own motor-cycle and engine firm. He started absorbing the craft of aeroplane design and construction, while making his own special contribution in the field of power-units, all the A.E.A. machines being fitted with Curtiss engines. He had then also produced the third A.E.A. biplane (*June Bug*), on which he won the *Scientific American* trophy in 1908.

Early in 1909, Curtiss started negotiations with Augustus M. Herring, former protégé of Chanute's, which led to the foundation of the Herring-Curtiss Company for building aeroplanes.

The first independent Curtiss aeroplane was the *Gold Bug*, built in the spring of 1909 for the Aeronautic Society of New York for $5,000; but it was soon loaned back to Curtiss, who on July 17th again won the *Scientific American* trophy this time for a non-stop flight of 24·7 miles. Naturally derived from the *June Bug*, the *Gold Bug* was a considerably smaller machine (with a weight of some 550 lbs.) and with significant differences (Fig. A). The *Gold Bug* had square-tipped (with "nicks" off the trailing edge tips), parallel-rigged biplane wings (single surfaced) instead of the tapered converging "droop", and large between-wing ailerons (each 2 × 6ft.) instead of the pointed ones on the wing tips: the wing area was 258 sq. ft., the span being 28 ft. 9 in. and the chord 4½ ft., with a wing-gap of 5 ft. There were outriggers placed fore and aft 12 ft. from the wings, which bore a Wright-type biplane elevator forward (24 sq. ft.) with a triangular fin — what the Wrights called a "blinker" — between (and extending a little above) the two surfaces: the tail-unit comprised a fixed tail-

A. Curtiss *Gold Bug*: 1909

B. Curtiss *Golden Flyer* at Reims: 1909

C. Curtiss *Golden Flyer* at Reims: 1909

plane of 12 sq. ft., and a rudder of $6\frac{1}{4}$ sq. ft. Control was by a wheel on a horizontal rod (turning the wheel to turn the rudder, and pushing or pulling the unit to operate the elevator), and a shoulder-yoke to work the contracting ailerons. The 4-cylinder 30 h.p. Curtiss engine was water-cooled and drove direct a 6 ft. propeller. There was a tricycle undercarriage.

Already, in June-July, Curtiss was building a similar machine with which to compete for the Gordon Bennett trophy at Reims in August, the differences being in weight-saving where possible, a new V-8 cylinder 50 h.p. water-cooled motor and a 7 ft. propeller.* There was so little time to spare that the motor had only had one day of bench-testing. This machine came to be called the *Golden Flyer* (Figs. B, C).

The *Golden Flyer*, bearing competition No. 8, flew at Reims with great distinction and proved itself (with the Blériot XII) one of the two fastest machines in the world, showing the surprised Europeans that a biplane could fly as fast as a monoplane. Curtiss intended only to enter the speed contests; so, as he had neither a spare airframe nor engine, he kept out of the other events, and conserved his resources. He won the Gordon Bennett cup for the U.S.A. at 75·7 km.p.h. (47 m.p.h.) on August 28th; won the "Prix de la Vitesse" at 75 km.p.h. ($46\frac{5}{8}$ m.p.h.) on August 29th; and was second in the "Tour de Piste" on the 28th.

The *Gold Bug* and *Golden Flyer* now set the style for the main U.S. rival machine to the Wrights.

* Dollfus tells me that Curtiss entered his machine as being powered by a 30 h.p. engine, which must have been deliberate, as he says all along in his own book (see Notes) that it was the new 50 h.p. This was, in fact, the subject of protest from some of the competitors at Reims.

63

The Year 1909:
ENGINES AND PROPELLERS—I

Four aero-engines had played a vital part in the conquest of the air by 1909; the three Wright engines (the 12 h.p. of 1903; the 15–16 h.p. of 1904 and 1905; and the 30 h.p. which first flew in 1908), and the 50 h.p. Antoinette. The former were designed and built by the Wright brothers, the latter was designed by Leon Levavasseur and built by the Société Antoinette, for which he designed both aircraft and engines. Of these engines, two were still in the forefront of flying at the time of the Reims meeting, the 30 h.p. Wright (Fig. A) and the 50 h.p. Antoinette (Fig. B). For a list of engines and the machines they powered, see Appendix IV.

The Wright engine, built both in Dayton and under licence in France by Bariquand and Marre, was a vertical 4-cylinder motor, water-cooled. It had no carburettor (the fuel being introduced by direct injection) and a high-tension magneto. The cylinders were of cast iron, the crankcase and cooling jackets of aluminium. Its weight was about 200 lb. including accessories, and its normal speed was 1,450 r.p.m., hence the weight per horsepower was about 6·5 lbs.

The 50 h.p. Antoinette was an 8-cylinder V-type: the 1909 engines had the cylinder head and barrel cast in one piece, with an aluminium crankcase. Part of its cooling system was evaporative, the water being converted into steam and condensed by a tubular condenser attached to the aircraft's fuselage. It weighed, with accessories, over 200 lbs. and had a speed of 1,100 r.p.m. Antoinette engines, first the 24 h.p. in 1906–07, and the 50 h.p. from 1906 onwards, virtually made European aviation viable (see Appendix IV).

Of a similar configuration, with much success attending it at Reims and after, was the excellent Curtiss 50 h.p. V-8 which powered his *Golden Flyer* and later machines.

The next advance in aero-engine design came with the arrival of the 50 h.p. rotary Gnome (Fig. C) which first powered an aeroplane — the Voisin (Paulhan) — in June of 1909; but it was made famous by Henri Farman substituting one of them for his Vivinus during the Reims meeting, and so winning the Grand Prix. The Gnome, designed by L. Seguin, was the world's first successful aero rotary: it was an air-cooled 7-cylinder motor rotating at a speed of 1,200 r.p.m. with a weight of some 165 lbs., *i.e.* about 3·5 lbs. per h.p. When

[205]

A. Wright 30 h.p. engine: 1909

B. Antoinette 50 h.p. engine: 1909

C. Gnome 50 h.p. engine and Chauvière propeller: 1909

D. Esnault-Pelterie 30 h.p. engine, and pr 1908–9

E. Anzani 25 h.p. engine and Chauvière propeller: 1909

right "bent end" propeller: 1909

B. Voisin propeller: 1909

C. Antoinette propeller: 1909

powering Farman, Voisin and other pusher types, the Gnome was always placed behind the propeller, *i.e.* the propeller revolved between the rear of the nacelle and the engine, the petrol intake being through the fixed crankshaft, around which the propeller (attached to the crankcase) revolved.

Esnault-Pelterie designed and built some promising radial engines, his 30 h.p. radial REP. being shown in Fig. D. But with engines, as with aeroplanes, he always seemed to be the "odd man out", and did not attain the success which often seemed due to him.

An engine which came into particular prominence in 1909 was the air-cooled 3-cylinder fan-type Anzani of 25 h.p. whose substitution for his 30 h.p. REP. helped Blériot to make a success of his cross-Channel No. XI (Fig. E), but it did not find much favour thereafter.

In use since 1908, but not to become fully successful until 1910 and later, were the 50 h.p. Renault and the 60 h.p. E.N.V.

PS. One of the more absurd of the statements made by Gabriel Voisin to discredit the Wrights in his autobiography (see Notes to Sect. 20) was that "the Wright aircraft was never able to leave the ground under its own power until the 1908 period when it was fitted with a French engine, built in France by the firm of Bariquand and Marre of Paris." Leaving aside the first absurdity, he cannot have been ignorant of the fact that the Bariquand and Marre engine was in fact the Wright 30 h.p. engine built under contract by that firm; also he could not have avoided knowing that Orville's spectacular flying at Fort Myer in September 1908 was carried out with the same type of machine as the one Wilbur used at Auvours, and was fitted with a Dayton-built Wright engine. It is quite extraordinary to what lengths the anti-Wright "faction" went — and still goes — to denigrate the brothers.

64

The Year 1909:
ENGINES AND PROPELLERS—II

One of the most remarkable features of the Wright brothers' work was their original research on propellers, and their design and construction of an excellent series of airscrews right from the start of practical powered aviation. Almost as remarkable was the inexplicable paucity of research on the subject in Europe (despite the many and able aviation pioneers at work) between 1902 and 1909.

The Wrights realised at the outset that propeller blades were in reality rotating aerofoils which produced "lift" forwards (*i.e.* thrust). They evolved highly efficient wooden airscrews by 1904, which were geared down and which produced a thrust of 185 lbs. at 400 r.p.m. They then produced, in 1905, their so-called "bent-end" propellers, which were used on all Wright machines from 1908 to 1910, and later (see Fig. A): they had found a tendency in their propellers to bend under pressure, and designed the bent-enders to correct this. These airscrews produced a thrust of 210 lbs. at 450 r.p.m., the sprocket ratio being 32:10.

The European propellers from 1906 to 1909 were of both metal and wood, and even of the fabric-over-frame type; but until the advent of the developed Chauvière in 1909, they were primitive to say the least. Most popular were the "spoon" types, consisting of slightly curved aluminium (or other metal) blades fixed to radial tubes, such as the Voisin (Fig. B), the Antoinette (Fig. C), and the REP. (previous Plate, Fig. D). They were not only inefficiently shaped, but were invariably direct-drive airscrews rotating at engine speeds of over 1,000 r.p.m. which gave very poor thrust.

Lucien Chauvière produced his first propellers in 1907, but it was not until 1909, when Blériot exchanged his metal REP. propeller for a Chauvière *Intégrale* on his No. XI, that proper attention was paid to these excellent airscrews (previous plate, Figs. C & E). Perhaps the most successful engine and propeller combination to be found in Europe in 1909 was the Gnome-cum-Chauvière *Intégrale* as seen in the production-type Henry Farman III's of late 1909 and after. As noted before, these propellers were always placed between the rear of the nacelle and the engine of pusher aircraft.

65

The Year 1909:
THE CHANNEL CROSSING

The outstanding aeronautical event of the year was Louis Blériot's flight across the Channel on July 25th in his No. XI (mod), thereby winning the *Daily Mail* £1,000 prize. By rights he should not have won it; for Hubert Latham — "gentleman de l'air" as one modern Frenchman has described him — was at first the only serious competitor for the prize. He had a fine robust aircraft in his Antoinette IV (Fig. 55-A), and the finest of engines in his 50 h.p. Antoinette. He set off from Sangatte (near Calais) on July 19th; but he was unlucky enough to suffer engine failure when seven or eight miles out, and had to "ditch" in the Channel, being then rescued by the accompanying French destroyer *Harpon* (Fig. A). Others also had had it in mind to attempt the Channel crossing, including the Comte de Lambert (Wilbur Wright's first pupil), and even Wilbur himself.

But success was to attend Louis Blériot, who — feeling none too fit after a recent accident when he was burnt on the leg — took off from Les Baraques (near Calais) at 4.41 a.m. and landed in the Northfall Meadow by Dover Castle (Fig. B) at 5.17½ a.m. on Sunday, July 25th, after a somewhat devious and perilous flight of about 23½ miles in his frail — and for this task quite unsuitable — No. XI (mod) monoplane, with its 3-cylinder 25 h.p. Anzani (Fig. 51-E & 67-E). "No pilot of today" says Charles Dollfus, "no matter how great, could repeat this exploit in such an aircraft and with such an engine." But luck was with Blériot, and he triumphed: it was a fitting climax to a courageous career. Blériot was widely fêted, and overnight became one of the world's popular heroes, so vividly had he struck the popular imagination (Fig. C).

This flight had as vivid and profound effect on Kings and Governments as it had on the general public. "The day that Blériot flew the Channel", wrote Sir Alan Cobham, "marked the end of our insular safety, and the beginning of the time when Britain must seek another form of defence besides ships." Although the writing on the wall was clear enough to most of those who controlled the destinies of Europe, there were still some military commanders who could not stomach the idea of an aeroplane being of any more service in war than a flying observation post. In this connection, it is lamentable to record that three months before this, in April, the British War Office had ordered ex-

[210]

A. Latham's Antoinette IV after its crash: July 19th, 1909

B. Blériot and his XI (mod), after the landing at Dover: July 25th, 1909

C. Blériot arrives in London: July 26th, 1909

periments with aeroplanes at Farnborough to cease "as the cost had proved too great": the cost was £2,500.

Two days after Blériot's Channel crossing — on July 27th — Latham again started from Sangatte in the Antoinette VII (with wing-warping), and again suffered the ill-fortune of engine failure, this time only a mile from England.

The resounding fame which attended Blériot's flight had an immediate and lasting effect on the embryo aviation industry; for Blériot himself, it resulted in orders for over a hundred aircraft, and the type XI — in various modifications — became known the world over, and remained in service as a reconnaissance and training machine even into World War I.

It is interesting to see this early aeronautical illustration of "nothing succeeds like success", where, simply because Blériot conquered the Channel, he received the orders which — from the point of view of all-round quality and efficiency — should have been placed for Antoinettes.

PS. A significant comment on Blériot's flight came from H. G. Wells, writing in the Daily Mail in July 1909. He says: "What does it mean for us? One meaning, I think, stands out plainly enough, unpalatable enough to our national pride. This thing from first to last was made abroad. . . Gliding began abroad when our young men of muscle and courage were braving the dangers of the cricket ball. The motor-car and its engine was being worked out "over there", ... Over there, where the prosperous classes have some regard for education, . . . where people discuss all sorts of things fearlessly and have a respect for science, this has been achieved. . . . It means, I take it, first and foremost for us, that the world cannot wait for the English. It is not the first warning we have had.

"It has been raining warnings on us — never was a slacking, dull people so liberally served with warnings of what was in store for them. . . . In the men of means and leisure in this island there was neither enterprise enough, imagination enough, knowledge, nor skill enough, to lead in this matter. . . . Either we are a people essentially and incurably inferior, or there is something wrong in our training, something benumbing in our atmosphere and circumstances. That is the first and gravest intimation in M. Blériot's feat. The second is that, in spite of our fleet, this is no longer, from the military point of view, an inaccessible island."

[212]

66

The Year 1909:
THE REIMS MEETING

The first great aviation meeting of history was held from Sunday, August 22nd to Sunday, August 29th in the year 1909 on the plain of Bétheny, three miles north of Reims, the scene (in 1901) of the military review in honour of the Tsar. The full official title of the meeting was "La Grande Semaine d'Aviation de la Champagne", and was under the patronage of the President of the Republic; the whole event was initiated, promoted and financed by the Champagne industry, and managed by a "comité d'organisation" under the presidency of the Marquis de Polignac. As an added inducement to the world of aviation, the Champagne industry offered a number of highly generous prizes (see below) which resulted in highly creditable performances. The aeroplane was thus finally ushered into civilisation by courtesy of the most civilised, urbane and sophisticated industry of France. The leading Champagne firms of 1909 might well have adopted as their motto these lines from the Greek Anthology:

"Wine to the poet is a wingèd steed;
Those who drink water gain but little speed."

The final list of entries numbered 38 machines, but only 23 took off during the eight days — some only briefly — with 22 pilots flying them, some sharing aircraft and some flying more than one. There were over 120 take-offs, which resulted in 87 flights of over 5 km. (3 miles), and some 7 of 100 km. (62 miles) or more, the longest being 180 km. ($111\frac{7}{8}$ miles). The best speed obtained was nearly 48 m.p.h., and the best height 155 m. ($508\frac{1}{2}$ ft.).

The meeting was an unqualified success, both technically and officially (in the way of its later influence), financially, and even socially. Many military and political chiefs, including Lloyd-George, attended and were deeply impressed. "Flying machines are no longer toys and dreams," said Lloyd-George, "they are an established fact. The possibilities of this new system of locomotion are infinite. I feel, as a Britisher, rather ashamed that we are so completely out of it."

Reims marked the true acceptance of the aeroplane as a practical vehicle, and as such was a major milestone in the world's history. The individual aircraft and pilots who became airborne, with the

[213]

approximate number of flights, is given at the end of this account; the types of machine (with numbers of each which flew) were as follows:

Biplanes		Monoplanes	
Breguet	1	Antoinette	3
Curtiss	1	Blériot type XI	2
Henri Farman	3	Blériot XII	1
Voisin	7	Blériot XIII	1
Wright	3	REP.	1

"La Piste" (race-track) at Bétheny for the flights was laid out as an oblong space with a "pylone" at each corner, one lap round which was 10 km. (6¼ miles). An elaborate layout of grandstands for 5,000 spectators, a restaurant to seat 600, the hangars, and the offices, was arranged along the west side, near both the Neufchâtel-Reims road and the railway. To make matters easy for the many visitors in Reims, signal pennants ("flammes") were hoisted on various public buildings in the city, black meaning "on ne vole pas"; white "on volera probablement"; and red "on vole."

It had been hoped that all the crops on the plain would have been cut and gathered, but this had not been completed: some crops were still uncut, and sheaves of others lay about elsewhere to provide serious hazards in the case of forced landings. But otherwise the location and surroundings were ideal.

Perhaps the greatest disappointment was the absence of the Wright brothers, who were weighed down with duties and occasions in America, and Orville making the Army acceptance trials in July. Reims was also deprived of Santos-Dumont, who had entered a *Demoiselle*, but — we do not know why — neither flew it nor appeared at the meeting. But most of the other famous aviators were there, with Henri Farman — always officially treated as English — undoubtedly the chief lion of the event,* closely rivalled by Latham.

The principal prizes at Reims, and their winners, were as follows:

"Grand Prix de la Champagne et de la Ville de Reims"; for the greatest non-stop distance, "la plus grande distance sans avoir été ravitaillés". Prize money of 100,000 francs donated by the Champagne industry and the city, with first prize of 50,000 francs (£2,000) and five others, won by Henri Farman on his

---

* *The Times* found it necessary to write, "In view of the misapprehension which apparently continues to exist with regard to Mr. Henry Farman's nationality, it may be repeated that he is the son of British parents and has remained a British subject." Farman became a naturalised French citizen in 1937.

original, but now Gnome-powered, Henry Farman III (mod) on August 27th with a flight of 180 km. in 3 hr. 4 min. 56$\frac{2}{5}$ sec. (the official time), but he kept on flying and landed after 3 hr. 15 min., the "record du monde de durée". Second was H. Latham on the Antoinette IV, with 154·5 km. (25,000 francs). Third was L. Paulhan on a Gnome-powered Voisin with 131 km. (10,000 francs).

"Prix de la Vitesse"; over a distance of 30 km. (three laps of the "piste"). Prize money of 20,000 francs donated by Heidsieck Monopole and Louis Roederer, with first prize of 10,000 (£400) and three others. Won by Glenn Curtiss on August 29th at 75 km.p.h. (46$\frac{5}{8}$ m.p.h.): second was Latham on his Antoinette VII at 68·9 km.p.h. (42$\frac{3}{4}$ m.p.h.)

"Prix des Passagers"; for one lap of the "piste" with the greatest number of passengers (excluding the pilot). Prize (one only) of 10,000 francs donated by Veuve Clicquot-Ponsardin. Won on August 28th by Farman on his own machine carrying two passengers, in 10 min. 39 sec.

"Prix de l'Altitude"; for the highest altitude (recorded on a sealed baragraph) above 50 m. Prize (one only) of 10,000 francs donated by Moët et Chandon. Won on August 29th by Latham on his Antoinette VII at 155 m. (508$\frac{1}{2}$ ft.): second was Farman with 110 m., a particularly good achievement as he strongly disliked flying high, and always felt dizzy.

"Prix du Tour de Piste"; for the fastest speed over 10 km. (1 lap). Prize money of 10,000 francs donated by Pommery et Greno with first prize of 7,000 francs and second of 3,000 francs. Won on August 28th by Blériot on his No. XII at 76·95 km.p.h. (47$\frac{3}{4}$ m.p.h.); second was Curtiss at 47$\frac{1}{4}$ m.p.h.

"Coupe d'Aviation Gordon Bennett"; an international inter-club trophy and prize (with the trophy going to the club and 25,000 francs to the pilot) for the fastest speed over 20 km. (2 laps). Won on August 28th by Curtiss (Aero Club of America) at 75·7 km.p.h. (47 m.p.h.): second was Blériot on his XII at 75·3 km.p.h. (46$\frac{3}{4}$ m.p.h.)

"Prix des Mécaniciens"; a prize decided on during the meeting to show appreciation of the work of the mechanics: the winning pilots (distance flown in a given time) received a percentage bonus for their mechanics (5 francs per km. flown). The winner was E. Bunau-Varilla on a Voisin, who covered 100 km. and won 2,000 francs for himself and 500 for his mechanics. Second was

[215]

H. Rougier, also on a Voisin for 90 km.; he received 1,000 francs and his mechanics 450.

There was also a "Prix des Aéronats" for airships, and a no-prize "Concours de Sphériques" (for balloons).

Even apparently reliable contemporary records differ about the speeds attained, so I have followed *L'Aérophile* (especially the later and more detailed tables given in the issue of November 1st, 1909).

The following is a list of aircraft which were airborne at the Reims meeting: trial flights which were made prior to August 22nd are not counted here. The Reims competition number follows the make of engine in each case.

BIPLANES

Voisin (Gobron): 60 h.p. Gobron: No. 5. Entered and piloted by Jean Gobrun. Made 5 flights; best lasted 50 min.

Voisin (De Rue) 50 h.p. Antoinette: No. 17. Entered by De Rue (pseudonym for Captain F. Ferber); piloted once by Ferber, and 4 times by Legagneux. Made 5 flights; best was 20 km.

Voisin (Paulhan) 50 h.p. Gnome: No. 20. Entered and piloted by Louis Paulhan. Made 7 flights; best was 133 km. 676 m. in 2 hr. 43 min. Won third prize in the Grand Prix (distance).

Voisin (Bunau-Varilla) 50 h.p. Gnome: No. 27. Entered and piloted by Étienne Bunau-Varilla (18 years old). Made 6 flights; best was 100 km., which won the mechanics prize.

Voisin (Rougier) 50 h.p. Antoinette: No. 28. Entered and piloted by Henry Rougier. Made 5 flights; best was 90 km.

Voisin (Fournier) 50 h.p. Itala: No. 33. Entered and piloted by Henry Fournier. Made 2 flights; best was 5 km. Crash-landed on August 25th, and was badly damaged.

Voisin (Sanchez-Besa) 50 h.p. Antoinette: No. 37. Entered and piloted by Sanchez-Besa, a Chilean citizen. Made 2 flights; best was 1 km.

Wright A (Lefebvre) 30 h.p. Wright: No. 25. Entered by the firm, Société Ariel, and piloted by Eugène Lefebvre. Made 9 flights; best was 30 km. in 29 min. 2 sec. All three of the Wright machines were made in Dayton and assembled in Europe.

Wright A (Tissandier) 30 h.p. Wright: No. 4. Entered by Société Ariel, and piloted by Paul Tissandier. Made 5 flights; best was 30 km. in 28 min. 59 sec.

Wright A (de Lambert) 30 h.p. Wright: No. 7. Entered and piloted by the Comte de Lambert. Made 3 flights; best was 116 km. in 1 hr. 55 min.

Henry Farman III and III (mod) (the original No. III) 50 h.p. Vivinus; then — changed during the meeting — 50 h.p. Gnome: No. 30. Entered and piloted by Henri Farman. Made 7 flights, 2 with the Vivinus (August 23rd), and 5 with the Gnome (August 27th–29th); best, which won the "Grand Prix" for distance, was 180 km. in 3 hr. 4 min. 56$\frac{2}{5}$ sec. on August 27th: also won the "Prix des Passagers" (Farman plus two up) on August 28th, and was second in the "Prix de l'Altitude".

Henry Farman III (Cockburn) 50 h.p. Gnome: No. 32. Entered and piloted by the Englishman George Cockburn. Made 3 flights; best was 10 km. in 11 min. 28 sec.

Henry Farman III (Sommer) 50 h.p. Vivinus: No. 6. Entered and piloted by Roger Sommer. Made about 10 flights; best was 60 km. It was in this machine, on August 29th (still at Reims), that Sommer took up Miss Gertrude Bacon, whose account of her flight is a minor classic of aviation literature.

Curtiss "Golden Flyer" 50 h.p. Curtiss: No. 8. Entered and piloted by Glenn Curtiss. Made 8 flights; best was 30 km. in 24 min. 15$\frac{1}{5}$ sec. Won the Gordon Bennett cup on August 28th and the "Prix de la Vitesse" at 75 km.p.h. on August 29th, and was second in the "Tour de Piste". Was often called the Herring-Curtiss at the time, as that was the firm the two men formed for constructing aeroplanes. The *Golden Flyer* was based on the previous machine, the *Gold Bug*.

Breguet I 60 h.p. Renault: No. 19. Entered and piloted by Louis Breguet. Made 3 flights; best was 500 m. Crash-landed on August 29th, and was badly damaged.

MONOPLANES

Antoinette IV 50 h.p. Antoinette: No. 13. Entered by the makers, Société Antoinette, and piloted by Hubert Latham. Fitted with ailerons. Made 7 flights; best was 154 km. 620 m. in 2 hr. 17 min. 21$\frac{2}{5}$ sec. Won second prize in the Grand Prix (distance). Latham's first attempt to cross the Channel on July 19th was made on this machine.

Antoinette VII 50 h.p. Antoinette: No. 29. Entered by the Société Antoinette and piloted by H. Latham. Fitted with warping. Made 12 flights; best was 70 km. in 1 hr. 1 min. 51$\frac{4}{5}$ sec.

Latham's second attempt to fly the Channel on July 27th, 1909 was made on this machine. Also won the Prix de l'Altitude on August 29th with 155 m., and was second in the Prix de la Vitesse.

Antoinette VIII 50 h.p. Antoinette: No. 11. Entered by the Société Antoinette, and piloted by Ruchonnet. Made one take-off only of 10 m., and crash-landed, but without much damage.

Blériot XI (Delagrange) 25 h.p. Anzani: No. 16. Entered and piloted by Leon Delagrange. Made 10 flights (one of which was piloted by Blériot); best was 50 km.(?) Had a tall rudder, as in the original XI.

Blériot XI (Leblanc) 25 h.p. Anzani: No. 23. Built for A. Leblanc. Entered by Louis Blériot and piloted by him (two flights) and Leblanc (1 flight of 5 km.) Made 3 flights; best was Leblanc's 5 km. Had a low rudder.

Blériot XII 50 h.p. E.N.V.: No. 22. Entered and piloted by Louis Blériot. Made 9 flights; best was 20 km. in 15 min. 56⅕ sec. Also won the Prix du Tour de Piste on August 28th, and was second in the Gordon Bennett competition: it made one flight with a passenger. It crash-landed, caught fire and was destroyed on August 29th, Blériot escaping without serious injury. The E.N.V. motor drove a four-bladed Chauvière propeller geared-down to 600 r.p.m.

Blériot XIII 40 h.p. Anzani. No. 21. Entered and piloted by Louis Blériot. Made 4 flights; best was 10 km. Also took a passenger on two ocasions. Was virtually identical with the XII, except for the engine.

REP. No. 2-bis 35 h.p. REP.: No. 3. Entered and piloted by Maurice Guffroy. Made one flight only, of 2 km.

No. of machines finally entered - - - - - -	38
No. of machines which were airborne (15 biplanes and 8 monoplanes) - - - - - - - - - -	23
No. of aircraft types which were airborne (5 biplanes and 4 monoplanes) - - - - - - - - -	9
No. of engine types used - - - - - - -	12
No. of pilots who were airborne - - - - - -	22
No. of take-offs made - - - - - - -	over 120
No. of flights made of more than 5 km. (3 miles) - - -	87

THE REIMS MEETING

Greatest timed distance flown (Farman) - - - 180 km.

Highest speed over 30 km. (Curtiss) - - 75 km.p.h. (46$\frac{5}{8}$ m.p.h.)

,, ,, ,, 20 km. (Curtiss) - 75·7 km.p.h. (47 m.p.h.)

,, ,, ,, 10 km. (Blériot XII) 76·95 km.p.h. (47$\frac{3}{4}$ m.p.h.)

Greatest altitude (Antoinette VII) - - - 155 m. (508$\frac{1}{2}$ ft.)

Note: Contemporary accounts of the Reims meeting will be found in Appendix VII.

THE SIX PRINCIPAL AEROPLANES OF 1909

There were six "key" aeroplanes flying at the Reims meeting in August 1909 — four biplanes and two monoplanes — which together stood for the coming-of-age of powered aviation, and the acceptance of the aeroplane as a practical vehicle. These six machines were:

Biplanes
- Wright Model A;
- Voisin;
- Henry Farman III [type];
- Curtiss Golden Flyer;

Monoplanes
- Blériot XI [type];
- Antoinette.

Of these six machines, all were in commercial production by August 1909, except the Curtiss *Golden Flyer*, which was soon to follow.

Each machine is presented here through a general arrangement drawing, a table of figures, and a contemporary description. All the drawings are from early issues of *Flight*, and are reproduced here by generous permission of Mr. H. F. King, M.B.E., the Editor of today's *Flight International*, as are also the contemporary descriptions, with the exception of the Wright machine.

As mentioned in the Introduction, accuracy and contemporary agreement concerning weights, measures and performances were impossible to arrive at, even in 1909; the situation is even more hopeless today, despite the survival of a few original machines, which — probably owing to warpage and other factors — make confusion worse confounded. Only one contemporary writer, the still-alive American, G. L. Loening, made a systematic attempt to arrive at accurate figures. Using data compiled mostly in late 1909, he submitted descriptions and specifications of a number of contemporary aircraft (1909–10) as a thesis for his M.A. (A.M.) degree at Columbia University: this was accepted by the University in June 1910, and the degree granted. This thesis was published as a series of articles in the supplements to the *Scientific American* magazine during the latter part of 1910. Loening consulted some dozen sources, mostly contemporary periodicals, and came to his own conclusions about what was correct among the conflicting figures. I have covered the most ostensibly reliable of his sources, and have also appealed to authorities in France. The result of my investigations has been thwarting and disappointing, the figures appearing even more confusing and contradictory than ever. I have, therefore, been forced to make my own assessments, and come to my own conclusions and approximations in the light of the available evidence.

It should be emphasised, however, that the basic and essential nature of each machine, its general dimensions, construction, performance and overall qualities, emerge clearly enough, despite the confusion of details noted above.

As a lone plate (67-G) at the end of this section, there is included the Breguet I biplane, as it was the machine at Reims which — although itself not then successful — was destined to exert most influence on future biplane design.

Note: In some of the extracts from *Flight* that follow, reference is made to illustrations: these have had to be excluded from the text, but the general arrangement drawings are included here, and those illustrating the control systems will be found in Appendix VI.

PS. The prices in pounds sterling given for each machine are those quoted (for delivery in England) in the catalogue issued by the Aeroplane Supply Co., of 111 Piccadilly, London, and dated November 1st, 1909.

WRIGHT MODEL A (1909)

Two-seat pusher biplane

Wings: span: 41 ft.
     chord: 6·5 ft.
     total area: 510 sq. ft.
     gap: 6 ft.
Elevators: span: 14 ft.
     chord: 3 ft.
     total area: 70 sq. ft.
Total Area of Rudders: 23 sq. ft.
Length: 29 ft.
Engine: 30 h.p. Wright (4 cyl.)
Propellers (2): Wright (geared-down): diam. 8·5 ft.: 420 r.p.m.
Weight (loaded): 1,000 lbs.   *Weight (empty):* 800 lbs.
Speed: 35–40 m.p.h.   *Price* (Short-built in England): £1,100

"The following notes were made chiefly from personal observation, though some of the facts were given by Mr. Wright or his associates. Most of the figures are therefore only approximate.

I was present on six different working days, and there were at least 3 or 4 flights on each day.

I twice made an ascent with Mr. Wright, but the first attempt only lasted a few seconds, the start being made in a light cross wind. It however gave one some experience of the start and landing. The second flight lasted 4 min. 25 sec.

.   .   .   .   .

The machine in general consists of a framework of spruce poles supporting two superposed main planes with two small superposed foreplanes in front and two parallel vertical rudders behind.

MAIN PLANES. These are both about 40 feet wide in front and about 6 feet from front to rear, the after corners being cut away. The frame of the planes is stoutly made of spruce consisting of an oval frame, about 1½ inches thick to which are attached the longitudinal ribs and the uprights. The ribs consist of an upper and lower batten of ash joined together at intervals by small blocks of wood which are nailed on.

There are 18 upright rods of wood, about 1½ by 2 inches and about 6 feet long. These have metal eye-bolts let in to each end, which engage in stout metal hooks fixed to the main frame. Wire pins prevent the eyes from coming unhooked.

[222]

A. Wright A (Lefebvre) at Reims: 1909

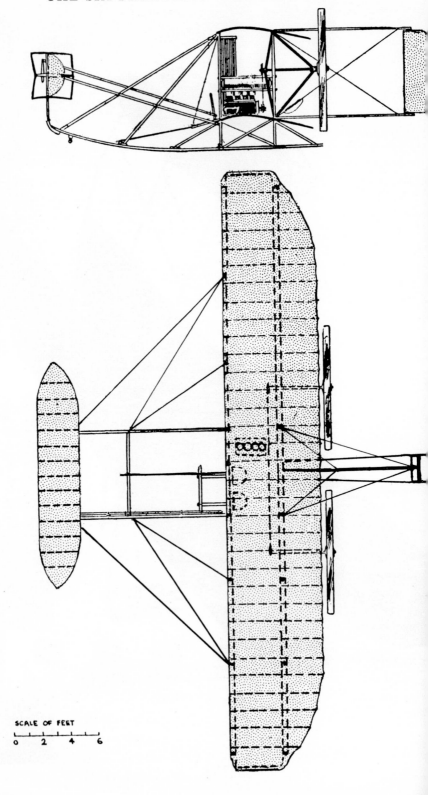

SCALE OF FEET

0   2   4   6

Diagonal wire stays run from the top of each rod to the bottom of the next. These are of soft steel (not piano wire) 14 S.W.G. with loops at either end wrapped round with thin metal and soldered. They are not tightly stretched.

The lower plane, on which rests the engine and the passengers etc. is supported about 18 inches off the ground on runners, which extend from just below the after edge to about 12 feet in front. The runners are of spruce, about $2\frac{1}{2}$ inches wide and $1\frac{1}{2}$ thick.

The planes are covered with an upper and lower sheet of grey cloth placed diagonally. This is nailed to the frame. The cloth, which is not varnished, is quite slack in dry weather, although said to become tight in damp. It is dirty and oil-spattered.

FORE-PLANES. These are each about 14 feet wide and 3 feet front to rear, but the last 3 feet at each end are formed into an ogival, so that the area would be about 35 sq. ft. each. They are 3 ft. apart. The frame consists of a transverse piece about one-third of the way from the front, a series of longitudinal ribs, and a frame all round the edge. The two planes are connected, about three feet apart, by a number of thin wooden vertical rods, two of which near the centre carry vertical vanes. The planes are practically flat. They are pivoted on a transverse steel rod in the middle. To this is clamped a short arm to which the connecting rod of the lever is attached.

VERTICAL RUDDERS. These are supported by two rods about 8 feet behind the main planes, these rods being so connected as to allow of considerable play in a vertical direction, but are held down by a strong spiral spring. If, in landing, the bottom of the rudders strike the ground, they rise against this spring. They are prevented from moving from side to side by wire stays. The rudders are about 6 feet high and 18 inches wide, and are covered (slackly) with cloth. The rudders are fixed about two feet apart by several small wooden rods, one at the top and one at the bottom being pivoted to the above mentioned rods. Wires from the ends of the lower cross-rod are fastened to the ends of a similar cross-rod pivoted to the frame of the lower main plane, which is actuated by the hand lever for steering.

STEERING DEVICES. There are three steering devices controlled by two levers on the right and left of the driver.

1. Front Control. The lever held in the left hand is pivoted at the bottom to the frame, and about six inches up is connected to a long rod, the far end of which is attached to the arm, already referred to, on the transverse steel tube which supports the foreplanes. When this lever is pushed forward the front planes are consequently depressed.

[225]

The connecting rod passes through a slot in the frame and is held tightly in it by a plate of metal, the friction of which prevents the rod from shifting.

2. Horizontal steering is effected by two means, by the right-hand lever. This lever has an ingenious double action. The lower end is fixed to a longitudinal steel tube mounted in bearings; when the lever is pushed towards or from the operator this tube is caused to turn. At its after end it carries a small upright arm which turns the same as the lever. To the end of this short arm are attached the wires which, passing round pulleys, cause the main planes to be 'warped'. These pulleys are placed at the top and bottom of the third upright connecting poles from each end (of the rear row of uprights). In order to prevent the wires breaking from the continual bending round the pulleys, short pieces of chain are inserted in the wires at those places.

3. The other action of the right-hand lever is that when pushed forward or back it causes the pivoted cross-piece (before referred to) to turn and move the vertical rudders to one side or other.

THE MOTOR. The engine has four vertical water-cooled cylinders. These are bolted to a solid-looking gear case which rests on the lower plane. It has automatic inlet valves, and the exhaust, in addition to valves, is conducted through a series of holes in the cylinder direct into the air. The motor developed 30 h.p. during long trials in America but, Mr. Wright says, since being set up in France it has not developed more than 22 to 24 h.p. It makes about 1,300 r.p.m.

The engine complete weighs about 90 kilos (200 lbs.) or 78 without coil, plugs, etc. The ignition is high tension magneto (though Wright prefers low tension). This weighs 20 kilos.

The petrol tank at first used was a vertical cylinder, but since then a larger tank, perhaps a foot in diameter, with conical ends, has been fitted. Horizontally this is said to contain enough petrol for three hours run. The radiator consists of four vertical sets of six flattened tubes, only about an eighth of an inch thick, about six feet high, with two small cylindrical tanks at the top. These sets of tubes are arranged parallel about an inch apart.

In practice a string is run across in front of where the passengers sit, which on being pulled (or accidentally struck) cuts off the ignition. This is a good precaution in case of accident.

PROPULSION. The engine shaft terminates in 2 small sprocket wheels with 8 cogs. From this, chains connect with sprocket wheels on the propellor shafts, which have 32 cogs, so that the reduction is 1:4. The chains are enclosed in tubes for most of their length.

The propellers are supported on a diamond shaped frame of steel tubes, the shaft running across the diagonal. This frame is only lightly attached to the upper and lower plane frames but is stayed with wires to keep rigid. The propeller shafts are about four feet long, the sprocket wheels being at the front end and the propellers at the after end. There are plain thrust bearings, without balls, well lubricated before each start.

Mr. Wright prefers not to give any facts relating to the propellers, but they appear to be of wood, about 9 foot in diameter and of considerable pitch. These are new ones, only just fitted on. They are said to be wider and slightly longer than the old ones. They have a considerable curve in the blade. The boss is about 5 inches long and about 2 inches thick. The blades are about a foot across at the tips.

The stationary thrust is said to be 80 kilos for the two screws.

ACCESSORIES. In order to move the machine about on the ground, two heavy wheels on frames are employed. These are affixed under the lower plane outside the runners, are tied on with bits of rope, and removed before a flight.

STARTING DEVICE. The pylon, or derrick, consists of four wooden poles, 25 feet high, with a large pulley near the top. The rope tackle draws up a weight consisting of (usually) 6 iron discs weighing 100 kilos each, and one of 200 kilos (800 kilos in all).

The rope, after leaving the block at the base of the derrick, runs round a pulley fixed to the far end of the track, and is attached to a second rope which is hauled on by a lot of men or by a motor car.

When the weight is thus raised to the top of the derrick, the rope after going round the pulley fixed to the track, is attached to a hook on the end of a wooden rod attached to the machine under the centre of the lower main plane.

The track consists of some seven beams of wood with an iron band on the top. Placed end to end, these beams are set upright on solid wooden legs, which are kept in position by pegs driven into the ground.

Each section of track is about 15 feet long, so that the whole is about 100 feet long.

The machine is held against the pull of the weights by a loop of wire fixed to the near end of the track, which engages a small hinged lever just below the operators seat.

When the machine is to be placed on the track, a thick piece of wood like a railway sleeper is placed across under the runners, which has 2 small wheels about 2 feet apart on a bar fixed longitudinally across its centre to run on the track. Another still smaller roller is fixed under a cross bar of the main frame to support the weight in front. The sleeper is left on the ground when the machine rises.

MANIPULATION. The methods of preparing the apparatus for flight appear somewhat crude and clumsy.

The machine with its wheels attached is drawn from its shed to the track. Here the wheels are detached and the machine caused to rest on the cross-bar on the track. A small trestle is placed under one end of the lower plane to keep the whole upright. The retaining wire is attached to the machine. Then the weight is drawn up, and the starting rope hooked to the hook.

(The track is laid so as to face the wind. If the wind changes in direction, as was the case in my first ascent, a false start is very likely to result).

All being ready, two men get on to the propellers, and counting 'one, two, three,' start the engine.

When the motor is seen to be running satisfactorily, the passengers take their seats, coats buttoned up and caps well adjusted. (In one case the passenger's cap flew off during the trip and was caught in the wire stays behind. Had it fallen on the transmission chain it might have led to an awkward incident.)

Then the driver opens the catch which releases the retaining wire, and the machine rapidly rushes along the track.

The foreplane is inclined slightly downward until about halfway along the track, when it is tilted upward, and the machine, hardly rising, skims through the air and gradually mounts. There are often slight undulations in the course at starting, but nothing great.

Should the wind be blowing down the track in the same direction as the machine is going, at a rate greater than 6 feet per second, Wright considers it impossible to rise.

The rate of ascent is about 3 ft. per second, or say 1 in 15.

The speed of travel is usually about 60 to 63 kilometres an hour, the fastest being 70 kilom. I timed one short bit and made it 60 yards in $3\frac{1}{2}$ seconds.

The machine travels very steadily, often going along for long distances within two or three feet of the ground so steadily that one could easily imagine it was running on wheels.

In turning corners the machine inclines over to a considerable angle. Wright says 25° is about the maximum.

It takes a very wide sweep to get round, the radius of curve being fully 200 yards, but it is possible that a much sharper turn could be made if necessary.

[228]

If the engine stopped when at a height, Wright says the machine would glide down at an angle of 1 in 8.

In landing, as a rule, the machine is brought down very low, and after skimming along just above the ground, the ignition is cut off, and the machine lands on its skids, and slides for some distance on the ground. I measured one track, from the point where the runners first touched, to the point of stoppage, and found it 30 yards."

(Notes made by Maj. B. Baden-Powell, Past President of the Aeronautical Society, at Auvours, October 3rd to 9th 1908, and communicated to the War Office in London.)

VOISIN (1909)

Single-Seat pusher biplane

Wings: span: 10 m. (32·8 ft.)
      chord: 2 m. (6·6 ft.)
      gap: 1·50 m. (4· 8 ft.)
Total wing area: 40 sq. m. (430·5 sq. ft.)
Elevator area: 4 sq. m. (43 sq. ft.)
Tailplanes: span: 2·10 m. (6·9 ft.)
      chord: 2 m. (6·6 ft.)
Total area of tailplanes (2) : 8·4 sq. m. (91 sq. ft.)
Total lifting area (i.e. wings and tail-unit): 48·4 sq. m. (521·5 sq. ft.)
Rudder area: 1·20 sq. m. (12·9 sq. ft.)
Length: 12 m. (39·3 ft.)
Engine: 50 h.p. Antoinette (8 cyl.)
Propeller: Voisin (direct drive); diam : 2 m. (6·6 ft.) 1,100 r.p.m.
Weight (loaded): 550 kg. (1,213 lbs.)   *Price* (with Gnome): £1,000
Speed: 55 km.p.h. (34·2 m.p.h.)   (with E.N.V.): £780

"The Voisin flyer is an original type of machine, and it is therefore the more important to specifically state its leading characteristics. Broadly speaking, the great point in the Voisin flyer is the fact that it has a tail, this member consisting of a kind of open-ended box carried at the rear upon a light outrigger framework extending some thirteen feet behind the main decks.

Having two principal supporting surfaces, the Voisin flyer belongs to the biplane class, and in this respect is similar to the Wright machine, with which it has another point in common, in the presence of an elevator. The elevator consists of a pivoted plane mounted about six feet in front of the main decks. Apart from the presence of the tail, the greatest contrast between the Voisin and Wright types lies in the absence of any wing warping or other special method of maintaining lateral stability in the Voisin flyer, beyond what is available from the effects of steering by the rudder.

Unlike the Wright flyer, which is supported upon runners or 'ski,' the Voisin machine, when on the ground, rests upon a wheeled chassis, and it is a leading characteristic in the construction of the machine that this chassis is attached to a kind of girder which supports the engine, contains the driver's seat, and carries an extension on which the elevator is mounted. This chassis-frame is one of the elements into which the machine can be dismantled for transport.

B. Voisin (Bunau-Varilla) at Reims: 1909

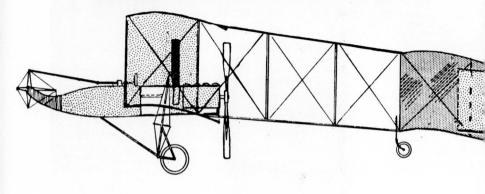

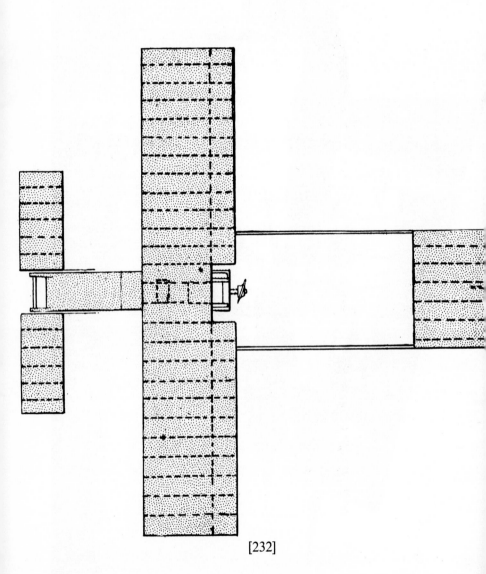

VOISIN BIPLANE

The last, but by no means the least important characteristic of the Voisin flyer is its use of a single high-speed propeller mounted direct on the crank-shaft of a 50 h.p. engine.

The main decks have a total span from tip to tip of approximately 33 ft., and a fore and aft chord of 6 ft. 9 ins. They are single-surfaced with fabric which is stretched over a foundation consisting of ash ribs lying across two transverse main spars. Two spars are placed about 5 ft. apart, and the ribs, which end up flush with the front spar, overlap the rear member a matter of 21 ins., whereby the trailing edge of the decks becomes flexible to a limited extent. This flexible trailing edge is a feature of Voisin construction, as also is the single-surfacing of the decks.

The 'Continental' surface fabric is so attached that it lies beneath the ribs, but these members are enclosed in pockets of the same material; it is this feature of the construction which gives the uneven appearance to the upper surface of the deck. In order to avoid sharp angles, the main transverse spars are also covered by strips of fabric so fastened that they give the spars a virtual triangular section.

All the ribs which lie between the two main spars are not alike, for at intervals coinciding with the vertical struts which separate the decks the ribs are considerably larger, and are built up to form an inverted T section. Before being mounted, the ribs are permanently set to the required shape, so that the decks when surfaced shall have the proper camber.

The tail, which is also of biplane form, is constructed on exactly similar lines to the main decks, and although it has a smaller gap, and a much shorter span, the chord is the same dimension. The area of the two decks of the tail is nearly one-quarter of the area of the main decks, and it is necessary to bear its value in mind when considering the effective supporting area of the whole machine. The aspect ratio of the tail is only a little more than unity.

Unlike the tail, the elevator does not resemble the main decks, either in its form or construction, for in the first place it is of the monoplane type, secondly it is double-surfaced. The elevator is, owing to its method of mounting, divided into two equal portions on either side of the girder frame, which juts out in front of the main deck. The area of both parts combined is 45 sq. ft. or a little more than one-tenth of the area of the main decks. Its effective span is 13 ft. 10 ins., and as its chord is 3 ft 3 ins. the aspect ratio of each portion is about 2.

The ribs which stiffen the elevator are sufficiently thick at the maximum section to allow the hinge-rod to pass through them, and fore and aft of this point, which lies $10\frac{1}{4}$ ins. behind the leading edge, the ribs taper to a point. The hinge-member consists of a $1\frac{1}{4}$-in. steel tube, and the maximum depth of the elevator at this point is about $2\frac{1}{2}$ ins. Being double-surfaced, that is to say, having a fabric covering top and bottom, the ribs and the hinge are entirely enclosed. The elevator is virtually cambered by its arched upper surface; the bottom surface is approximately flat.

The operation of the elevator is carried out by means of a connecting-rod attached to the steering-wheel spindle. This latter member is mounted so that it can slide in its bearings, and the pilot is thus able to set the elevator by pushing and pulling the steering-wheel bodily to and fro.

The rudder resembles the elevator in form and construction. It is situated between the decks of the tail, being mounted upon a vertical hinge pivoted upon the rear transverse spars of the tail decks. Owing to the tail itself having a flexible trailing edge most of the rudder lies wholly within the tail, only about 1 ft. 3 ins. of its chord projecting in the normal position. The hinge of the rudder is about 18 ft. 4 ins. behind the rear edges of the main decks.

The operation of the rudder is effected by wires, which pass round a wooden drum on the steering spindle.

Another feature which characterises the Voisin flyer is the presence of side-curtains between the main decks and also between the decks of the tail, these members being thereby converted into a kind of box-kite construction. Between the main decks there are four side-curtains, one at each end and another between the vertical struts adjacent to those at each end. They consist of sheets of the same surface material as is employed for the decks, and are stiffened by flat ribs enclosed in pockets. To a certain extent they may also receive support from the diagonal wire-ties which lie adjacent to them.

The real utility of side-curtains has been questioned by some aviators, and M. Delagrange has flown a Voisin machine without them. Leaving aside all considerations affecting those employed between the main decks, it appears to us that the possible influence on the effectiveness of the rudder, of those in the tail, ought certainly to be taken into consideration. We have already pointed out that the rudder is almost entirely enclosed within the tail, and it is difficult to believe that the side-curtains do not affect its action.

The part played by the side-curtains between the main decks is not altogether too well defined. They afford a considerable extent of cut-water, which doubtless assists the machine in turning, and it is possible that they also tend to minimise the direct effect of side gusts suddenly striking the machine obliquely.

After trying various different engines, Mr. Moore-Brabazon finally selected an E.N.V. motor of 50 h.p. [it was, I believe, rated at 60 h.p. — C. H. G-S.] It is an engine of the 8-cyl. 'V' type, and of very substantial construction, although specially designed for flight.

The propeller is mounted direct on an extension of the crank-shaft, and is a two-bladed construction in steel. The blades are riveted to detachable arms, which are bolted to a separate boss in a manner which is clearly illustrated in an accompanying sketch. Some observations on the pitch and efficiency of the Voisin propulsion will be found in *Flight*, vol 1, p. 16. In front of the engine, and immediately behind the pilot's seat, is a large honeycomb radiator.

The engine is mounted on a light girder framework of steel, an arrangement which is well illustrated in the accompanying photographs.

The control of the Voisin flyer is carried out entirely by the aid of the elevator and the rudder, the former being operated by pushing and pulling the steering wheel bodily to and fro, and the latter by turning the wheel upon its axis. The steering follows the same direction as on a motor car; pulling the steering wheel tilts the front edge of the elevator for temporary ascents. The purpose of the elevator is to produce temporary ascents or jumps by altering the angle of incidence of the main planes to the relative wind, and also to check any longitudinal oscillations which may occur. The elevator, although a means of beginning an ascent, is not itself endowed with any capacity for causing ascent to be maintained; that alone can result from an increase in the engine power beyond what is necessary to sustain horizontal flight. Lateral stability is maintained by suitably steering the machine, so as to give the depressed wing tip such an increased relative velocity to the air as will cause it to have a greater lift.

The weight of the machine, with the exception of that part represented by the tail, which is independently supported by a pair of small wheels, rests upon two bicycle wheels shod with 650 by 65 mm. tyres. These wheels are mounted upon a tubular framework, and have a track of 4 ft. $8\frac{1}{2}$ ins. They are so arranged that they can swing, together, to one side or the other of their normal position, like the castors of a chair, a feature which is essential in order to preserve the equilibrium of the machine when it runs along the ground. In order to restrain these movements on the part of the wheels, their hubs, which are joined by a hinged axle, are anchored to the chassis frame by tension springs, which always tend to draw the wheels back again to their normal positions.

The suspension of the flyer upon the chassis is effected by a pair of long helical springs. Each spring is mounted about a steel column which extends upwards from the chassis and passes through a bracket attached to the girder frame which carries the engine. This bracket serves as an abutment to the upper end of the spring, and it also carries a rubber pad to cushion the effect of the recoil. This point forms one of the attachments of the chassis to the frame, the other attachment being formed by a radius-rod which is hinged directly to the frame at a point further in front. When the springs compress, the effect of these radius-rods is to cant the uprights about which the springs are mounted, a point which should be borne in mind when considering the stresses to which the supporting brackets are liable to be subjected.

The pilot's seat in the Voisin flyer is situated about a third of the chord behind the leading edge of the main plane, and is contained within the girder frame which carries the engine and the elevator. On Mr. Moore-Brabazon's machine the seat consists of a simple board, hinged so that it can be raised for access to the starting-handle of the engine, which lies almost immediately beneath it. The relative position of the seat to the other principal members is clearly shown by an accompanying sketch.

From a constructional point of view a flyer presents a series of special problems in girder work, and it is therefore always instructive to consider the design on this basis. The main planes of the Voisin machine constitute together a kind of lattice girder, in which vertical wood struts alternate with diagonal piano-wire ties. Here and there extra struts and tie wires have been introduced in the manner illustrated by an accompanying diagram which shows the staying of the main spars forming the leading edges of the decks.

A point which is always of considerable importance to observe in this connection, is the continuity or otherwise of the girder from end to end, and special attention should therefore be paid to the manner in which the lower spars of the main decks are carried across through the supplementary frame used for the engine. In the Voisin construction the front spar is divided at this point and fastened to the engine girder by a bracket, an intermediate member belonging to the girder bridging the gap.

Another example of girder work in the Voisin flyer is the outrigger carrying the tail, but this consists of four rectangular spars attached by brackets to the rear transverse spars of the main decks. Each pair of spars in a vertical plane constitutes a lattice girder, and is braced in a similar manner to the spars in the main decks. There is no bracing, however, between the spars in a horizontal plane, other than that afforded at each end by the tail and the main decks respectively.

The girder, to which the chassis is attached, which carries the engine, the pilot's seat, and the elevator, is a semi-elliptic construction formed by four longitudinal spars braced together by wood struts and diagonal wire-ties. In the vicinity of the engine, tubular steel struts are used instead of ash, and the blank end of the girder is finished off with a pressed steel member, which braces three sides simultaneously.

Considerable attention has already been given to the joints and fastenings of the Voisin flyer in other issues of *Flight*, so that our readers are already familiar with the aluminium socket-brackets by means of which the struts of the machine are fastened to the spars. This in itself is a feature of the Voisin construction, not alone as a detail, but also because of the rigid system which it represents. The joints in the Voisin flyer are designed to be quite rigid throughout, and the tie-wires have tighteners fitted to them, so that they can always be kept taut. On the contrary, the Wright flyer has hook-and-eye joints between the struts and the spars, and the tie-wires are not specially stretched in place; the whole machine is, in fact, built so as to be slack, and therefore able to give when strained.

Ash is used throughout in the construction of the machine, with the exception of the steel tube work employed in the chassis. As timber, ash is characterised by its flexibility, and on the Voisin machine it must be confessed that there is not lacking evidence of its capacity in this respect, many of the struts and spars being very much inclined to bend under the load imposed upon them. In flying machine design every effort is, of course, made to keep down the weight, and sections have to be reduced to a minimum in consequence.

For the small fittings such as the socket-brackets for the struts, aluminium is employed, and this metal was also used for the main supporting brackets above the springs, until it gave way during a rough landing. Messrs. Short Brothers then introduced a pair of manganese steel brackets when making the repair, and as these members are in any case not large, the increase in weight is in no way comparable with the value of the additional strength thus obtained for such an important member.

The fabric used for covering the decks is Continental rubber-proofed material.

THE SIX PRINCIPAL AEROPLANES OF 1909

Most of the important dimensions likely to be of primary interest to the reader are given on the full-page plan and elevation. There are a few others, however, which it may be of interest to summarise here. The spacing of the ribs in the main decks is approximately 1 ft. 3 ins.; their camber is given by an accompanying diagram. The main transverse spars in the decks are $1\frac{1}{2}$ ins. fore and aft and $\frac{3}{4}$ in. deep, but the section is not symmetrical, being cut away to sharpen the leading edge. The ordinary ribs have a section of about $\frac{5}{16}$ in. by $\frac{3}{4}$ in., while the main ribs of the section are $1\frac{1}{2}$ ins. wide at the base. The struts have a maximum width of $1\frac{1}{2}$ ins. and a maximum depth of 2 ins. They taper slightly towards the extremities, and have a sharp-pointed elliptic section. The longitudinal spars forming the outrigger which carries the tail have a mean section of $1\frac{1}{2} \times 1 \times 1\frac{1}{4}$ ins., while the main spars in the central girder which carries the engine and elevator have a section $1\frac{1}{8}$ ins. square. The ribs in the elevator are spaced 1 ft. $4\frac{1}{2}$ ins. apart.

The smallest wire used has a diameter of about $\frac{1}{16}$ in., but their size varies in different places and is much larger where it is employed for staying the chassis. The tubular steel work of the chassis is mostly $1\frac{1}{4}$ ins. in diameter. The helical springs used in the suspension are 3 ft. long, 2 ins. mean diameter, and of $\frac{3}{4}$ in. circular section."

(Flight)

Note: The machine described above was the Voisin specially built for Henri Farman, which the Voisins sold secretly to Moore-Brabazon, and which became the *Bird of Passage*. Although it differed in some respects from the standard Voisins, the above description well fits the standard type.

HENRY FARMAN III (type) (1909)

Single seat pusher biplane

Wings: span: 10 m. (32·8 ft.)
    chord: 2 m. (6·6 ft.)
    gap: 2 m. (6·6 ft.)
Total wing area: 40 sq. m. (430·5 sq. ft.)
Elevator area: 4 sq. m. (43 sq. ft.)
Tailplanes: span: 4 m. (13 ft.)
    chord: 1 m. (3· 25 ft.)
Total area of tailplanes (2) : 8 sq. m. (86 sq. ft.)
Total area of rudders (2) : 3 sq. m. (32 sq. ft.)
Length: 12 m. (39·3 ft.)
Engine: 50 h.p. Gnome.
Propeller: Chauvière (direct drive); diam: 2·60 (8·53 ft.); r.p.m. 1,100
Weight (*loaded*): 550 kg. (1,213 lbs.)
Speed: 60 km.p.h. (37 m.p.h.)   *Price* (with Gnome): £1,120

"One of the most successful pioneers in the practical side of aviation — winner of the historic Deutsch-Archdeacon prize by the accomplishment of the first circular kilom., and hero of the first cross-country flight — Henry Farman has only latterly taken up the design and construction of the machines which bear his name. In his early work he used a Voisin flyer, and throughout the many succeeding experiments, in which one modification or another was made in respect to detail, the machine still retained most of what are, after all, the essential characteristics of the Voisin type.

The Farman flyer of to-day is a biplane; it has a biplane tail, carried on a rearwardly projecting outrigger, and it has a monoplane elevator in front. Where the Farman design differs materially from the Voisin system, however, is that the machine is totally devoid of vertical panels, either between the main decks or the supporting members of the tail. There is, of course, a rudder, or to be more precise two rudders which work in unison, but there is no prow, not even so much as exists on the Voisin flyer, where the covering in of the elevator outrigger serves this purpose to a certain extent.

One very natural consequence of the absence of this vertical surfacing in the Farman machine, is that it has a much lighter appearance, for there is nothing so well calculated to make a flyer look heavy as to

[239]

FARMAN BIPLANE

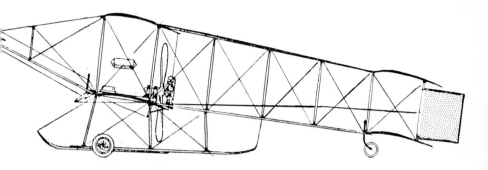

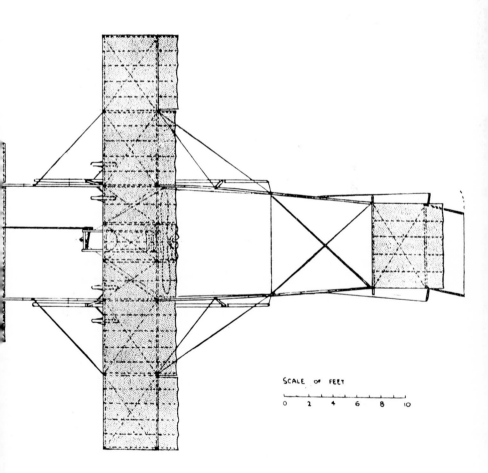

SCALE OF FEET

0   2   4   6   8   10

[241]

box it in with side curtains. Another important feature of the Farman flyer, and one which originated on this machine, is the combination wheel-and-ski chassis. Being designed for launching by running along the ground, wheels are essential in the construction, but Mr. Farman was one of the first to appreciate the advantages of the ski on the Wright machine when it came to landing after a flight. A suspension which is in every way satisfactory for running about over smooth ground, preparatory to the start, is by no means necessarily adequate to meet the very severe shocks which are apt to be associated with descents on ground which has not exactly been chosen for the purpose. Here the advantages of skis assert themselves, the extent of their tread and of their strength to resist impact being particularly valuable under such circumstances.

The main decks have a span of 32 ft. 6 ins., and measure 6 ft. 4 ins. on the chord; their aspect ratio is thus 5 : 1. The framework of the decks consists of two parallel transverse main spars, which pass from one extremity of the span to the other and lie parallel about 4 ft. 9 ins. apart. Across these spars are fastened curved ribs which overlap the rear spar by a distance of 1 ft. 7 ins.; the ribs are flush with the front spar which forms the leading edge of the deck.

The decks are single-surfaced with ordinary fine canvas, but the spars and the ribs are nevertheless enclosed in pockets of the same material. This is done in order to avoid sharp angles. The strips of fabric forming pockets for the ribs are sewn on to the upper surface. The pocket for the front spar is formed by turning back the main sheet of fabric, the edge of which is then stuck down on to the under surface. The pocket for the rear spar is formed by similarly attaching another strip of fabric to the under surface of the deck.

That part of the deck formed by the projection of the ribs beyond the rear spar constitutes a flexible trailing edge. It is not, however, continuous either in the top deck or the bottom deck, owing to the provision of hinged balancing flaps and the necessity for accommodating the propeller. The hinged balancing planes are constituted by those portions of the trailing edge lying between the last pair of main struts at each end of the span. The accommodation of the propeller involves the cutting away of the trailing edge of the lower deck only between the main spars of the outrigger frame.

The main decks are separated by vertical ash struts, 6 ft. 4 ins. in height. The section of the struts forms a pointed oval. Diagonal wire ties crossing between the extremities of the struts brace the whole structure into a lattice girder.

FARMAN BIPLANE

In addition to the framework of the main decks, the complete machine includes two outriggers for the elevator and tail respectively, and a chassis for the support of the machine upon the ground. All of these members are constructed of timber and wire, ash being the principal wood used.

The tail outrigger is built up of four longitudinal ash spars, having a rectangular section. These are braced by vertical ash struts set in flanged aluminium sockets, and lugs attached to these sockets afford an anchorage for the adjustable diagonal tie-wires. There are no transverse struts between the spars, except those formed by the transverse spars of the main decks and tail. It will be noticed on reference to the drawing of this machine, that the longitudinal spars in the tail outrigger converge as they recede from the main decks.

The elevator outrigger forms, in elevation, an isosceles triangle with its apex pointing forwards and upwards. Each pair of converging spars is braced by a single vertical member and a pair of diagonal wires. The transverse bracing between the two pairs of struts forming the complete outrigger is constituted by the bar on which the elevator hinges.

The chassis frame is formed by two longitudinal skis, attached by six struts to the main-frame of the flyer, as shown in our drawing; diagonal wires are used to complete the bracing as in other parts of the framework. The most interesting detail in the construction of the chassis is the method of mounting the wheels on the ski. They are carried by an axle which is strapped at its centre to the ski by an arrangement of rubber bands, as shown in an accompanying sketch. Radius rods diverge from the ski to opposite ends of the axle in order to prevent slewing when one wheel strikes an obstacle, but as each radius-rod is separately hinged the axle can tilt as much as is required. When the elastic spring has been stretched to its permissible limit, the ski comes in contact with the ground, and takes the load direct.

Another frame member which is of particular importance, although eminently simple in the Farman flyer, is that which supports the engine and the pilot's seat. It is shown separately in an accompanying sketch, and [see in Appendix VI on Control Systems] consists in the main of two wood spars and a simple pressed-steel bracket. The spars lie fore and aft across the main-deck spars, to which they are clamped by U-bolts in order to avoid drilling the wood. A foot-rest, and a light seat for the pilot, are fastened direct to these spars at one end, while a pressed steel bracket for the support of the engine is attached at the other extremity. The bracket itself is of quite unusual shape,

[243]

since its purpose is to provide a support for the stationary crank-shaft of the Gnome rotary engine. Its shape and position are sufficiently well illustrated by the accompanying sketch to need no further reference. [See Appendix VI.]

The elevator, tail, rudders and balancing planes comprise the supplementary surfaces of the Farman flyer. The elevator is a mono-plane constructed in three sections in order to clear the outrigger which supports it, its span being greater than the distance between the main spars of that member. The leading edge of the elevator has been made continuous throughout the span, which is 15 ft. in length. The tail is a biplane of approximately 7 ft. span. Its decks are constructed like the main decks, and are similarly surfaced. The rudder is in duplicate, the two vertical planes constituting this member working in unison. They are hinged to the rear struts of the tail, and project some little distance beyond the trailing edge of that member. Their bracing, which is an interesting constructional detail, is well illus-trated by an accompanying sketch. The balancing planes are the hinged portions of the main decks, to which reference has already been made. They are so mounted that they are free to adjust themselves to any natural position, and in flight would lie in the air stream line.

Situated at the driver's right hand, is a universally-pivoted lever, to which four wires are attached. Two of these wires operate the elevator, while the other two control the balancing flaps which form a portion of the trailing edge of the main decks, as already described. A to-and-fro motion of the lever controls the elevator, backwards movement, tilting the leading edge for ascent, and *vice versa*.

Sideways motion of the lever works the balancing flaps, the con-nections being such that when the lever is moved to the pilot's right the flaps on the pilot's left are deflected downwards, thus causing that end of the deck to be raised upwards by the increased air-pressure which results from the movement. This manoeuvre also increases the resistance on that side of the machine, and in order to obtain the increased lifting effect required it is essential that the velocity at which that end of the deck travels through the air should be maintained, otherwise the increased angle of incidence will not have the desired effect, but will only serve to slew the machine from its proper course. The desired path is maintained by operating the rudders, which are controlled by wires attached to a pivoted foot-rest. Pressing with the right foot sets the rudder so that the machine steers to the pilot's right, a manoeuvre which would be used to counteract the slewing effect of depressing the left-hand balancing flaps.

FARMAN BIPLANE

It will be observed that the connections have been designed to accommodate as far as possible what might be expected to be the natural actions of a pilot in emergency. If the machine cants so that the extremity on the left of the pilot is depressed, the pilot would naturally try to correct this by leaning over to the right, and in so doing he would automatically move the balancing-lever in that direction, and would probably also automatically press harder upon the right hand end of the foot-rest. Both actions are those which it is intended should be performed as a means of righting the machine in the case indicated.

The engine at present fitted to the Farman flyer is a 7-cylinder Gnome rotary motor. A peculiarity in the arrangement of this engine is that it is situated behind the propeller. The engine itself is of the radial type, and has its cylinders and the crank-chamber constructed entirely of steel. The cylinders are air-cooled, and have the exhaust-valves situated in the centre of the heads. The inlet-valves are in the piston-heads, the mixture being admitted through the hollow stationary crank-shaft. One of the principal problems in the development of this engine has been the balancing of the valves against the disturbing influence of centrifugal force, a difficulty which seems to have been satisfactorily surmounted, as the engine is apparently being used with success. The rotation of the cylinders affords, we are led to believe, a satisfactory solution of the air-cooling problem.

The propeller is made of wood, and has been built by Chauvière, whose workmanship invariably shows great care and high finish. The diameter is 8 ft. 6 ins., and it has two blades."

(Flight)

CURTISS GOLDEN FLYER
Single seat pusher biplane

Wings: span: 28·75 ft.
      chord: 4·5 ft.
      gap: 5 ft.
Total wing area: 258 sq. ft.
Elevators (total) area: 24 sq. ft.
Tailplane area: 15 sq. ft.
Length: 28·5 ft.
Engine: 50 h.p. Curtiss (8 cyl.) (water-cooled)
Propeller: Curtiss (direct drive); diam: 6 ft.: 1,600 r.p.m.
Weight (loaded): 550 lb.
Speed: 45 m.p.h.   *Price:* £800

"It has been left to Mr. Curtiss in America to evolve what may be termed the first rational type of one-man machine, although even in his flyer we are of the opinion that the power plant which is said to be capable of 30-h.p. has been designed on unnecessarily generous lines, and that it might have led to a much greater achievement had the same skill been exercised in the design of an engine of but little more than half that power.

The weight of the engine itself without its accessories is only 85 lbs. The radiator, magneto, &c., add another 107 lbs., and thus bring the power plant complete up to 192 lbs., which is still considerably below anything of this power actually in successful use. It is, of course, very easy to understand why a pioneer of a new type does not want to take too many risks simultaneously, and having, as Curtiss has, cut down the supporting area of the main plane to 272 sq. ft., whereas those on the Wright flyer are about 560 sq. ft., it is perhaps not to be wondered at that he should hardly desire in the first instance to take risks also with the engine. [Unknown to most writers at the time, the engine which Curtiss fitted to his Reims *Golden Flyer* was his new 50 h.p. 8-cylinder V, see page 204 — C. H. G-S.]

The Curtiss flyer is a biplane having two decks spaced 5 feet apart by laminated struts, which, like the main spars, are of Oregon spruce. Each deck is 28 ft. 9 in. span, and has a chord of 4 ft. 6 in. The decks are considerably cambered, the maximum height of the curvature being about one-ninth the chord. Baldwin rubberised silk, similar to that employed in the U.S.A. Army dirigible 'No. 1,' is

[246]

D. Glenn Curtiss flying his *Gold Bug*: 1909

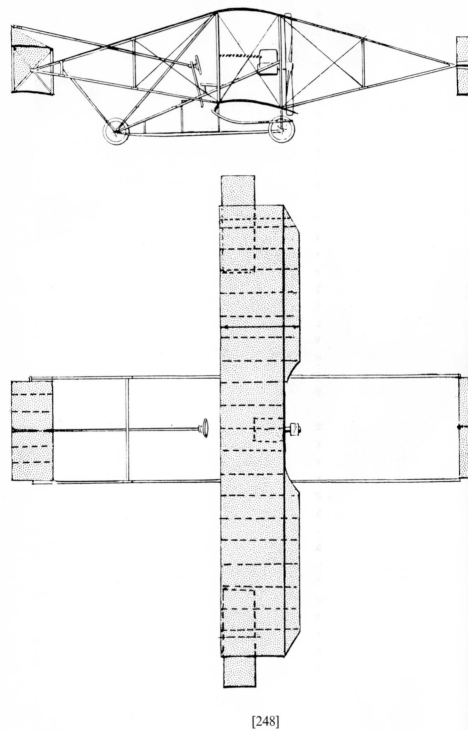

used as surfacing, and the fabric is mounted in sections, those at the outside being fastened by a system of lacing. The fabric is stretched as tight as possible, and its rigidity is augmented by spruce ribs. The decks are single surfaced, and the ribs are enclosed in pockets sewn to the upper side of the fabric. These ribs overlap the rear spar and form a flexible trailing edge, through which a wire is run for bracing purposes. When at rest on the ground the chord of the decks is inclined at an angle of about 6° to the horizon, but this does not represent the horizontal flight position. The angles of entry and trail have not been made known.

The aspect ratio, *i.e.*, ratio of span to chord, is 6 : 4, which is fairly high value, and should result in correspondingly good lift efficiency.

At the extremities, the rear edges of the main decks have their corners cut away, similarly in the centre, where this is done in order to accommodate the propeller. It will be observed that the main decks are in no way arched on the present machine, as they were on the earlier Curtiss designs.

Extending fore and aft to a distance of 10 ft. 6 ins. from the edges of the main decks are two triangular outrigger frames, carrying the elevator and tail.

The elevator consists of a pivoted biplane of 6 ft. span by 2 ft. chord, and having an area, therefore, of 24 sq. ft., or less than one-eleventh of the total area. This is a smaller ratio than exists in the large machines.

Between the decks of the elevator, and also extending a little above the top deck, is a triangular prow, which serves the purpose of a cutwater to give sensitiveness to direction.

On the other outrigger which extends rearwards, is a horizontal tail of 12 sq. ft., and a vertical rudder of $6\frac{1}{4}$ sq. ft. area divided into two parts so that it is symmetrical above and below the tail.

In addition to these supplementary surfaces, there are two others situated between the extremities of the main decks, where they serve the same purpose as is performed by warping on the Wright machine. These balancing planes, as they may be called, have each the same dimensions (2 ft. by 6 ft.) as the decks of the elevator and tail, and it will be noticed on reference to our drawing that they extend some little distance beyond the extremities of the main planes, although the greater part of their area is between decks. This feature we consider to be of very considerable importance on the score that it is questionable practice to put supplementary planes of this description between the main decks, both because it tends to throttle the gap and thereby possibly interfere with the lift efficiency, while conversely the decks themselves may be expected to have a restricting influence on the action of the righting planes when they are tilted or dipped. The fact that a portion of the righting planes on the Curtiss flyer are quite outside the extremities of the main planes is therefore a detail which should not be overlooked.

The machine as a whole is mounted upon a three-wheeled chassis, of which the framework is made of wood. Two of the wheels are placed immediately beneath the lower deck of the main planes, while the third is mounted on an outrigger some distance in front. All wheels are shod with 20-in. diam. pneumatic tyres.

The system of control on the Curtiss biplane is naturally much the same in its essential features as that on other machines of the type. Steering to the right or left is accomplished by a joint manipulation of the righting planes and the rudder, which may be employed either in the same or in opposite senses, according as it is required to increase or minimise the cant. Longitudinal oscillations are damped out by the elevator, and any tendency to capsize is checked by using the balancing planes. Ascent and descent automatically accompany variations in engine power, although the elevator can be used as a means of producing temporary jumps for adjusting the line of flight.

The operating mechanism by means of which the pilot is enabled to perform these various manoeuvres, consists of a steering wheel and a lever formed by the pivoted back of his seat, which has extensions embracing his shoulders so that it can be operated by a swaying motion of his body. The steering wheel is mounted on a sliding shaft, and is pulled bodily to and fro for the purpose of tilting and dipping the elevator. Turning the steering wheel upon its axis operates the rudder, and swaying the pilot's body to the right or left controls the righting planes.

Some mention has already been made of the engine, the power capacity of which is stated to be 30-h.p. at 1,200 r.p.m. It is a petrol motor of the 4-cyl. type, the cylinders being cast separately, and with a thickness of only $\frac{5}{32}$ in. Set diagonally in the heads are the inlet and exhaust valves, both of which are operated by a single pivoted rock lever, controlled from a double acting tappet rod.

Surrounding the cylinders are copper-jackets fastened in place with welded joints. On one end of the camshaft is a gear wheel water pump and from the other end a Bosch high-tension magneto is driven through spur gearing. In the centre an oil pump is driven, but splash lubrication is also provided in the crank chamber. The radiator carries 2 gallons of water and the fuel tank 2½ gallons of petrol.

Direct coupled to the crank-shaft is a two-bladed propeller 6 ft. in diameter and 6 ft. pitch. At 1,200 r.p.m. it develops a thrust of 180 lbs., which is considerably in excess (it is conceivably twice as much) of that required for horizontal flight.

Timber is employed throughout in the construction of the Curtiss biplane, and for the most part the selected wood is Oregon spruce, although it is a feature of the details that some parts of the elevator and tail are made of bamboo. The main spars and ribs of the main deck are of spruce, and the propeller is also of this material. The surfacing consists, as mentioned elsewhere, of Baldwin rubberised silk.

All the principal dimensions, together with the leading weights, will be found on the accompanying drawing, and some have already been referred to in the text above. The engine alone weighs 85 lbs., the magneto 12½ lbs., the radiator 40 lbs. Altogether the accessories bring the engine weight up to 192 lbs. The weight of the machine mounted is 550 lbs., so that as a glider it would weigh mounted 358 lbs., and allowing 170 lbs. for the pilot, the machine alone comes out at 188 lbs., which is an amount that ought to have given the constructors a fair chance of making a sound strong job of their work."

(Flight)

PS. As mentioned previously the writer above, as with most of his contemporaries, believed Curtiss was using his 4-cylinder 30 h.p. motor; but he did in fact fit his 50 h.p. motor.

P.PS. The general arrangement drawings illustrated on page 248 show both the elevator outrigger and the tail outrigger as too short.

BLÉRIOT XI (mod)
(1909)

Single seat tractor monoplane

Wings: span: 7·80 m. (25·6 ft.)
  chord: 2 m. (6·6 ft.)
Total wing area: 14 sq. m. (150·7 sq. ft.)
Elevator area: 2 sq. m. (21·5 sq. ft.)
Rudder area: 0·4 m. (4.5 sq. ft.)
Length: 8 m. (26·25 ft.)
Engine: 25 h.p. Anzani (3 cyl.)
Propeller: Chauvière (direct drive); diam: 2 m. (6·5 ft.); 1, 400 r.p.m.
Weight (loaded): 300 kg. (661 lbs.)
Speed: 58 km.p.h. (36 m.p.h.)   *Price:* £480

"M. Blériot has constructed, at one time and another, many flyers. That to which the accompanying illustrations refer is known as 'No. 11,' and its special feature lies in the fact that it is one of the smallest practical machines ever built. Its greatest achievements are the crossing of the Channel on Sunday, July 25th, 1909, and a cross-country journey of 25 miles. The appearance of this machine at the first Paris Aero Salon in December of last year was the occasion of considerable comment on the part of all interested in the science of aviation, for no one other than M. Santos-Dumont — whose Demoiselle was hardly to be regarded in the category of full-size machines — had at that time attempted to build anything quite so compact as the short-span flyer which M. Blériot exhibited. As the result of preliminary experiment some modifications were made of the original dimensions, but the machine itself is still wonderfully compact, and is altogether quite the smallest-looking flyer which has hitherto met with any sort of success.

From the time that M. Blériot abandoned his over-water experiments in 1906 he has been a champion of the monoplane principle, and none have shown greater perseverance than he in the mastery of the problem of flight along these lines. He experienced innumerable difficulties in his early attempts and he met with delay after delay, for he was always having mishaps which damaged his flyer, although they never once placed him *hors de combat* personally. This latter fact was, it may almost be said, his only consolation, for there were not wanting critics in those days who doubted his ultimate success, and it

[252]

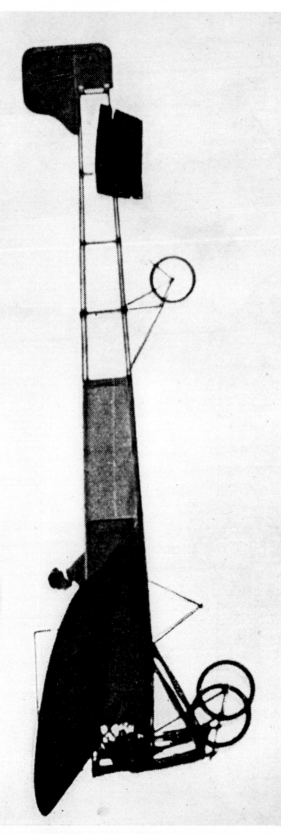

E. Blériot XI (mod) at Port Aviation (Juvisy): 1909

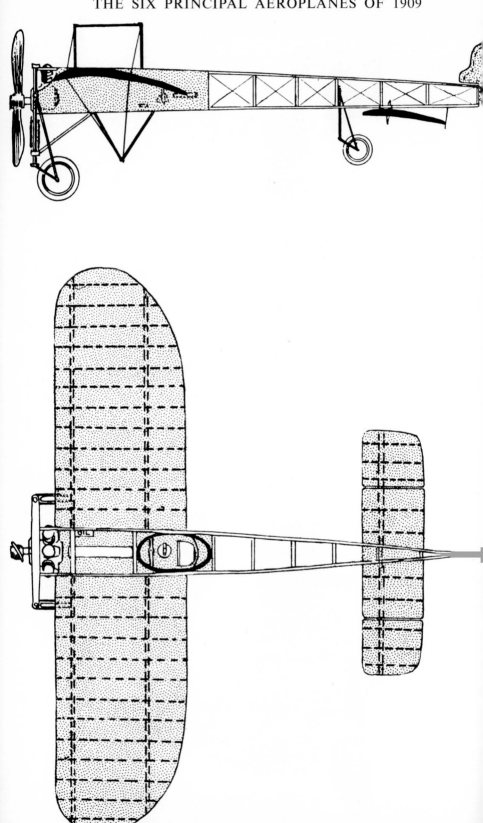

must be remembered that Wilbur Wright had not then encouraged Europe with his epoch-making demonstrations of what could be done in the air. That patience and perseverance won the day, there needs no better proof than that his name must go down in history as the man who first flew across the Channel, and, as some will have it, thereby destroyed for ever the insular position of England.

M. Blériot not only taught himself to fly, but he achieved flight with a monoplane of his own design; further, in his 'No. 11' he developed the one-deck principle in a manner which has placed the seal of success on this type of machine, although it has not altered the fact that the monoplane still remains the racer of the air.

Being a monoplane, the Blériot flyer 'No. 11' has of course only one deck, or, to be more descriptive, one pair of wings, for it is common to refer to the deck of a monoplane as a pair of wings, since the construction differs from that common in biplanes on account of the position of the main frame which divides the deck in the centre and thus causes each half to jut out like an extended wing from the body. It is a feature of the Blériot construction that these wings can be readily dismounted in order to facilitate the transport of the flyer. The member to which they are attached consists of a lattice-work box girder having a square section in front, but tapering to an edge behind, so that in plan it somewhat resembles the lines of the after-part of a racing skiff. At this extremity there is a rudder, and a little farther forward a supplementary plane forming a tail. This member is mounted beneath the girder, and its extremities are pivoted so as to be independently movable for the purpose of control.

The pilots sits in the main frame, slightly forward of the rear edge of the main wings, and the engine is situated a corresponding amount in front of the leading edge, and is immediately above a two-wheeled chassis which carries the weight of the fore part of the machine when it is resting on the ground: the rear part of the flyer rests on a single wheel of smaller dimensions.

Direct-coupled to the crank-shaft of the motor is a two-bladed tractor-screw, made of wood. Jutting out above the main-frame, between the pilot's seat and the engine, is a light triangular steel frame, which originally carried a small fin, but has since been deprived of this member. The frame itself remains, however, as it is used in connection with the staying of the main wings.

The main wings, which, as already explained, consist of two single members which are independently detachable from the main frame-work, are each built up around two transverse wood spars having a solid rectangular section measuring about 3 by $\frac{3}{4}$ ins. At frequent intervals, about 7 ins. apart, these two spars are joined by curved ribs, some of which are quite slender pieces of wood having a square section of only about $\frac{1}{4}$ in. square, while others are formed by strips of aluminium, reinforced in front by a strip of wood. The main rib at the inner extremity of each wing is entirely of wood, and has a built-up channel section. The wings are double-surfaced with Continental fabric, that is to say, the ribs and spars are entirely enclosed top and bottom by this water-proof material, and therefore present a perfectly smooth contour on both faces. At the maximum point, the thickness of the wings is about $3\frac{1}{2}$ ins., but the front edge and the trailing edge are both sharp. Transversely the wings form a straight line, but in fore and aft section they are cambered in accordance with the usual practice, and the maximum amount of camber is about $3\frac{1}{2}$ ins. This point occurs a little less than a third of the distance from the leading edge. The extremities of the wings are rounded off in a manner which is clearly indicated in our accompanying drawing.

Having a span of 28 ft. and a chord of 6 ft., the aspect ratio is only 4·65 and the area 150 sq. ft.

The supplementary surfaces on the Blériot flyer consist of a monoplane tail having pivoted extremities, and a rudder. The overall span of the tail, including the tip, is approximately two-thirds that of the main wings, and the area is about one-fourth as great. The pivoted tips are approximately square, and have an individual area of about one-fourth that of the full area of the tail. The rudder, which is shaped in accordance with the constructional requirements, has an area of approximately $4\frac{1}{2}$ sq. ft. It is situated about 13 ft. behind the rear edge of the main wings, and is pivoted about 18 ins. behind the rear edge of the tail.

The construction of the tail is similar to that of the main wings, except that the principal transverse spar consists of a steel tube. The central portion of the tail, which is rigid in flight, can be adjusted in respect to its angle of incidence.

The Control. The pilot of the Blériot monoplane 'No. 11' sits on a low board raised but a few inches above the floor of the main girder, and rests his back against a leather strap. His feet are placed upon a pivoted cross-bar, by means of which the rudder is operated, and vertically in front of the pilot's seat is a lever for warping the wings and controlling the pivoted tips on the tail by means of wires. This lever is mounted in a somewhat peculiar manner, and has a curious inverted cup-shape fitting upon its lower end, which forms the subject of a Blériot patent No. 21497 of 1908. It is manipulated with the left hand, while the right is free to control the throttle and ignition-levers, and also, as occasion requires, to operate a rubber bulb of the scent-spray variety for the purpose of increasing the pressure in the lubricating tank, as the sight-feed fitting has, for convenience, been placed somewhat above its lowest level.

Balancing is controlled by warping the main wings, while the tips of the tail — which work together — perform the usual functions of an elevator.

Constructive Detail. First and foremost in the constructive details of the machine comes the mounting of the main wings. Mention has already been made of the fact that each wing is built up about two main spars, and it is these members which are employed for the attachment. The front spar, which is the more important of the two, juts out from the shoulder of the wing for a matter of 12 ins. or so, and spigots into a socket formed by a hollow rectangular strut of aluminium, mounted rigidly on the main frame of the machine. When in place, the joint is secured by small bolts. The other main spar projects only a few inches, and is merely bolted to a simple aluminium bracket fastened at the side of the frame.

The main frame itself is constructed of ash and is braced at intervals with wood struts and diagonal wire ties, which are fitted with tighteners.

The attachment of the tail is another interesting detail equally remarkable for its simplicity. The weight of this member is carried by the lower principal longitudinal members of the main frame, to which it is fastened by a pair of channel-section aluminium clips. It is important to bear in mind that the clips are of channel section and therefore partially embrace the rectangular ash beam, thus necessitating only the lightest of bolts to complete the fastening. The bracket extension of these clips carry the main transverse bar of the tail which, as before-mentioned, is a steel tube, and the mounting is so arranged that the tail can pivot upon this bracket as a hinge. The trailing edge of the tail is fitted with a little lug which is bolted to a bracket drilled with holes at frequent intervals so that the angle of incidence of the tail can be set with some nicety.

A pair of large bicycle wheels mounted on castor brackets serve to support the fore part of the machine when it is on the ground, and enable the initial run which precedes flight to be accomplished. The rear part of the machine rests upon a single wheel of smaller dimensions. The chassis to which the two principal wheels are attached consists of a pair of tubular steel columns braced together by two wooden beams, upon one of which the front end of the main frame of the machine rests. This beam is stayed to the heads of the steel columns by a steel strap so arranged that the girder frame rests in a kind of cradle. The upper beam is merely a strut between the two columns.

The columns themselves are stayed to the frame, but the forks which carry the wheels are hinged as well as pivoted to the lower ends of the columns, and the wheel hubs are stayed independently to loose collars that ride upon a portion of the upper ends of the columns which are there turned smooth to receive them. These collars are anchored to the lower ends of the columns by a pair of very strong elastic bands, and it is these pieces of elastic which constitute the main suspension. Inside the hollow columns are springs used for the purpose of returning the wheels to their normal positions after they have been deflected to one side or the other while running along the ground. The connection between the springs and the wheel brackets is carried out by means of a single flexible wire, working over a swivelling pulley.

As the chassis wheels rise and fall over uneven ground they cause the sliding collars to which they are braced to ride up and down on the vertical columns, and the wear which has taken place on this part of the machine is distinctly noticeable; in fact, the marking is suggestive that the collars are apt to jam, behaviour which might otherwise have been expected on account of their extremely short bearing surface, and the obliquity of the thrust which they have to resist.

The engine with which the Blériot 'No. 11' is fitted is a 25-h.p. 3-cylinder Anzani of the semi-radial type, which means to say that the cylinders jut out radially from the upper half of the crank-chamber. The motor is air-cooled, and has auxiliary exhaust ports in the cylinder walls, which are uncovered by the piston at the end of its stroke. The main exhaust valves are, of course, mechanically operated, but the induction valves are automatic, and are situated immediately above the exhaust valves.

As the result of the semi-radial construction, the engine is extremely compact, great economy being especially noticeable in the length. The engine is attached to the machine by four channel-steel brackets which are bolted to the faces of the crank-chamber, and are drilled at intervals to the web for the sake of lightness.

The bore and stroke of the motor are 100 by 150 mm.

During the Channel flight an inflated air-bag was attached inside the frame between the pilot and the tail to act as a float in water."

(*Flight*)

ANTOINETTE (1909)

Single seat tractor monoplane (wing-warping type)

Wings: span: 12·80 m. (42 ft.)

chord: 3 m. (9·8 ft.) tapering to 2 m. (6·5 ft.)

Total wing area: 50 sq. m. (538·2 sq. ft.)

Length: 11·50 m. (37·7 ft.)

Engine: 50 h.p. Antoinette (8 cyl.)

Propeller: Antoinette (direct drive): diam: 2·20 m. (7·2 ft.): 1,100 r.p.m.

Weight (loaded): 520 kg. (1,146 lbs.)

Speed: 70 km.p.h. (43·5 m.p.h.)   *Price:* £1,000

———————

"While it doubtless required Mr. Latham's splendid failures in his attempted cross-Channel flights to bring the Antoinette monoplane into that extreme prominence which it undoubtedly occupies in the public eye to-day, the work of its designer, M. Levavasseur, has ever been deserving of recognition during the long while that he has been working on the problems of flight. If fortune has denied him the greater honours, he has not been discouraged thereby from putting his best into the development of his machine, which stands out to-day not only as one of the most interesting, but also as one of the most carefully-built flyers on the market.

Of the various reasons which led M. Levavasseur to adopt the monoplane system of construction, its simplicity of form, and lower resistance to flight, have been leading factors, although the designer frankly admits that increased difficulties of construction scarcely allow the matter of its simplicity to go further than the appearance. Certainly, however, the Antoinette firm have ably taken advantage of their opportunity in this latter direction, for its clean, neat 'cut' is, perhaps, the most marked of the external characteristics of this machine.

In summarising the leading features of the design of the Antoinette monoplane, it is essential to mention two details relating to the main wings. One is their great thickness, the other is their upward slope, which embodies in the machine the principle of the dihedral angle.

This principle has for its object the provision of a certain amount of automatic lateral stability by means of the restoring couple brought into play by the difference in the upward components of the air

[259]

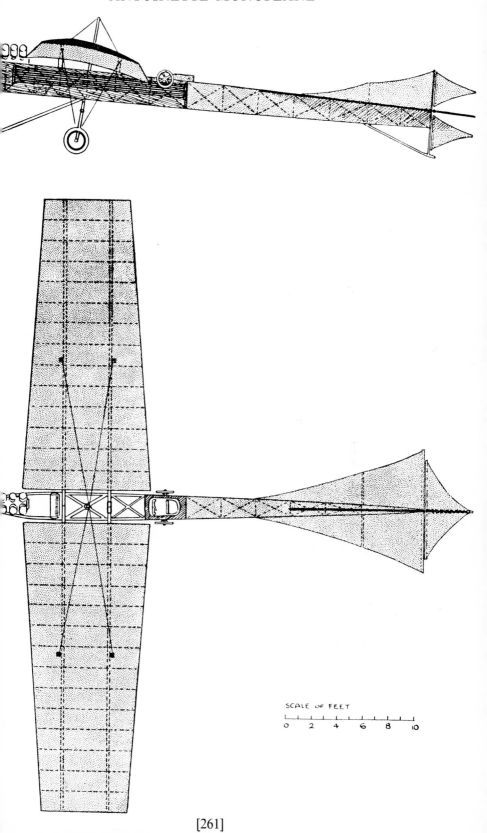

SCALE OF FEET

0   2   4   6   8   10

pressure under the wings when the flyer is canted from its normal position of equilibrium. . . .

Long as it has been known, the dihedral angle has, however, been little used in practice on full-sized machines for the reason that many designers see in the arrangement a source of danger far more serious than any advantage likely to accrue from the otherwise favourable points of the system. It is argued that the most likely cause of canting is a side gust of wind which, persisting after the cant has been started, will find an increasing area of action on the uplifted wing and so tend to capsize the flyer before the restoring force has time to assert itself.

Wilbur Wright in his early gliding experiments tried and abandoned the scheme, and, in fact, it is now nowhere quite so much in evidence as on the Antoinette flyer; hence the reason for drawing early attention to the peculiarity.

The thickness of the wings already mentioned is a result of adopting a system of construction designed to secure a maximum of strength with a minimum of weight, but it may be remarked *en passant* that the volumetric capacity which this thickness confers on the wings showed itself to be of more than incidental advantage in the matter of buoyancy when Mr. Latham so unfortunately had to alight on the sea in his cross-Channel flights.

Of the other special features, it is necessary only to mention the boat-like body and the distance of the tail behind the main planes, which distinctly seems to be relatively greater than on other machines.

The wings are built up upon two transverse main spars, neither of which, however, forms the edge of the wing, as is so commonly the case in the decks of biplanes. Both the leading and trailing edges of the Antoinette wings are sharp, and their upper and lower surfaces (made of Michelin rubber-proofed fabric) are kept exceptionally taut by the large number of ribs that go to make up the wing framework.

The outstretched wings form a pair of cantilevers, of which the main transverse spars are the principal members. Each spar is constructed on the lattice-girder principle, and tapers in depth towards the extremity. At its inner end it is mounted in a substantial bracket, which is attached to the body of the machine. This bracket, in the case of the rear pair of spars, is pivoted, as shown in an accompanying sketch, so that it can rock bodily when the wings are warped.

In addition to these main transverse spars there are other transverse-members unattached to the body of the machine, but serving, nevertheless, to give strength to the wing framework. Across these spars pass the curved main ribs, which are spaced at intervals of about 18 ins.; they are also built up lattice-girder fashion. Between the main ribs light open ribs, constructed without the lattice bracing, are provided for the additional support of the surface fabric. Near the body of the machine these latter members have a spacing of only about 2 ins., but elsewhere their distance apart is twice as much. As the result of this very carefully thought-out system of construction, the manufacturers claim that their wing framework for wings of 15 to 25 square metres in surface can be produced as light as 1 kilog. per square metre, not including the fabric.

In addition to their mounting on the body of the machine, to which reference has already been made, the wings are further supported by wires, which radiate from a central wooden mast projecting above the body. These wires are attached to the main transverse spars about the centre of their length, and each spar is itself independently trussed by a vertical post and diagonal wires. The posts used for this purpose are, like the main-mast, of hollow construction, and each is one continuous member from top to bottom. It is placed a little to the side of the main-spar which it trusses, being notched to receive that member.

This arrangement avoids the necessity of dividing the post at the centre. Each end of the post is fitted with a steel ferrule, on the outside of which is a screw thread. A suitable attachment for the stay-wires is provided by a light steel plate threaded over the ferrule, and clamped between two nuts.

The body of the machine consists of a hollow V-section lattice girder, the fore part of which is encased with a veneer of cedar, and pointed like the bows of a boat. Farther aft the cedar gives place to a covering of rubber-proofed fabric, and this material is also carried over the top side of the frame, thus forming a kind of deck. An open cockpit is provided for the accommodation of the pilot's seat.

The machine is supported on the ground by a pair of small pneumatic shod wheels, attached to an axle which is provided with pneumatic suspension. This latter is obtained by means of a plunger in a steel tube; the tube is a downward continuation of the main-mast already mentioned. The bracing of the axle to a sliding collar which rides on the outside of the stationary tube, and thereby prevents the axle from tilting, is effected by hollow wood struts fitted with steel forks spliced in their extremities.

An ash skid is provided in front of the machine to prevent the propeller from hitting the ground, and there is a very light skid at the rear to protect the rudder. The forward skid is made of ash, and has a maximum square section of about $2\frac{1}{4}$ ins. Its extremity is laminated and curved upwards, the tip being protected by a steel plate.

At the rear of the body is the tail, consisting of two fixed planes, and three movable planes. The fixed members include a vertical and a horizontal plane arranged like the feathers on the shaft of an arrow, and their object is to fulfil much the same purpose in respect to the flight of the machine. The movable members are virtually extensions of these planes; the continuation of the horizontal plane, forming an elevator, while the continuation of the vertical plane makes a rudder. An additional rudder working in unison with the first is provided beneath the elevator.

The control of the machine is effected by means of two hand wheels and a pedal. The wheels are placed vertically on each side of the pilot's seat, and lie just outside the body of the machine. That on the right when moved forward, dips the trailing edge of the elevator. A similar movement of the left-hand wheel warps the trailing edge of the right-hand main-wing downwards. Pressing forward the right foot puts the trailing edge of the rudder over to the right, and therefore steers the nose of the machine in the same direction. In the above, the terms right and left apply to the pilot, who sits facing in the direction of flight.

Adjacent to the main control-wheels are two smaller wheels for adjusting the throttle and the ignition.

The warping of the wings is effected by the intermediary of a cog-wheel and chain mechanism.

The cog-wheel is mounted in a case attached to the lower end of the stationary tube which forms an extension of the main-mast. It is operated by a lever attached to its spindle, and the extremities of this lever are controlled by wires from the hand wheel already mentioned. In mesh with this cog-wheel is a chain, the extremities of which are coupled by wires to the rear main spars of the wings. Partially rotating the cog-wheel draws the chain from one side to the other of the machine, and thus pulls downwards one main spar while it allows the other to rise.

This movement takes place with the greatest freedom and nicety, owing to the careful construction of the wings and to the method of mounting the rear spars on a pivot as already described. The forward spars, being fixed rigidly to the body of the machine, remain stationary, and thus the result of the manoeuvre is that helicoidal deformation of the wing surfaces which is commonly described by the term 'warping'.

[264]

ANTOINETTE MONOPLANE

In some cases the Antoinette flyer is fitted with balancing flaps instead of the warping device.

The engine on the Antoinette is placed right up in the bows, the crank-chamber being supported on two transverse girders in the body. The crank-chamber is cast so that it extends up to the boss of the propeller, which is fastened direct to the crank-shaft. The engine is of the multi-cylinder V type, having eight or sixteen cylinders, according to the power which it is intended to provide. Each cylinder is a separate steel forging, and is complete with its head and valve-chamber. The inlet valves are atmospheric, and instead of a carburettor the petrol is injected by means of a pump. The water jackets are made of copper. A feature of the cooling system is that very little water is carried, the idea being to allow the water to be converted into steam, which is then condensed into water again by a tubular aluminium condenser lying outside the body of the machine. The arrangement of this condenser is very well illustrated in the accompanying illustrations, but it is important to remark that the cedar panelling of the body, which elsewhere gives the appearance, and possibly some of the buoyancy, of a boat, is cut away behind the radiator to facilitate freer air-circulation round the tubes."

(Flight)

APPENDICES

Appendix I

EARLY AIRCRAFT NOMENCLATURE
(December 1903 to August 1909)

The nomenclature of the first powered aeroplanes from
the Wright brothers to the Reims meeting of 1909.

The following pages present an abbreviation of Pt. II of my Science Museum book, *A Directory and Nomenclature of the First Aeroplanes* (1965). It has become growingly necessary to adopt some such nomenclature, so that machines can be conveniently and consistently referred to in indexes, tables, lists, and the like, as well as in historical texts. I have therefore put forward this suggested nomenclature in the hope that it will be found acceptable to historians.

The man or organisation responsible for a given machine — generally the first word of its designation — is given in the centre of the pages, with the individual aircraft tabulated below in bold type. To make the list more useful for reference, some of the historically important gliders are included, and a few aircraft which never flew, the designations in both categories being enclosed in brackets.

The date immediately following the designation indicates the period during which the machine was in service. I have purposely avoided including an exact date for each first take-off, since the records often make it next to impossible to determine the precise day on which a machine well and truly took off, as opposed to making one or more minuscule hops and jumps.

The "coding" in brackets which precedes each machine shows at a glance the calibre of its achievement, in terms of its best duration up to the end of August 1909, which coincides approximately with the end of the great Reims meeting. The coding is as follows:

(00) Indicates that the machine's best airborne duration was less than 15 seconds.

 (0) Indicates a best airborne duration of between 15 seconds and 1 minute.

(1) One minute or more.	(60) One hour or more.
(10) Ten minutes or more.	(120) Two hours or more.
(30) Thirty minutes or more.	(180) Three hours or more.

It will be found in practice that this somewhat rough and ready calibration provides a surprisingly accurate assessment of a machine's overall achievement, except of course, in the cases where the dates of the first take-offs were near to August 1909.

The "sub-designations" of the aircraft are given in the original French manner if they were used at the time, *i.e. -bis* (= second form) and *-ter* (= third form). Otherwise I have generally used the abbreviation "mod" (modification) and — in extreme cases — "2nd mod." and even "3rd mod." if the contemporary usage seems today to have been inadequate for our purposes. Where no satisfactory usage was in force at the time, I have adopted what in each case seems the most practical for the use of present-day — and, I hope, future — historians.

The abbreviation "(contd.)" indicates that the machine flew beyond August 1909.

A.E.A.
(Aerial Experiment Association)

All machines designed and built collectively by the Association at Hammondsport, N.Y.; all of them were powered by Curtiss engines. Tested and flown by various members of the Association. All were pusher biplanes, and were flown only at Hammondsport, N.Y., except for the **Silver Dart.** For the Curtiss **Gold Bug,** etc. see under CURTISS.

(00) **A.E.A. Red Wing.** March 1908.
   Piloted by F. W. Baldwin.
 (0) **A.E.A. White Wing.** May 1908.
   Piloted by various members of the A.E.A.
 (1) **A.E.A. June Bug.** June to August 1908.
   Piloted by Curtiss, Selfridge and McCurdy. Has sometimes been called the **Curtiss June Bug.** Won the Scientific American Trophy, July 4th, 1908, at Hammondsport, N.Y.
(10) **A.E.A. Silver Dart.** February 1909.
   Flown by J. A. D. McCurdy and others (?) at Baddeck, Nova Scotia. Made the first flights in the British Empire outside Britain.

ANTOINETTE
(Société Antoinette)

All machines and their engines designed by Leon Levavasseur for, and built by, the Société Antoinette. The name "Antoinette" was given to both aircraft and engines after the daughter of M. Gastambide, the head of the firm. In 1903 Levavasseur built and tested a propeller-driven bird-form machine, but it did not fly. The designation numbers shown were all adopted at the time, but not apparently inscribed on the aircraft.

(**Antoinette I.** 1907. Pusher monoplane. Not completed.)

(00) **Gastambide-Mengin I.** February to August 1908. First form. Tested at Bagatelle.

(1) **Antoinette II.** August 1908.
The Gastambide-Mengin I modified. Also called Gastambide-Mengin II. Tested at Issy.

(**Antoinette III** (Ferber IX). See under FERBER.)

(120) **Antoinette IV.** October 1908 to August 1909 (contd.).
The first "typical" Antoinette machine. Had ailerons. Flown by H. Latham from March 1909, who attempted the first Channel flight on it and crashed, July 19th, 1909. No. 13 at Reims.

(10) **Antoinette V.** December 1908 to September 1909.
Had ailerons. Built for R. Demanest; flown by him and others.

(10) **Antoinette VI.** April to July 1909.
Had warping, which all future Antoinettes were to have. Built for, and flown by, Capt. Burgeat.

(60) **Antoinette VII.** July, August 1909 (contd.).
Flown by Latham, who attempted his second Channel crossing on it, and again crashed, July 27th, 1909. Flew at Reims, No. 29.

(10) **Antoinette VIII.** August 1909 (contd.).
Flown by Ruchonnet. Flew at Reims, No. 11.

ARCHDEACON

(Ernest Archdeacon)

(**Archdeacon No. 1 glider.** 1904. Copied from the Wright No. 3 glider (modified) of 1902).

(**Archdeacon No. 2 glider.** 1905. Modification of the No. 1, with a tailplane and twin fins.)

Note (1): the so called Archdeacon float-glider of 1905 is given under Voisin.

Note (2): the name Archdeacon is pronounced "Arsh-dek."

APPENDIX I

Blériot
(Louis Blériot)

All machines from the No. V onwards were designed and built by Blériot, but sometimes with important assistance from others. The No. I was also designed by Blériot, but it cannot be determined what part, if any, he played in the design of Nos. II, III and IV. Only Blériot tested and flew the Nos. III to XIII.

(**Blériot I.** 1901–02. Experimental ornithopter model.)

(**Blériot II.** 1905. The Voisin-Blériot float-glider: see under Voisin.)

(**Blériot III.** 1906. Powered float-biplane, with ellipsoidal wings and tail-unit. Did not fly.)

(**Blériot IV.** 1906. The III modified, with conventional wings but ellipsoidal tail: was first a float-plane, then a land-plane. Did not fly.)

(00) **Blériot V.** April 1907.
Canard pusher monoplane (propeller in tail). Sometimes called Blériot IV.

(0) **Blériot VI** (Libellule). July, August 1907. First form.
Tandem tractor monoplane, derived from Langley. Sometimes called Blériot V.

(0) **Blériot VI (mod).** September 1907.
The VI modified, now with 50 h.p. Antoinette. Sometimes called Blériot VI.

(0) **Blériot VII.** November, December 1907.
Tractor monoplane.

(0) **Blériot VIII.** June 1908.
Tractor monoplane.

(1) **Blériot VIII-***bis.* July to September 1908.
The VIII modified, with small triangular ailerons.

(10) **Blériot VIII-***ter.* October 1908.
The VIII-*bis* modified, with large flap-type ailerons.

(**Blériot IX.** 1908. Tractor monoplane. Did not fly.)

(**Blériot X.** 1908. Pusher biplane. Was not completed.)

(1) **Blériot XI.** January to April 1909. (First form.)
Tractor monoplane. With 30 h.p. REP.

(30) **Blériot XI (mod).** May to July 1909.
With 25 h.p. Anzani, and other modifications. Made first aeroplane crossing of the Channel, July 25, 1909.

APPENDIX I

(1) **Blériot XI (Leblanc).** August 1909 (contd.).

First production type XI. Built for, and flown by, Alfred Leblanc. Flew at Reims, No. 23.

(60) **Blériot XI (Delagrange).** August 1909 (contd.).

Second production type XI. Built for, and flown by, Leon Delagrange. Flew at Reims, No. 16.

(30) **Blériot XII.** May to August 1909.

Tractor high-wing monoplane, with 60 h.p. E.N.V. No. 22 at Reims, where it crashed and was burnt, Blériot escaping uninjured.

(1) **Blériot XIII.** August 1909 (contd.).

Similar to the XII, but with 50 h.p. Anzani.

BREGUET
(Louis Breguet)

Designed and flown by Breguet; built by the Ateliers Breguet.

(0) **Breguet I.** June to August 1909 (contd.).

Tractor biplane. First tested at Douai. No. 19 at Reims. Had been exhibited in March 1909 at Olympia (London) in uncompleted form.

BREGUET-RICHET
(Louis and Jacques Breguet and Charles Richet)

Designed and tested by the Breguet brothers and Richet; built by the Ateliers Breguet at Douai.

(**Breguet-Richet I.** 1907. Helicopter, called a "giroplane". Just rose with a man, but was steadied by the ground crew.)
(**Breguet-Richet II.** 1908. Helicopter. Did not fly.)
(**Breguet-Richet II-***bis*. 1908. Convertiplane. Did not fly.)

CATERS. See DE CATERS

CODY
(Samuel Franklin Cody)

Machines designed and flown by Cody, with assistance from the officials at Farnborough (then known as the Balloon Factory). All until 1910 were pusher biplanes, with two propellers revolving between the wings. They were tested at the Balloon Factory, and at Laffan's Plain nearby. The full nomenclature of the Cody aircraft (1905–13) has now been agreed with the Farnborough authorities.

(**Cody Kite-Glider.** 1905. This machine was probably used once or twice to glide down from its tethered position.)

(**Cody Motor-Kite.** 1907. An adapted Cody man-lifting kite fitted with a 12 h.p. Buchet engine. Flew, suspended from a wire).

(**Cody 1–A.** September 1908. Called "British Army Aeroplane No. 1". Did not fly.)

(0) **Cody 1–B.** September, October 1908.
The 1–A modified. Called "British Army Aeroplane No. 1". Made the first powered flight in Britain, October 16th, 1908. Had 50 h.p. Antoinette, with pilot sitting behind engine.

(1) **Cody 2.** January to July 1909.
This machine underwent a number of modifications, which are now broken down into sub-letters A to E. Occasionally called the "Army Aeroplane".

(10) **Cody 3.** August (onwards) 1909.
The 2 rebuilt, with 60 h.p. E.N.V. engine, and the pilot sitting in front of engine. This was Cody's first practical machine, on which he took passengers. This machine underwent modifications, now shown by the sub-letters A to C.

CORNU. (See postscript on page 287.)

CURTISS
(Glenn Curtiss)

Designed and flown by Curtiss. Built by the Herring-Curtiss Co. in U.S.A. Pusher biplanes. These machines were also designated "Herring-Curtiss" (see also A.E.A.).

(30) **Curtiss Gold Bug.** June to August 1909 (contd.).
First flown at Morris Park, U.S.A.: 30 h.p. Curtiss. Flown also once each by Baldwin, Williams and Willard.

(10) **Curtiss Golden Flyer.** August 1909 (contd.).
This name is seldom used in aviation history, but it has contemporary authentication. First flew at Reims, No. 8. Was similar to the **Gold Bug,** but with a 50 h.p. Curtiss.

[273]

APPENDIX I

De Caters
(Baron de Caters)
Designed and flown by De Caters; built by Voisin.

(1) **De Caters.** October 1908.
Tractor triplane, similar to the Goupy I. Tested at Issy and Brecht (Belgium). (For De Caters biplane, see Voisin.)

De la Vaulx. See La Vaulx

De Pischoff
(Alfred de Pischoff)
Designed and tested by De Pischoff: built by Chauvière.

(00) **De Pischoff 1.** December 1907 and January 1908.
Tractor biplane: tested at Issy.

Dunne
(John William Dunne)
Dunne was employed by the War Office to proceed with the design of his swept-wing stable biplanes. The chronology of his early machines can now be established. They were built at the Balloon Factory, Farnborough, and tested at Blair Atholl (Scotland) by Dunne, Col. Capper (the C.O. at Farnborough) and others. The first successful powered machine was the Dunne D.5 of 1910, which comes outside this survey.

(**Dunne D.1–A.** 1907. Swept-wing tailless biplane glider.)

(**Dunne D.1–B.** 1907. The D.1–A, fitted with two 12 h.p. Buchet engines driving two propellers. Destroyed during its first take-off. Both the glider and powered version were called at the time simply D.1.)

(**Dunne D.2.** The designation given to a proposed triplane glider, which was never constructed. A powered version flew in 1911.)

(**Dunne D.3.** 1908. A smaller glider, derived from the D.1, tested September-October 1908.)

(00) **Dunne D.4.** 1908. The D.1 rebuilt and modified, resembling the D.3, and fitted with a 30 h.p. REP. engine driving 2 propellers. Tested November-December 1908.

[274]

APPENDIX I

ELLEHAMMER
(J. C. H. Ellehammer)

All machines designed, built and tested in Denmark (and once in Germany) by Ellehammer, who also designed and built the engines.

(**Ellehammer I.** January (onwards) 1906. Tractor Monoplane. Tested tethered on circular track. Did not fly. Wrongly stated to have been tested in 1904.)

(00) **Ellehammer II.** September (and on) 1906.
Semi-biplane. Tested tethered, as with the I. Wrongly stated that it made a free take-off and flight, on September 12th, 1906: it flew tethered.

(00) **Ellehammer III.** 1907.
Triplane.

(00) **Ellehammer IV.** 1908.
Tractor biplane. Made the first hop-flights in Germany (at Kiel) in June, 1908.

(**Ellehammer V.** 1909. Tractor biplane seaplane. Did not fly.)

(**Ellehammer VI.** 1909. Tractor monoplane, Blériot-derived. Did not fly.)

ESNAULT-PELTERIE
(Robert Esnault-Pelterie)

Designed and constructed — also the engines — by Esnault-Pelterie. All were tractor monoplanes, and bore the designation in large letters and arabic figures on the rear fuselage, i.e. "REP. No. 1", etc., R.E.P. being Esnault-Pelterie's initials.

(**Esnault-Pelterie Wright-type glider.** 1904.)

(**Esnault-Pelterie aileroned glider.** 1904.)

(1) **REP. 1.** October, November 1907. [5]
Flown by Esnault-Pelterie at Buc.

(1) **REP. 2.** June (onwards) 1908.
Flown by Esnault-Pelterie at Buc.

(1) **REP. 2-*bis*.** February to August 1909.
Flown by Guffroy at Buc and Reims. No. 3 at Reims.

FARMAN
(Henri(y) Farman)

All machines designed, built, and flown by Farman; although he was born and spent all his life in France, he was of British nationality —

[275]

both his parents were British — until he became a French citizen in 1937. He used both the "i" and "y" in his christian name, but with "i" appearing on his Voisin-built machines, and "y" on his own.

(**Henri Farman I.** 1907–08. See under VOISIN.)

(**Henri Farman II.** 1908. Originally the designation given to his tandem monoplane *Flying Fish* which was not completed; then to the 2nd machine he commissioned from the Voisins, which was sold by Gabriel Voisin behind his back to Moore-Brabazon, without the latter knowing it was Farman's. See under VOISIN, Voisin (Bird of Passage).)

(180) **Henry Farman III** and **III (mod).** April to August 1909 (contd.). Pusher biplane, fitted with ailerons. Farman's own first design. Fitted first with a 50 h.p. Vivinus engine, then (at Reims) with a 50 h.p. Gnome (Henry Farman III (mod)). First tested at Bouy. When first completed, it had side-curtains on the tail-unit, with the designation "Henry Farman No. III" painted on them. No. 30 at Reims, where it won the Grand Prix.

(120) **Henry Farman III (Sommer).** July, August 1909 (contd.). First production machine of the III type. Built for Roger Sommer. Had 50 h.p. Vivinus engine. Flew at Reims, No. 6.

(10) **Henry Farman III (Cockburn).** July, August 1909 (contd.). Second production machine of the III type. Built for the Englishman George Cockburn. Had a 50 h.p. Gnome. Flew at Reims, No. 32.

FARMAN

(Maurice Farman)

Designed and piloted by Maurice Farman: built by Mallet. Farman was associated with MM. Kellner and Neubauer in the construction.

(10) **Maurice Farman I.** February to August 1909 (contd.). Pusher biplane. Sometimes called "Maurice Farman-Neubauer." Tested at Buc.

FERBER

(Captain Ferdinand Ferber)

Designed, built and tested by Ferber. Ferber's own book *L'Aviation* (1909) is inconsistent and confusing in the nomenclature of his machines, and it is impossible to understand what he meant by his numbers. One can only therefore make the available numbers fit the aircraft known to have existed (all of them photographed), with the help of sub-letters. While in the army, he used the pseudonym "F. de Rue" when flying. Ferber was killed in 1909 after landing his standard Voisin (see VOISIN — Voisin (Ferber)).

(**Ferber I.** 1899. Glider with diamond-shaped wing.)
(**Ferber II.** 1899. Glider with squarish diamond-shaped wing.)
(**Ferber III.** 1900–01(?). Glider with hexagonal wing.)
(**Ferber IV.** 1901. Lilienthal-type glider.)
(**Ferber V–A.** 1902. Wright-type glider.)
(**Ferber V–B.** 1904. Tailed version of V–A.)
(**Ferber VI–A.** 1903. Powered tractor biplane, Wright-derived; no elevator and tailless. Did not fly.)
(**Ferber VI–B.** 1905. Tailed glider conversion of VI–B.)
(**Ferber VI–C.** 1905. Powered tractor version of VI–B. Launched from overhead cable. Could not sustain itself.)
(**Ferber VII.** No aircraft can be identified with this number.)
(**Ferber VIII.** 1906. Powered tractor biplane. Did not fly. Destroyed by a gale on the ground.)
(0) **Ferber IX.** July to September 1908.
Tractor biplane, similar to the VIII. Also called Antoinette III, as Ferber was then employed by the Antoinette firm.

GASNIER
(René Gasnier)
Designed, built, and piloted by Gasnier.

(0) **Gasnier I.** August, September 1908.
Pusher biplane. Tested at Rochefort-sur-Loire.
(**Gasnier II.** 1908. Pusher biplane. Did not fly.)

GASTAMBIDE-MENGIN. See ANTOINETTE

GOUPY
(Ambroise Goupy)
Designed and flown by Goupy.

(00) **Goupy I.** September to December 1908.
Tractor triplane. Built by Voisin. Tested at Issy.

APPENDIX I

(0) **Goupy II.** March (onwards) 1909.

Tractor biplane. Goupy was assisted in the design by Lieut. Calderera (Wilbur Wright's first Italian pupil) who piloted the machine on one of its two take-offs. Built by Blériot. Tested at Buc. Was later modified.

GRADE
(Hans Grade)
Designed, built and piloted by Grade.

(00) **Grade I.** January, February 1909.

Tractor triplane. Tested at Magdeburg, Germany.

HERRING-CURTISS. See CURTISS

JATHO
(Karl Jatho)

Jatho will always remain a somewhat shadowy figure. He appears to have built a pusher semi-biplane and tested it in 1903. It is said to have made hops of up to 60 metres, but it is not known whether this was on the level, or down-hill. In any case the machine did not fly, and no serious claims have been advanced that it did.

KOECHLIN-DE PISCHOFF

Designed and built by MM. Koechlin and De Pischoff. Probably piloted by Koechlin.

(0) **Koechlin-De Pischoff.** October 1908.

Tandem monoplane (3 pairs of wings); tested at Villacoublay.

LA VAULX
(Comte Henry De La Vaulx)

Designed by Victor Tatin for De La Vaulx; built by Mallet. Piloted by De La Vaulx.

(00) **De La Vaulx.** November 1907.

Pusher monoplane, with two propellers. Tested at Saint-Cyr.

[278]

APPENDIX I

ODIER-VENDOME

Designed by MM. Odier and Raoul Vendome. Built by Les Fils de Régy Frères. Piloted by Odier. See also under Vendome.

(1) **Odier-Vendome.** June, July 1909.
    Pusher biplane. Tested at Issy.

PEARSE
(Richard William Pearse)

It was once claimed, but since disproved, that Pearse in New Zealand flew a powered aeroplane in 1903. He may have taken off — but did not fly — in 1904 and/or 1905, but plays no significant part in history. See GS–A (in the Commentary).

PHILLIPS
(Horatio Phillips)

Designed, built and tested by Phillips at Streatham, near London.
    (**Phillips I.** 1904. Multiplane with superposed slats. Did not fly.)
(00) **Phillips II.** 1907.
    Multiplane (slats arranged in frames). Made the first tentative hop-flight in Britain, at Streatham in the spring (?) of 1907.

PISCHOFF. See DE PISCHOFF

RAOUL VENDOME. See VENDOME

REP. See ESNAULT-PELTERIE

ROBART
(Henri Robart)

Designed, built and tested by Robart.

(00) **Robart.** December 1908.
    Tractor semi-biplane, with curved dihedral of the main wings, and a small wing above. Tested at Amiens.

APPENDIX I

ROE
(Alliott Verdon Roe)

Designed, built and flown by Roe. His first successful machine was the Roe III (triplane) of late 1909.

(00) **Roe I.** June 1908.
Pusher biplane. Tested at Brooklands, England.

(00) **Roe II.** July 1909 (contd.).
Triplane. Sometimes called "Roe Triplane No. 1", and "Bullseye". Tested at Lea Marshes, England.

SANTOS-DUMONT
(Alberto Santos-Dumont)

Designed, built, and flown by Santos-Dumont. Nos. 1 to 14 were lighter-than-air aircraft. Nos. 14-*bis*, 15 and 17 were biplanes. Nos. 19 and 20 were monoplanes. No. 16 was an airship-cum-aeroplane. No. 18 was a wingless hydroplane.

(00) **Santos-Dumont 14-*bis*.** September 1906. (First form.)
Canard pusher biplane: 24 h.p. Antoinette. The number 14 refers to his airship No. 14, suspended from which this aeroplane was tested.

(0) **Santos-Dumont 14-*bis* (mod).** October and November 1906; April 1907.
The 14-*bis* powered by a 50 h.p. Antoinette, and fitted with ailerons: made the first official flights in Europe at Bagatelle, 1906, the best being 220 m. in $21\frac{1}{5}$ sec.

(**Santos-Dumont 15.** 1907. Tractor biplane. Did not fly.)

(**Santos-Dumont 16.** 1907. Airship-cum-aeroplane. Did not fly. Destroyed before first take-off.)

(**Santos-Dumont 17.** 1907. Development of the No. 15. Did not fly.)

(0) **Santos-Dumont 19.** November 1907.
Small tractor monoplane. Tested at Bagatelle, Issy, and Buc.

(**Santos-Dumont 19-*bis*.** 1907. Development of the No. 19. Did not fly.)

(10) **Santos-Dumont 20 (Demoiselle).** March to August 1909 (contd.).
Tractor monoplane, developed from the No. 19. Flown at Issy, St. Cyr, and Buc.

APPENDIX I

V AULX. See L A V AULX

V ENDOME
(Raoul Vendome)

Designed and piloted by Vendome. Built by Les Fils de Régy Frères. See also under Odier-Vendome.

> (**Vendome I.** 1908. Tractor monoplane. Did not fly.)
>
> (00) **Vendome II.** January 1909.
> Tractor monoplane. Tested at Issy.

V ENDOME (O DIER -) See O DIER -V ENDOME

V OISIN
(Gabriel and Charles Voisin)

All machines were biplanes, and pushers when powered. Designed and built by the Voisins, often in collaboration with others. Piloted mostly by their clients. Names and numbers given in "quotes" are those of the clients; these were generally inscribed in large letters and arabic numbers on the side-curtains of the tail-units of the machines, with the Voisin name and address given either above or below it in discreetly small letters. This practice of naming the aircraft was adopted by the Voisins to flatter their clients, and has often proved confusing to historians.

> (**Voisin-Archdeacon float-glider.** 1905. Box-kite glider with box-kite tail-unit. Built for Ernest Archdeacon.)
>
> (**Voisin-Blériot float-glider.** 1905. Similar to the above machine, with shorter span, and dihedral on the outer side-curtains.)
>
> (**Voisin hang-glider.** 1907. Chanute-type biplane, but with box-kite tail-unit. Built for Henri Farman; next owned by the Voisins; and finally by the Aéronautique-Club.)

(*Powered pusher biplanes*)

> (**Voisin-Kapferer.** 1907. Built for Henry Kapferer. Did not fly.)
>
> (00) **Voisin-Delagrange I.** March to November 1907.
> Called "Leon Delagrange No. 1". First tested at Vincennes and Bagatelle; then on floats on Lake d'Enghien in spring, 1907 (when it was sometimes called the "Delagrange-Arch-

deacon" because Archdeacon shared in the experiments); then back to a wheeled undercarriage (November 1907), but with one (instead of two) rudders.

(1) **Voisin-Delagrange II.** January, March, April 1908.

The I re-built after crashing: now with smaller tail-unit. Called "Leon Delagrange No. 2".

(10) **Voisin-Delagrange III.** May to July 1908.

The II with two (inner) side-curtains added. Called the "Leon Delagrange No. 3".

(30) **Voisin-Delagrange III (mod).** September 1908 to July 1909.

The III fitted with four side-curtains. Still called the "Leon Delagrange No. 3".

(1) **Voisin-Farman I.** September to November 1907.

Called "Henri Farman No. 1". Built for Henri Farman, who piloted this and all the following five modifications. Farman himself was responsible for many of the modifications which made the machine successful. First flown at Issy.

(1) **Voisin-Farman I (mod).** November 1907 to January 1908.

Tail-unit is now smaller. Still called "Henri Farman No. 1". Flew the first European circle, January 13, 1908, at Issy.

(10) **Voisin-Farman I-*bis*.** March to September 1908.

The I (mod) now with further minor modifications. Called "Henri Farman No. 1-*bis*".

(30) **Voisin-Farman I-*bis* (mod).** September, October 1908.

The I-*bis*, now with four side-curtains. Still called "Henri Farman No. 1-*bis*".

(10) **Voisin-Farman I-*bis* (2nd mod).** October to November 1908.

The I-*bis* (mod), now with four large ailerons. Still called "Henri Farman No. 1-*bis*".

(10) **Voisin-Farman I-*bis* (triplane).** November 1908 to May 1909.

The 1-*bis* (2nd mod), now made into a semi-triplane by the addition of a small plane above the upper wings. Still called "Henri Farman No. 1-*bis*". For a short time in November 1908 it was converted back to a biplane; then, also in November, it was re-converted to a triplane.

(The first Standard Voisins)

The following were the first of the "Standard" Voisin pusher biplanes; all were similar, and had only minor differences, such as depth of wing-gap, etc. For these machines, the practice has here been adopted of naming them "Voisin" followed in brackets by whatever was the surname of the client, or other name, inscribed by the Voisins on the tail-unit.

(1) **Voisin (Moore-Brabazon).** December 1908 to February(?) 1909. Called "J. T. C. Moore-Brabazon No. 3". Built for Moore-Brabazon (the late Lord Brabazon), the No. 3 referring to his previous attempts to design an aeroplane. This machine was not the "Bird of Passage", as so often asserted, for which see below.

(?) **Voisin (Études).** February (onwards) 1909. Called "Biplan d'Études", and placed at the disposal of the Voisin clients for training.

(1) **Voisin (Bird of Passage).** February (onwards) 1909. Originally commissioned by Henri Farman, and called "Henri Farman No. 2"; but sold, when nearing completion, to Moore-Brabazon and re-named "J. T. C. Moore-Brabazon No. 4, Bird of Passage". Flown mostly in England, and was the first machine to be flown (1909) by a British-born pilot, Farman being British, but born in France, and Cody not yet naturalized. It was fitted with a 60 h.p. E.N.V.

(10) **Voisin (Alsace).** April to August 1909 (contd.). Called "Alsace". Built for the Ligue Nationale Aérienne.

(120) **Voisin (Rougier).** April to August 1909 (contd.). Called "Henry Rougier", and built for him. He used the English form of "Henry". No. 28 at Reims. This was the first Voisin to be fitted with a nose-wheel (off the ground) under the elevator: most Voisins were to include this feature from now on.

(10) **Voisin (De Caters).** April to August 1909 (contd.). Called "Baron de Caters No. 2". and built for him. The De Caters I was a triplane, included in this list under De Caters.

(30) **Voisin (Gobron).** May to August 1909 (contd.). Called "Jean Gobron", and built for him. No. 5 at Reims. Powered by a 60 h.p. Gobron.

(1) **Voisin (Hansen).** May to August 1909 (contd.). Called (?) "Hansen", and built for a Swedish client of that name.

(120) **Voisin (Paulhan).** June to August 1909 (contd.). Called "Octavie No. 3", won as a prize by Louis Paulhan. The significance of both the name and number has not yet been determined. No. 20 at Reims. Powered by a 50 h.p.

Gnome: this was the first aircraft to be powered by a Gnome engine.

(1) **Voisin (Legagneux).** June to September 1909.

Called "Georges Legagneux", and built for him.

(10) **Voisin (Ferber).** July to September 1909.

Called "F. de Rue", which was the pseudonym of Capt. F. Ferber when flying as a civilian, for whom it was built. Ferber was killed when taxying this machine on September 22nd, 1909, at Boulogne. No. 17 at Reims.

(30) **Voisin (Fournier).** July, August 1909 (contd.).

Called "Henry Fournier", and built for him. He used the English form of "Henry". No. 33 at Reims.

(10) **Voisin (Odessa).** July, August 1909 (contd.).

Called "Aéro-Club d'Odessa", for whom it was built.

(1) **Voisin (Daumont).** August, September 1909.

Called "Daumont No. 1"; built for the Comte de Beau-regard, but flown by Gaudart. The significance of the name Daumont is not yet understood.

(120) **Voisin (Bunau-Varilla).** August 1909 (contd.).

Called "Etienne Bunau-Varilla", and built for him. No. 27 at Reims.

(1) **Voisin (Sanchez-Besa).** August 1909 (contd.).

Called (?) "Sanchez-Besa", and built for the Chilean of this name. No. 37 at Reims. Powered by a 60 h.p. E.N.V.

VUIA

(Trajan Vuia)

Designed, constructed and tested by Trajan Vuia. All tractor mono-planes. The I and I-*bis* had a carbonic acid gas motor.

(00) **Vuia I.** March to August 1906.

Tested at Montesson and Issy. Had no elevator.

(00) **Vuia I-*bis*.** October 1906 to March 1907.

Tested at Issy and Bagatelle. Now with rear elevator.

(00) **Vuia II.** June, July 1907.

Tested at Bagatelle. A new machine, with 24 h.p. Antoinette.

APPENDIX I

WATSON
(Preston A. Watson)

The claim that Watson, in Scotland, flew before the Wrights, has been disproved and the claimant has admitted that no such flight took place. For a full discussion of the Watson case, see GS-A (pages 208-213). Watson designed a machine with a small rocking-wing (above a monoplane structure) for control. It is possible that he built a conventional glider in 1903 and attempted to power it in 1906. When it comes to the powered rocking-wing aircraft, I have named them "Rockers". The first to make short flights was the Watson Rocker No. 2 of 1910; and the Rocker No. 3 had a limited success, but the configuration was not practical.

> (**Watson Rocker 1.** 1908 or 1909. Possibly took off; but did not fly.)

WHITEHEAD
(Gustave Weisskopf, called Whitehead)

The story that Whitehead started flying powered aeroplanes in 1901, and made a 7-mile flight in 1902, has long been exploded as a myth, put about by a group of people who were set on denigrating the Wright brothers. There is no reason to believe Whitehead ever flew a machine of any kind. See GS-A (pages 207-208).

WRIGHT
(Wilbur and Orville Wright)

All machines and engines were designed and built by the Wrights, or — in one case in the period covered here — built under licence from them. The Wright brothers did not adopt any formal nomenclature for their aircraft until they named the "Model B" in 1910. From the start of their powered flying, they simply referred to their machines as "Flyers", with or without a capital "F". Although they never called their first standardised type the "Model A", I feel they must have so regarded them, since they adopted the "B" for their second basic type. I have therefore adopted an informal descriptive nomenclature for the gliders; then followed the practice, sanctified by the Europeans, of giving roman numerals to the first three classic powered machines; and then adopted the "A" for the famous machines of 1908–09, followed by the most appropriate name with

[285]

which to identify the individual machine; this is sometimes the name found in the brothers' papers.

All the machines were biplanes, and the powered machines pusher biplanes.

> **(Wright Warping Kite:** 1899.)
> **(Wright No 1 glider:** 1900.)
> **(Wright No 2 glider:** 1901.)
> **(Wright No 3 glider:** 1902.)
> **(Wright No 3 glider (mod):** 1902. The glider which embodied the vital combined use of warping and rudder.)
> **(Wright No 3 glider (2nd mod):** 1903. The modified No. 3 glider with a double rudder.)

------

(0) **Wright Flyer I:** December 17th, 1903.
The first powered machine.
(1) **Wright Flyer II:** May to December 1904.
(30) **Wright Flyer III:** June to October 1905.
(1) **Wright Flyer III (mod):** May 1908.
Modified to take pilot and one passenger, seated upright, for the refresher flights prior to flying in France and the U.S.A.

(*Note:* All these machines were piloted by the brothers.)

------

(120) **Wright A (France).** August 1908 to May 1909.
Flown by Wilbur and others in France at Hunaudières, Auvours, and Pau.
(60) **Wright A (Fort Myer).** September 1908.
Flown by Orville at Fort Myer, Washington, September 1908. Crashed on September 17th, 1908, killing the passenger Lieut. Selfridge and injuring Orville.
(30) **Wright A (Rome).** April to August 1909 (contd.).
Flown by Wilbur and his first Italian pupil Lieut. Calderera at Rome (Centocelle), and by the latter at Brescia.
(60) **Wright A (de Lambert).** May to August 1909 (contd.).
Sold to and flown by the Comte Charles de Lambert at Cannes (La Napoule), Reims, and elsewhere. No. 36 at Reims.
(30) **Wright A (Tissandier).** May to August 1909 (contd.).
Sold to and flown by Paul Tissandier at Pont-Long, Reims, and elsewhere. No. 4 at Reims.

[286]

(60) **Wright A (Signal Corps).** June to August 1909 (contd.).
Built for the U.S. Signal Corps and flown by Orville, and others, at Fort Myer, and elsewhere. This machine was the only Model A markedly different from the others, with less wing area and higher undercarriage, and without a sprung rudder outrigger. The world's first military aeroplane. It is preserved in the National Air Museum, Washington, D.C.

(30) **Wright A (Lefebvre).** July to August 1909.
Flown by Eugéne Lefebvre at the Hague, Reims, and elsewhere. No. 25 at Reims. Lefebvre was killed on September 7th, 1909 at Port-Aviation (Juvisy), when testing a new, French-built, Wright.

(—) **Wright A (Baratoux).** August 1909 (contd.).
Built for, and flown by Marcel Baratoux at Dunkerque, etc. The first French-built Wright.

(—) **Wright A (Berlin).** August 1909 (contd.).
Flown by Orville and others at Berlin (Tempelhof), and elsewhere. First flown — for 15 min — on the last day of August. This is the only surviving standard Model A, now in the Deutsches Museum, Munich.

Note: All these, with the exception of the Baratoux machine, were made at Dayton. Those flown in Europe were assembled in Europe.

Zipfel

(Armand Zipfel)

Designed, under Voisin influence, and flown by Zipfel. Built by the Ateliers d'Aviation du Sud-Est, at Lyon.

(1) **Zipfel.** November 1908 to February 1909.
Pusher biplane. Called "Armand Zipfel". This machine was, in all essentials, a standard Voisin. Flown at Lyon and Berlin (Tempelhof).

Postscript

Cornu

(Paul Cornu)

(**Cornu Helicopter,** 1907. Two-rotor machine which made — only just — the first free ascent with a man on Nov. 13th, 1907 near Lisieux. Had 24 h.p. Antoinette.)

Appendix II

CHRONOLOGICAL LIST OF THE FIRST POWERED AEROPLANES IN ORDER OF THEIR FIRST TAKE-OFFS

(December 1903 to August 1909)

This list is intended as a supplement to the Nomenclature presented in Appendix I; the designations here follow those in the Nomenclature, and the same "coding" is used before each aircraft to provide a quick assessment of its overall achievement. Also, as before, the month is given during which its first take-off was accomplished.

This Chronology should be taken in conjunction with the table of first flights (Appendix III), and Appendix I, which deals with the nomenclature of the same aircraft as listed here.

Prior to December 1903, each of the following man-carrying machines was briefly airborne — for some 5 seconds at best — most of them after a down-ramp run: none made a sustained or controlled flight of any kind:

>   *c.* 1874   Du Temple monoplane (France).
>   1884   Mozhaiski monoplane (Russia).
>   1890   Ader *Eole* monoplane (France).
>   1894   Maxim biplane test-rig (Britain).
>   1903   Jatho semi-biplane (Germany).

The following three machines were wrecked either before or during take-off:

>   1897   Ader Avion III monoplane.
>   1901   Kress tandem-wing monoplane flying boat (Austria).
>   1903   (twice)   Langley   tandem-wing   monoplane,   called   *Aerodrome* (U.S.A.).

. . . .

The first achievement of powered, sustained and controlled flying was by the Wright brothers, tentatively in 1903, and decisively in 1905. Then came a succession of experiments and achievements in Europe and America which culminated in the great Reims aviation meeting of August 1909, which signalised the world's acceptance of the aeroplane as a practical vehicle.

. . . .

(0) 1903 (December 17th) Wright Flyer I.

[288]

APPENDIX II

(1)	1904 (May)	Wright Flyer II.
(30)	1905 (June)	Wright Flyer III.
(00)	1906 (March)	Vuia I.
(00)	,, (September)	Ellehammer II.
(00)	,, (,,)	Santos-Dumont 14-*bis*.
(00)	,, (October)	Vuia I-*bis*.
(0)	,, (November)	Santos-Dumont 14-*bis* (mod).
(00)	1907 (March)	Voisin-Delagrange I.
(00)	,, (April)	Blériot V.
(00)	,, (Spring?)	Phillips II.
(00)	,, (June)	Vuia II.
(00)	,, (July)	Blériot VI (*Libellule*).
(0)	,, (September)	Blériot VI (mod).
(1)	,, (,,)	Voisin-Farman I.
(1)	,, (October)	REP. 1.
(0)	,, (November)	Voisin-Delagrange I (mod).
(0)	,, (,,)	Blériot VII.
(0)	,, (,,)	Santos-Dumont 19.
(00)	,, (,,)	De La Vaulx.
(00)	,, (December)	De Pischoff I.
(1)	,, (,,)	Voisin-Farman I (mod).
(00)	1907–08	Ellehammer III.
(1)	1908 (January)	Voisin-Delagrange II.
(00)	,, (February)	Gastambide-Mengin I.
(00)	,, (March)	A.E.A. *Red Wing*.
(10)	,, (,,)	Voisin-Farman I-*bis*.
(10)	,, (May)	Voisin-Delagrange III.
(1)	,, (,,)	Wright Flyer III (mod).
(0)	,, (,,)	A.E.A. *White Wing*.
(00)	,, (June)	Ellehammer IV.
(1)	,, (,,)	REP. 2.
(0)	,, (,,)	Blériot VIII.
(00)	,, (,,)	Roe I.
(1)	,, (July)	Blériot VIII-*bis*.
(1)	,, (,,)	A.E.A. *June Bug*.
(0)	,, (,,)	Ferber IX (Antoinette III).

[289]

(120)	1908	(August)	Wright A (France).
(1)	,,	(,,)	Antoinette II (Gastambide-Mengin II).
(0)	,,	(,,)	Gasnier I.
(30)	,,	(September)	Voisin-Delagrange III (mod).
(00)	,,	(,,)	Goupy I.
(60)	,,	(,,)	Wright A (Fort Myer).
(30)	,,	(,,)	Voisin-Farman I-*bis* (mod).
(10)	,,	(October)	Voisin-Farman I-*bis* (2nd mod).
(10)	,,	(,,)	Blériot VIII-*ter*.
(1)	,,	(,,)	Antoinette IV.
(0)	,,	(,,)	Cody 1-B.
(1)	,,	(,,)	De Caters.
(0)	,,	(,,)	Koechlin-De Pischoff.
(1)	,,	(November)	Zipfel.
(10)	,,	(,,)	Voisin-Farman I-*bis* (triplane).
(1)	,,	(December)	Voisin (Moore-Brabazon).
(10)	,,	(,,)	Antoinette V.
(00)	,,	(,,)	Robart
(00)	,,	(,,)	Dunne D.4.
(1)	1909	(January)	Cody 2.
(00)	,,	(,,)	Grade I.
(00)	,,	(,,)	Vendome II.
(1)	,,	(,,)	Blériot XI [first form].
(10)	,,	(February)	REP. 2-*bis*.
(10)	,,	(,,)	Maurice Farman I.
(?)	,,	(,,)	Voisin (Études).
(1)	,,	(,,)	Voisin (*Bird of Passage*).
(10)	,,	(,,)	A.E.A. *Silver Dart*.
(1)	,,	(March)	Santos-Dumont 20 (*Demoiselle*).
(0)	,,	(,,)	Goupy II.
(60)	,,	(April)	Henry Farman III [first form].
(10)	,,	(,,)	Voisin (*Alsace*).
(120)	,,	(,,)	Voisin (Rougier).
(30)	,,	(,,)	Wright A (Rome).
(10)	,,	(,,)	Antoinette VI.
(10)	,,	(,,)	Voisin (De Caters).
(30)	,,	(May)	Blériot XI (mod).
(30)	,,	(,,)	Voisin (Gobron).
(1)	,,	(,,)	Voisin (Hansen).
(60)	,,	(,,)	Wright A (de Lambert).

APPENDIX II

(00)	1909	(May)	Roe II (No. 1. Triplane, *Bullseye*).
(30)	,,	(,,)	Wright A (Tissandier).
(30)	,,	(,,)	Blériot XII.
(1)	,,	(June)	Odier-Vendome.
(120)	,,	(,,)	Voisin (Paulhan).
(30)	,,	(,,)	Curtiss *Gold Bug*.
(1)	,,	(,,)	Voisin (Legagneux).
(60)	,,	(,,)	Wright A (Signal Corps).
(0)	,,	(,,)	Breguet I.
(120)	,,	(July)	Henry Farman III (Sommer).
(10)	,,	(,,)	Voisin (Ferber).
(10)	,,	(,,)	Henry Farman III (Cockburn).
(30)	,,	(,,)	Wright A (Lefebvre).
(30)	,,	(,,)	Voisin (Fournier).
(10)	,,	(,,)	Voisin (Odessa).
(60)	,,	(,,)	Antoinette VII.
(1)	,,	(August)	Blériot (Leblanc).
(1)	,,	(,,)	Voisin (Daumont).
(10)	,,	(,,)	Cody 3.
(60)	,,	(,,)	Blériot XI (Delagrange).
(10)	,,	(,,)	Antoinette VIII.
(–)	,,	(,,)	Wright A (Baratoux).
(10)	,,	(,,)	Curtiss *Golden Flyer*.
(120)	,,	(,,)	Voisin (Bunau-Varilla).
(1)	,,	(,,)	Voisin (Sanchez-Besa).
(1)	,,	(,,)	Blériot XIII.
(180)	,,	(,,)	Henry Farman III (mod).
(–)	,,	(,,)	Wright A (Berlin).

Note: Not listed above are the aircraft built by Pearse, Watson and Whitehead, for which see the Nomenclature.

Addenda: The Watson Rocker No. 1 made one or more take-offs in 1908 or 1909, but could not fly.

Appendix III

TABLE OF THE FIRST POWERED FLIGHTS AND TAKE-OFFS (1903–08)

On the following pages is a table of words and diagrams showing the best airborne duration times achieved up to the end of 1908 by every powered aeroplane which can be said to have made one or more successful take-offs from December 1903 to the end of 1908. Flight duration is the best indication of sustentation and controllability — thus of success — in those early days, when calm weather was a sine qua non for most pilots. In the case of the more significant aircraft, a number of their best flights have been included, the abbreviation "ctd" being placed in columns six and eight for the second and subsequent entries.

Duration time and/or distance, when known, are given in columns four and five: in view of the unreliability of contemporary records, these are often approximate. In those few cases where neither duration nor distance is recorded, there is ample documentary evidence for the diagnosis given. Despite this general nature of approximation in the figures, the calibre of achievement emerges clearly enough from a study of the circumstances, and the unreliability of the records in no way affects the general picture.

In assessing the historical importance of many of the early performances recorded here, it could be argued that their achievements were so minuscule that they do not even merit bare inclusion in such a table as this. The reason for their inclusion is to show the number of machines constructed after 1903 which were brought to the stage of being at least able to take off. Many more were built which could never get off the ground. Those take-offs which lasted for less than 15 seconds — they were in no sense proper flights — have therefore been included, but are recorded simply as dots on the zero line of the chart: their duration times or distances are recorded in the left-hand columns. Even in terms of distance travelled through the air, none of these take-offs represented more than about 200 metres (say 650 ft.) at most, the majority of them were much less.

If the pilot's name was not that incorporated in the aircraft designation, it is given immediately beneath the latter in column seven.

In column eight is given the approximate number of take-offs accomplished until the end of 1908: such totals were very hard to come by, and in a few cases may be wide of the mark; but taken as a

[292]

whole, they appear to be reliable enough as a guide to the "useful lives" of the aircraft.

The abbreviations used are as follows:

B   Biplane

SB   Semi-biplane (*i.e.* what later would have been termed a sesquiplane)

Ctd.   "Continued" (*i.e.* a further flight by an aircraft already included)

M   Monoplane

TM   Tandem-monoplane

P   Passenger flight (*i.e.* pilot plus one passenger)

T   Triplane

ST   Semi-triplane

m.   metre

min.   minute

ml.   mile

List No.	Date	Location	Duration	Distance	Type	Aircraft and pilot	Tot take (
1	Dec. 17 1903	Kill Devil Hills	12 sec.	120 ft. (500 ft. air dist.)	B	**Wright Flyer I** (Orville)	4
2	Dec. 17 1903	Kill Devil Hills	59 sec.	852 ft. ($\frac{1}{2}$ ml. air dist.)	(ctd.)	**Wright Flyer I** (Wilbur)	
3	Nov. 9 1904	Dayton	5 min. 4 s.	$2\frac{3}{4}$ ml.	B	**Wright Flyer II** (Wilbur)	80
4	Sept. 29 1905	Dayton	19 min. 55 s.	12 ml.	B	**Wright Flyer III** (Orville)	40
5	Oct. 4 1905	Dayton	33 min. 17 s.	$20\frac{3}{4}$ ml.	(ctd.)	**Wright Flyer III** (Orville)	
6	Oct. 5 1905	Dayton	38 min. 3 s.	$24\frac{1}{8}$ ml.	(ctd.)	**Wright Flyer III** (Wilbur)	
7	Aug. 19 1906	Issy		24 m.	M	**Vuia I**	3
8	Sept. 12 1906	Lindholm	4 sec. (tethered)	42 m.	SB	**Ellehammer II**	(?)
9	Sept. 13 1906	Bagatelle		7 m.	B	**Santos-Dumont 14-*bis***	1
10	Oct. 14 1906	Issy	$\frac{7}{8}$ sec.	6 m.	M	**Vuia I-*bis***	8
11	Nov. 12 1906	Bagatelle	$21\frac{1}{8}$ sec.	220 m.	B	**Santos-Dumont 14-*bis* (mod)**	4
12	Mar. 30 1907	Bagatelle	6 sec.	60 m.	B	**Voisin-Delagrange I** (C. Voisin)	6
13	Apr. 5 1907	Bagatelle		6 m.	M	**Blériot V**	4
14	Spring/Summer 1907	Streatham		500 ft.	MP	**Phillips II**	(?)
15	July 5 1907	Bagatelle		20 m.	M	**Vuia II**	2
16	July 25 1907	Issy	10 sec.	150 m.	TM	**Blériot VI Libellule**	11
17	Sept. 17 1907	Issy	17 sec.	184 m.	TM	**Blériot VI (mod)**	6
18	Nov. 5 1907	Issy	40 sec.	500 m.	B	**Voisin-Delagrange I (mod)** (Delagrange)	2
19	Nov. 9 1907	Issy	1 min. 14 s.	1,030 m.	B	**Voisin-Farman I** (H. Farman)	20
20	Nov. 16 1907	Buc	55 sec.	600 m.	M	**R.E.P. 1** (Esnault-Pelterie)	5

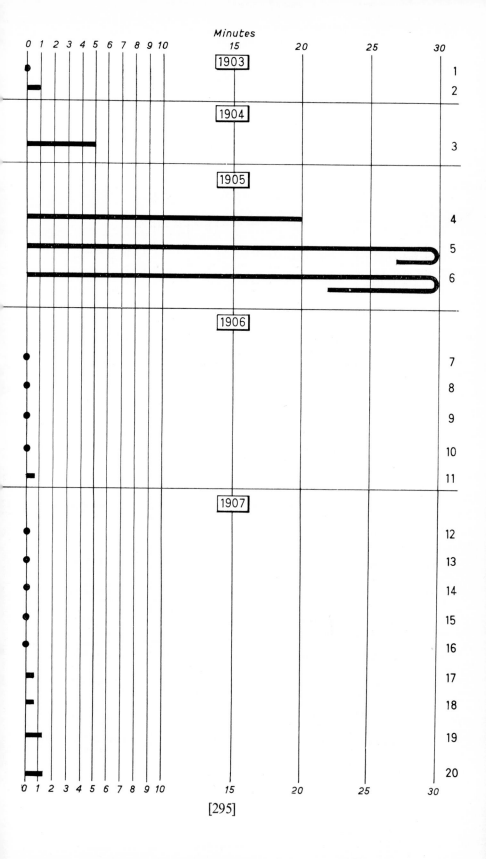

List No.	Date	Location	Duration	Distance	Type	Aircraft and pilot	To take
21	Nov. 16 1907	Issy	45 sec.	500 m.	M	**Blériot VII**	6
22	Nov. 17 1907	Issy	18 sec.	200 m.	M	**Santos Dumont 19**	3
23	Nov. 18 1907	Saint-Cyr	7 sec.	70 m.	M	**De La Vaulx**	2
24	Dec. 6 1907	Issy		7 m.	B	**De Pischoff I**	7
25	1907–08	Lindholm			T	**Ellehammer III**	(
26	Jan. 11 1908	Issy	1 min. 45 s.		B	**Voisin-Farman I (mod)** (H. Farman)	9
27	Jan. 13 1908	Issy	1 min. 28 s.	1 km.	(ctd.)	**Voisin-Farman I (mod)** (H. Farman)	
28	Jan. 15 1908	Issy	7 sec.	80 m.	(ctd.)	**De Pischoff I**	
29	Feb. 13 1908	Bagatelle		150 m.	M	**Gastambide-Mengin I** (Boyer)	(
30	Mar. 12 1908	Hammond-sport		319 ft.	B	**A.E.A. Red Wing** (Baldwin)	2
31	Apr. 11 1908	Issy	6 min. 30 s.	3,925 m.	B	**Voisin-Delagrange II** (Delagrange)	1
32	May 14 1908	Kill Devil Hills	3 min. 40 s.	2½ ml.	B	**Wright Flyer III (mod)** (Orville takes Furnas)	1
33	May 14 1908	Kill Devil Hills	7 mins. 29 s.	5 ml.	(ctd.)	**Wright Flyer III (mod)** (Wilbur)	
34	May 22 1908	Hammond-sport	19 sec.	1,017 ft.	B	**A.E.A. White Wing** (Curtiss)	3
35	June 8 1908	Buc	1 min.	800 m.	M	**R.E.P. 2** (Esnault-Pelterie)	(
36	June 23 1908	Milan	18 min. 30 s.	14.27 km.	B	**Voisin-Delagrange III** (Delagrange)	3
37	June 28 1908	Kiel	11 sec.	400 m.	B	**Ellehammer IV**	(
38	June 29 1908	Issy	50 sec.	700 m.	M	**Blériot VIII**	
39	June 1908	Brooklands		150 ft.	B	**Roe 1**	(
40	July 4 1908	Hammond-sport	1 min. 42.5 s.	5,090 ft.	B	**A.E.A. June Bug** (Curtiss)	3
41	July 6 1908	Issy	8 min. 25 s.		M	**Blériot VIII-*bis***	2
42	July 6 1908	Issy	20 min. 20 s.	20 km.	B	**Voisin-Farman I-*bis*** (H. Farman)	6
43	July 8 1908	Turin	15 sec.	150 m.	(ctd.)	**Voisin-Delagrange III** (Delagrange)	
44	Aug. 8 1908	Hunaud-ières	1 min. 45 s.		B	**Wright A (France)** (Wilbur)	1

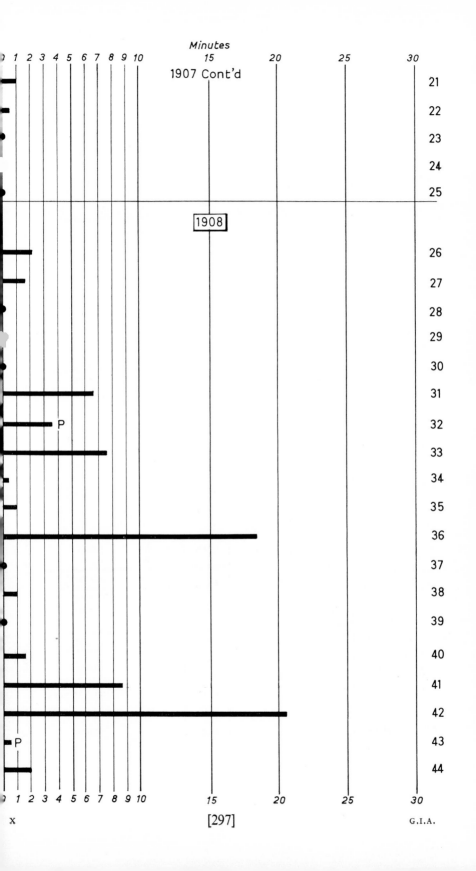

List No.	Date	Location	Duration	Distance	Type	Aircraft and pilot	Tot take
45	Aug. 21 1908	Issy	1 min. 36 s.		M	**Antoinette II** (Welferinger)	(1
46	Aug. 29 1908	Hammond-sport	3 min.	2 ml.	(ctd.)	**A.E.A. June Bug** (Curtiss)	
47	Sept. 12 1908	Fort Myer	1 hr. 14 min. 20 s.	50 ml.	B	**Wright A (Fort Myer)** (Orville)	1
48	Sept. 16 1908	Auvours	39 min. 18 s.		(ctd.)	**Wright A (France)** (Wilbur)	
49	Sept. 17 1908	Issy	30 min. 27 s.		B	**Voisin-Delagrange III (mod)** (Delagrange)	4
50	Sept. 17 1908	Rocheforte-sur-Loine	40 sec.	500 m.	B	**Gasnier**	1
51	Sept. 19 1908	Issy	40 sec.	500 m.	B	**Ferber IX** (Antoinette III)	8
52	Sept. 21 1908	Auvours	1 hr. 31 min. 25 s.	41½ ml.	(ctd.)	**Wright A (France)** (Wilbur)	
53	Oct. 2 1908	Bouy	44 min. 31 s.	40 km.	B	**Voisin-Farman-*bis* (mod)** (H. Farman)	6
54	Oct. 3 1908	Auvours	55 min. 37 s.	34¾ ml.	(ctd.)	**Wright A (France)** (Wilbur)	
55	Oct. 10 1908	Auvours	1 hr. 9 min. 45 s.	45–50 ml.	(ctd.)	**Wright A (France)** (Wilbur)	
56	Oct. 16 1908	Farn-borough	27 sec.	1,390 ft.	B	**Cody 1-B**	3
57	Oct. 25 1908	Issy	1 min.	800 m.	T	**De Caters**	3
58	Oct. 29 1908	Villa-coublay	40 sec.	500 m.	M	**Koechlin de Pischoff** (Koechlin)	1
59	Oct. 30 1908	Bouy to Reims	20 min.	27 km.	B	**Voisin-Farman 1-*bis*** (2nd mod) (H. Farman)	8
60	Oct. 31 1908	Toury to Artenay	11 min.	14 km.	M	**Blériot VIII-*ter***	6
61	Nov. 2 1908	Magde-burg		60 m.	T	**Grade I**	1
62	Nov. 17 1908	Bouy		10 km.	ST	**Voisin-Farman 1-*bis*** (3rd mod)	3
63	Nov. 18 1908	Issy	1 min.	900 m.	M	**Antoinette IV** (Welferinger)	4
64	Dec. 1 1908	Lyon	1 min.	900 m.	B	**Zipfel**	4
65	Dec. 1 1908	Issy		200 m.	B	**Voisin** (Moore-Brabazon	3
66	Dec. 7 1908	Issy		150 m.	T	**Goupy I**	4
67	Dec. 18 1908	Auvours	1 hr. 54 min. 53 s.	62 ml.	(ctd.)	**Wright A (France)** (Wilbur)	
68	Dec. 21 1908	Amiens		10 m.	SB	**Robart**	1
69	Dec. 25 1908	Issy	1 min. 30 s.	1 km.		**Antoinette V** (Welferinger)	2
70	Dec. 31 1908	Auvours	2 hr. 20 min. 23 s.	78 ml.	(ctd.)	**Wright A (France)** (Wilbur)	

[298]

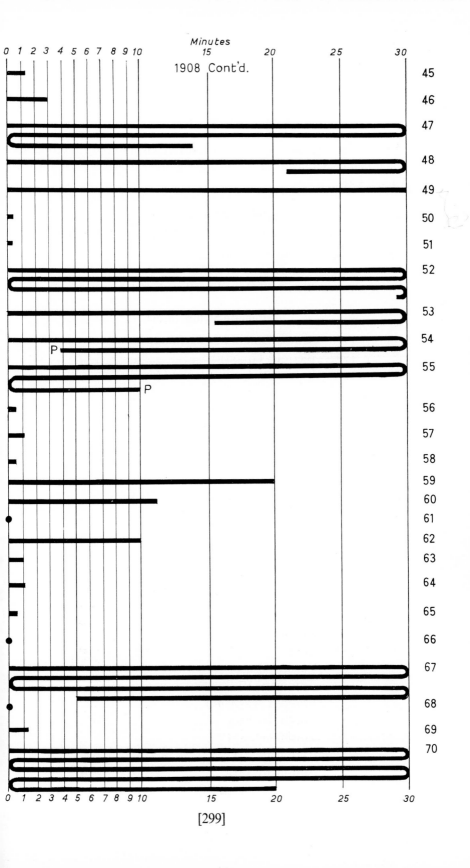

Minutes

1908 Cont'd.

Appendix IV

THE FIRST AERO-ENGINES (1903–09)

An alphabetical list of the aero-engines which powered all aeroplanes which made significant take-offs and flights from December 1903 to August 1909.

Antoinette 24 h.p. (8-cyl.)

1906	Santos-Dumont 14-*bis* [first form]
1907	Blèriot V [canard]
,,	Vuia II
,,	Blériot VI (Libellule) [first form]

Antoinette 50 h.p. (8-cyl.)

1906	Santos-Dumont 14-*bis* (mod)
1907	Blériot VI (mod)
,,	Voisin-Delagrange I, and I (mod)
,,	Voisin-Farman I, and I (mod)
,,	Blériot VII
,,	De La Vaulx
1908	Voisin-Delagrange II and III
,,	Gastambide-Mengin I and II
,,	Voisin-Farman I-*bis*, and modifications
,,	Blériot VIII, VIII-*bis*, and VIII-*ter*
,,	Ferber IX [Antoinette III]
,,	Gasnier I
,,	Antoinette IV
,,	Cody 1–B
,,	Zipfel
,,	Voisin (Moore-Brabazon)
,,	Antoinette V
,,	Robart
1909	Cody 2
,,	Voisin (Alsace)
,,	Antoinette VI
,,	Voisin (Legagneux)
,,	Voisin (Ferber)
,,	Voisin (Odessa)
,,	Antoinette VII
,,	Antoinette VIII

APPENDIX IV

Anzani 25 h.p. (3-cyl.)

1907 De Pischoff
1909 Vendome II
,, Blériot XI (mod)
,, Blériot XI (Delagrange)

Anzani 50 h.p.

1909 Blériot XIII
,, Raoul Vendome II

Curtiss 40 h.p. (8-cyl.)
(air-cooled)

1908 A.E.A. Red Wing
,, A.E.A. White Wing
,, A.E.A. June Bug

Curtiss 30 h.p. (4–cyl.)
(water-cooled)

1908 A.E.A. Silver Dart
1909 Curtiss Golden Flyer

Curtiss 30 h.p. (4–cyl.) (water-cooled)

1909 Curtiss Gold Bug

Darracq 30 h.p. (2-cyl.)

1909 Santos-Dumont 20 (Demoiselle)

Dutheil-Chalmers 20 h.p. (2-cyl.)

1907 Santos-Dumont 19
1908 Koechlin-De Pischoff

Ellehammer 18-20 h.p. (3-cyl.)

1906 Ellehammer II
1907 Ellehammer II (triplane)

Ellehammer 35 h.p. (6-cyl.)

1907 Ellehammer III (triplane)
1908 Ellehammer IV
1909 Ellehammer VI

[301]

E.N.V. 60 h.p. (8-cyl.)

1909   Voisin (Moore-Brabazon)
,,   Blériot XII
,,   Voisin (Sanchez-Besa)

Esnault-Pelterie. See REP.

Gnome 50 h.p. (7-cyl.)

1909   Voisin (Paulhan)
,,   Henry Farman III (Cockburn)
,,   Henry Farman III (mod)
,,   Voisin (Daumont)
,,   Voisin (Bunau-Varilla)

Gobron 60 h.p. (8-cyl.)

1909   Voisin (de Caters)
,,   Voisin (Gobron)

Grade 35 h.p. (6-cyl.)

1909   Grade I [triplane]

Itala 50 h.p. (8-cyl.)

1909   Voisin (Fournier)

J.A.P. 9 h.p. (2-cyl.)

1909   Roe II [triplane]

Renault 50 h.p. (8-cyl.)

1908   Voisin-Farman I-*bis*
,,   Goupy I [triplane]
1909   Maurice Farman I
,,   Voisin (Rougier)
,,   Breguet I

REP. 30 h.p. (7-cyl.)

1907   REP. 1
1908   REP. 2
1909   REP. 2-*bis* [? improved engine]
,,   Blériot XI [first form]
,,   Goupy II

Serpollet (carbonic acid gas) 25 h.p.

1906 Vuia I and I-*bis*

Turcat-Méry 20 h.p.

1909 Odier-Vendome

Vivinus 50 h.p. (8-cyl.)

1908 De Caters [triplane]
1909 Henry Farman III [first form]
,, Voisin (Hansen)
,, Henry Farman III (Sommer)

Wright 12 h.p. (4-cyl.)

1903 Wright Flyer I

Wright 15–16 h.p. (4-cyl.)

1904 Wright Flyer II
1905 Wright Flyer III [and the III (mod) in 1908]

Wright 30 h.p. (4-cyl.)

1908 Wright A (France)
,, Wright A (Fort Myer)
1909 Wright A (Rome)
,, Wright A (de Lambert)
,, Wright A (Tissandier)
,, Wright A (Signal Corps)
,, Wright A (Lefèbvre)
,, Wright A (Baratoux)
,, Wright A (Berlin)

Appendix V

THE WRIGHTS AND THE REVIVAL OF
EUROPEAN AVIATION: 1901–03

It can now be shown precisely and explicitly how the Wright brothers were directly responsible for the revival of European aviation during the years 1901–08. This influence has been described in the main text of the present book, but only recently has it been possible to uncover in detail the initial steps by which this influence came to Europe.

It is well known that the Wright influence on Europe was first effected through Capt. F. Ferber, and for long I had been content with Ferber's own statement on page 56 of his book *L'Aviation* (1909) that in January 1902 he had read an unsigned article on aviation in the *Revue Rose* (the popular title for the Paris technical Weekly *Revue Scientifique*); that he wrote to the editor; that the editor put him in touch with Professor G. H. Bryan at Cardiff; that Bryan in turn put him in touch with Octave Chanute in America; and that finally Chanute sent him a "dossier" of information which led to his abandonment of the Lilienthal-type glider, and the adoption of the Chanute-Wright configuration.

A short time ago I decided to try and identify the article which had thus "sparked" Ferber, for such an item must clearly be of considerable historical, and even sentimental, significance in this absorbing story. To my dismay, the four January issues of the *Revue Rose* revealed nothing remotely resembling the article in question. As he might have read an old issue, I went through those for the winter months of 1901, and again found nothing. Feeling sure that Ferber would not have "mis-remembered" the name of the periodical, but might well have forgotten when he actually read it, I continued with my search backwards through the formidable 1901 volume — formidable in size and complexity — of the *Revue Rose*. In the issue dated June 1st, 1901 (pp. 689–92), I found it at last. The piece was entitled "La Locomotion Aérienne", and was an unsigned resumé of a discourse with the title "History and Progress of Aerial Locomotion" given to the Royal Institution in London on February 8th, 1901, by Professor G. H. Bryan, F.R.S., a founder-member of the Aeronautical Society. It dealt with various nineteenth century efforts and accomplishments in gliding, ending with a description of Chanute and Herring; it did not mention the Wrights, as they were as yet unknown.

This seemed a long way back in 1901, but there can be no doubt that it was the article Ferber read. To obtain more details of this vital sequence of events, I wrote to my friend Miss Pearl Young in the U.S.A. (the biographer of Chanute), asking if the date of the first letter from Ferber was known, and for the dates of subsequent letters: she generously delved into every detail of the Chanute-Ferber correspondence for me with surprising and important results. The first point to emerge was that Ferber, even in the few years between his first contact and the writing of his book in 1908 (published in 1909) had completely forgotten the dates involved. Miss Young revealed that Ferber first wrote to Chanute on November 10th, 1901: allowing for his two previous letters and the answers to them, this meant that Ferber probably first read the article in the *Revue Rose* in October 1901: it was still certainly a fairly old number, but not so old as at first appeared. His first letter, referred to by date in Chanute's reply, has unfortunately not survived, but Miss Young transcribed Chanute's reply (dated November 24th), and it forms one of the most interesting links in aviation history. Chanute wrote in French (both his parents were French and they brought him to the U.S.A. in 1839 at the age of seven):

"I have your kind letter of November 10th. As I rarely write in French, I pray you to excuse me if I make mistakes in my reply.

"I am posting to you four fairly recent brochures which provide a popular account of my experiments. Quite recently, a Mr. Wright has done still better than I ("a fait encore mieux que moi") but he has not published anything.

"I had a book published in 1894 [*Progress in Flying Machines*], of which I send you the title, etc., and I have written several articles in the *Aeronautical Annual* for 1896 and 1897, giving some particulars of my experiments, to which Mr. Herring has also contributed. I regret that I have no more copies of these, but I enclose the address of the publisher."

Ferber wrote thanking Chanute on December 10th.

Here, in November 1901, was the first significant news of the Wrights to reach Europe. It was, of course, not the first time the name of Wright had crossed the Atlantic: Wilbur had previously had his article "Angle of Incidence" published in the *Aeronautical Journal* for July 1901; and another article, "Die wagerechte Lage während des Gleitfluges" (the horizontal pilot-position in gliding flight) published in the *Illustrierte Aeronautische Mitteilungen*, also for July 1901. The first of these articles was a theoretical paper on aerodynamics, and did not mention any practical flying, and was unillustrated. The second did in fact speak of their piloted glides in 1900, but only briefly and in general terms, and was accompanied — somewhat inappropriately in view of the title of the paper — by one illustration, the photograph of the 1900 glider being flown as an unmanned kite (Fig. 10-B in this book). No particular notice was taken in Europe of either article; but the photograph in the German periodical has the historical distinction of being the first illustration to appear anywhere in the world of a Wright aircraft.

Then on January 8th, 1902, Chanute sent Ferber what was to be the decisive document in the latter's career, and the first "sparker" of the European revival; it was a copy of the *Journal of the Western Society of Engineers* (Chicago) — or an off-print — of December 1901 containing Wilbur Wright's now famous first paper on "Some Aeronautical Experiments", describing and illustrating the work with the 1900 and 1901 Wright gliders, read before the Society on the preceding September 18th. On January 22nd, 1902, Ferber wrote to Chanute asking him to convey his "felicitations" to Wilbur.

Ferber thereupon decided to abandon his Lilienthal-type glider, and adopt the Wright type. It is important to note that he never attempted to copy the Chanute hang-glider which figured in the first batch of material he received from Chanute; after receiving Wilbur's paper, he immediately decided to espouse the Wright configuration with the forward elevator and (as yet) no tail surfaces *à la* the 1901 Wright glider, although his copy was sadly primitive in construction, and even lacked any warp-control. But it was the Wright configuration alone which now conditioned Ferber. Later on he even entitled the relevant chapter of his own book (*L'Aviation* 1909) "Ferber à la poursuite des Wright de 1902 à 1906".

In the issue of *L'Aérophile* for February 1903, Ferber published an account of his gliding experiments to date, with the title "*Expériences d'Aviation*"; he signed it with his pseudonym "De Rue". In this article he described his Lilienthal and Wright-type gliders with six prominent illustrations; four of them were of his machine "du type Chanute et Wright" as he called it, which in fact was his copy of the Wright No. 2 glider of 1901: the linkage of Chanute's name with the Wrights came about partly because of the Wrights' admitted copying of Chanute's method of rigging a biplane (their only technical debt to him), and partly owing to Chanute's somewhat paternal attitude toward the brothers, which led him to suggest — quite improperly — that they were his pupils. Near the end of the article he refers to

Wilbur's best glide of 622½ ft. in 1902, news which he had received in a letter from Chanute. These illustrations were the first published to show man-carrying Wright-type gliders in action, and the first to bring home forcibly to Europe the early Wright configuration. The German periodical noted above was little read in France, and the 1900 Wright machine shown there (being flown unoccupied as a kite) meant very little at the time, especially since in that particular photograph it is not at all clear that the structure out front (seen sideways on) is an elevator, and the controls were not referred to in the article. *L'Aérophile*, on the other hand, was the official organ of the Aéro-Club de France, and was "required reading" for every French pioneer.

It was in the April 1903 issue of *L'Aérophile*, published after Chanute's lecture on April 2nd (see below), that there appeared not only Archdeacon's passionate appeal to his countrymen not to allow the air to be conquered by foreigners, but an equally impassioned outburst by Ferber: "the aeroplane must not be allowed to be perfected in America!"

On June 24th, 1903, Wilbur read his second paper to the Western Society of Engineers at Chicago — "Experiments and Observations in Soaring Flight" — which was published in their Journal for August 1903. In a letter of June 28th to Ferber, Chanute promised to send the paper, which he did in August or September.

Ferber never forgot the debt he owed to Wilbur, and in a letter to George Besançon, published in the June 1907 issue of *L'Aérophile*, he wrote "without this man I would be nothing, for I should not have dared, in 1902, to trust myself to that flimsy fabric if I had not known from his accounts and his photographs that 'it would carry'. . . . without him, my experiments would not have taken place and I should not have had Voisin as a pupil (etc.)".

The second and even more powerful instigator of the European revival was Chanute's lecture to the Aéro-Club de France on April 2nd, 1903, which also gave rise to the second series of Wright-type gliders, and both strengthened and continued more forcibly Ferber's introduction of the Wright configuration to Europe; this led direct to the main stream of European powered flying. Equally explicit demonstrations and admissions of this new direct influence of the Wrights on Europe are available from contemporary sources, and are noted elsewhere in this work.

PS. A detailed study by the present writer of the Wrights' influence on European aviation is shortly being published by the Science Museum: it is entitled *The Birth of European Aviation*.

Appendix VI

CONTROL SYSTEMS IN 1909

I have discussed in some detail the history of aircraft control systems in my book *The Aeroplane* (GS-A), so I have here only described the operation of the mature control systems of the six chief machines of 1909. The illustrations are mostly from contemporary sources, those of the Voisin, Antoinette, and Henry Farman III being reproduced by courtesy of the Editor of *Flight International*.

THE WRIGHT CONTROL SYSTEM

The Wrights were the first who could properly control an aeroplane in flight — the control of Lilienthal's and Pilcher's hang-gliders being primitive in the extreme — and hence the first to evolve a successful control system. All modern flight control, and control techniques, derive directly from the Wrights, who evolved theirs from flying experience in their three gliders (1900–02), and in their first three powered machines (1903–05).

When the Wrights started to build their first "standard" (1907–09) model — which for convenience we call their Model A — they adopted no less than three methods of operating their elevator, warp, and rudder controls. The elevator system remained the same throughout, with one hand working the elevator lever. Until they started training their pupils, the elevator lever was always the left-hand lever; but when they had pupils under instruction, the latter sat in the right-hand seat, and had the duplicated elevator lever on the *right*, with the warp and rudder controls on the left. The Wrights' own pupils, therefore, learnt to fly their machines using reversed controls.

There was one highly ingenious and original feature of the Wright biplane elevator which has seldom been described, even at the time. This comprised a device which reversed the curvature of the surfaces as between the up and down position, as shown below. The normal elevator position on a Wright biplane is shown in the centre sketch, the elevator always being held at a slight negative angle of attack in level flight.

On the left is shown the down-position, with a concave curvature to provide additional "lift" downwards. On the right is the up-position, with a convex curvature to provide additional lift upwards. This potentiating of elevator effect provided the pilot with a highly

[308]

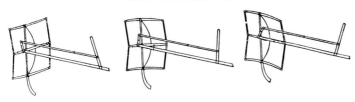

sensitive longitudinal control. The half-moon shape between the surfaces represents the one (and later, two) "blinkers" which provided forward keel area.

The Wright warping system as standardised in their Model A machines, provided for the centre bays of the machine — in which the engine and occupants were housed — to be rigid, with the outer two bays capable of being warped for lateral control, with special flexible joinings where the struts met the wing-spars. The warping system is sketched here:

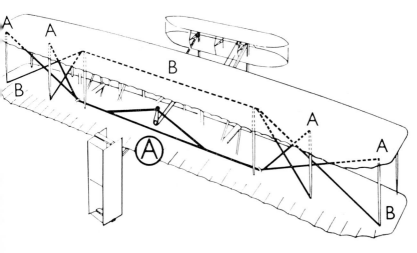

The warp control consisted of two cable systems, an active (positive) one A,A, and a passive (negative) one B,B. When, for example, the rocker arm (above the circle A) was put over to port — for a port bank — the active system produced a positive down-warp on the starboard side, the down-pressure on the outer starboard struts forcing down the outer trailing edge of the lower starboard wing in concert with the upper wing. Simultaneously, the passive system (B,B) exerted an upward pull on the outer port struts, which raised the trailing edges of the port wings in a negative warp. When it came to the warp and rudder control levers, the Wrights were to adopt no less than three systems between 1908 and 1910, when they arrived at a single standard system. It seems to have been Orville who initiated their sophisticated series of warp and rudder systems; this consisted of two right-hand levers mounted — and clamped stiffly — side by side on a common axle, one working the warp, the other the rudder: it was virtually impossible to move these two levers together, using one hand to achieve varying degrees of both simultaneously. This unsatisfactory system was rejected by Wilbur, who altered his epoch-making machine — Wright A (France) — during its assembly at Le Mans.

The Wilbur Wright System

The standard Model A Wright machines used in France 1908–10, starting with Wilbur's machine, were warp and rudder controlled by the universal lever system shown here:

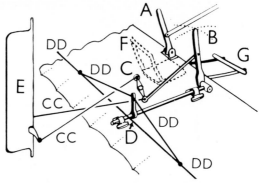

The lever (B) could be moved in any direction: if moved fore and aft, it activated the rudder (E) via the horizontal pivoted arm (C), and the crossed cables CC, CC. If rocked laterally, the lever activated the warping system via the rocking lever (D) and the cables DD, DD, along with the passive warping cables shown previously. If rocked obliquely, warp and rudder control were effected simultaneously. The pilot, sitting in the seat F (there were two seats in all the Model A machines) operated the elevator lever (A) with his left hand, and the warping-cum-rudder with the right (B). His feet were supported by the rest (G). The rudder (E) is shown here as a single unit.

The Orville Wright System

The standard Model A Wright machines used in the U.S.A. and Germany were controlled by the "bent wrist" system invented by Orville Wright, shown here (seen from $\frac{3}{4}$ front):

The control column (A) could only be moved fore and aft: fixed to its base was the semi-disc (B) to which the warping cables (C,C) were

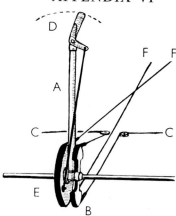

attached: thus, moving the column forward put positive down-warp on the starboard wings and negative on the port. The rudder was operated either separately, or together with the warping, by the side-to-side movement of the handle (D) of the control column: such movements were communicated to the rudder first via the rod from the handle (D) to the disc (E) — which was not attached to the control column, and could rotate freely on the common axle — and then via the cables (F,F) which were attached to the disc, and ran aft (crossing one another) to the rudder.

But a feature of the rudder system which had puzzled us until recently was the evident automatic movement of the rudder over to the banked side when the column was moved forwards or backwards to operate the warping, even when no wrist movement was made. The Dutch engineer, Mr. C. W. A. Oyens first pointed this out to me, drawing attention to the position of attachment on the disc (E) of the rudder rod. (On my sketch here, the attachment is shown too low down). We could not understand its significance until I happened to mention the matter to my friend Bruno Jablowsky, who flew with Orville and was trained on a Wright machine of this type. He said that Orville had deliberately gone back to the old idea of the automatic warp-rudder linkage, so that the pilot had some rudder put on to counteract the warp drag, as had first been adopted on the modified No. 3 glider of 1902; but if pure warping was necessary, a slight opposite movement of the wrist one way or the other would hold the rudder straight: by the same token, if more rudder was needed with the warping, the pilot bent the handle over in whichever direction was required.

The Wright control systems, whether Wilbur's or Orville's, were not satisfactory psychologically, since there were always at least two levers moving backwards and forwards, one of which was "suggestive" of the movement of the aircraft — i.e. the elevator lever — and the other "unsuggestively" working the warping and rudder. Nor was it satisfactory to have both hands occupied all the time.

But I feel it should always be borne in mind that all modern flight control derives, in its functions, direct from the Wright brothers; their unique contribution being not only in the proper use of lateral control, and the co-ordination of lateral control with rudder control, but in the mastery of flight control in the practical business of actual flying.

THE VOISIN CONTROL SYSTEM

The entire Voisin control system was operated by the hands:

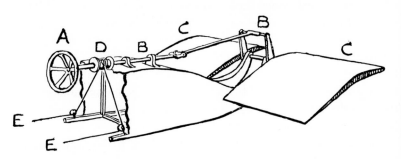

The system comprised a wheel (A) on a sliding shaft. To operate the double forward elevator (CC), the pilot thrust the wheel forward to lower it, and pulled the wheel back to raise it, these movements were effected by means of the shaft and elevator rod (B,B). To operate the rudder at the rear, the pilot rotated the wheel (A): this rotated the drum (D) over which was wound the continous rudder cable (E,E). There was no lateral control. This contemporary sketch shows almost a "kink" in the aerofoil section: this was inadvertent, the curvature being somewhat flatter.

The Voisin control system cannot reasonably be compared with any of the other developed 1909 systems, as it was the only one which omitted all lateral control. Control in two dimensions is very simple to operate and, within this simplicity, the Voisin system was satisfactory.

THE BLÉRIOT XI CONTROL SYSTEM

The Blériot system was one of the best of the early systems. In this sketch the controls are seen from $\frac{3}{4}$ rear, with the rudder-bar omitted.

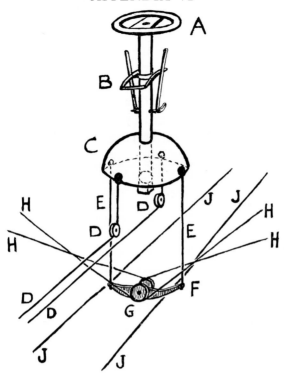

The control column was mounted on a universal joint at its base (shown dotted). A "wheel" (A) was fixed rigidly to the top of the column; the latter pierced, and was fixed rigidly to, the "cloche" (C). To the "cloche" were attached four cables D,D, and E,E: D,D ran down over pulleys, then aft to the elevator at the rear: E,E ran down to the rocker-arm (F), to whose pivot (G) were fixed one disc (forward) and one wheel (aft). Around the forward disc were attached the main positive-warping cables (the lower ending H,H) which pulled the trailing edge down on one side: running free, under the pulley-wheel, was the continuous inner bracing wire attached to the trailing edge of each wing between the attachment of the warping cable and the fuselage: this wire simply adjusted itself to whatever degree of warp was being exerted. Thus, to bank to port the column was rocked to port, which pulled down the starboard trailing edge and raised the port trailing edge.

The "passive" warping cable — which connected the upper surfaces of the trailing edges, and automatically pulled up one wing when the other was lowered — ran over a king post above the centre section.

The cables, J,J, ran back from the rudder bar forward (not shown) to the rudder at the rear. The engine controls are shown at B.

The Blériot system — using the Wrights' wing-warping — was simple, robust and psychologically "sound": like the Henry Farman, it was basically the control-system of today, with elevator and lateral control effected by one unit which could be used in any desired combination, and the rudder worked by the feet. It thus involved the coordination of two units to perform three functions.

The Antoinette Control System

The Antoinette was controlled by two side-wheels, and a rudder-bar. The starboard wheel operated the elevator at the rear (see sketch below): turning the wheel forwards applied down-elevator via the crossed cables (A,A); turning it backwards applied up-elevator:

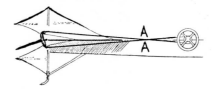

The port side-wheel operated the wing-warping mechanism (see sketch below); turning the wheel forwards produced a positive (down) warp on the starboard wing via the cables (A,A), which operated the rocker-arm pivoting on the vertical pillar (shaded black) which in turn pulled on the starboard cable (right-hand B). The negative warp was effected by a passive cable connecting the upper surface of each wing via a pulley on the king-post set on the centre section:

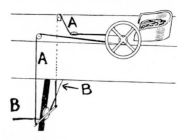

The next sketch (below) shows the vertical pillar (C) which was rigidly fixed to the axle-tree of the undercarriage (D), and bore the lever-arm operated by the cables (A,A): this lever arm was in turn

[314]

fixed to a cog-disc, which engaged (beneath) a chain attached to the warping cables (B,B):

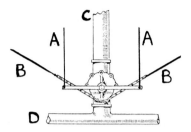

The warping cables ran from the disc-cog to the rear spars of the wings. When, for example, a positive (down) warp was to be produced on the starboard wing, a pull was exerted on the starboard warping cable: this pull lowered the whole trailing edge of the starboard wing; it simultaneously resulted in a corresponding raising of the trailing edge of the port wing. The simultaneous lowering and raising of the rear portions of the wings as a whole was effected by the initial setting of the wings at a dihedral angle, with the rear spars of the wings pivoted on the centre section of the fuselage as shown here:

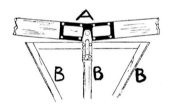

In this sketch, the wings are pivoted at A on the strengthened V-section fuselage (B,B,B). With a strong pull or push on the warping wheel, a further down-twist of the positively warped wing on its outer portion would also result.

Despite the many admirable qualities of the Antoinette as a flying machine, the operation of its control system was the least satisfactory of the 1909 machines, primarily owing to the bad "psychological lay-out" of the two wheels, with their axles at right angles to the fuselage, and the separation of function into three separate units — two wheels and a rudder-bar — used by each hand separately, and the feet. The turning of the (starboard) elevator wheel, forwards or backwards, was in itself satisfactory; but the similar forward and backward turning of the (port) warping wheel was a bad arrangement, as it was not "associationally" linked with port or starboard, or any directional function.

[315]

APPENDIX VI

As Levavasseur gave up ailerons in favour of warping on the Antoinette VI and all subsequent Antoinettes, I have here concentrated on the warping. The ailerons were worked by the same wheel (left) as the warping, and by a similar set of cables, the ailerons being contra-acting.

THE HENRY FARMAN III CONTROL SYSTEM

The Henry Farman was controlled by one hand, and the feet.

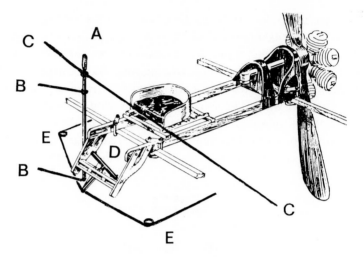

The forward elevator, and the ailerons, were operated by a single control column (A) on a universal joint attached to the starboard side of the rudder-bar support, as shown above.

The aileron cables (C,C) were attached just below the handle of the column, their operation being shown in a sketch above. The elevator cables (B,B) were also attached to the column, one below the aileron cable attachment, the other at the base.

The aileron control shown below consists of the control column, to which are attached a single, then bifurcating, cable on each side running over pulleys (on the leading edge of the lower wings) to under-

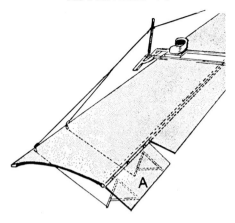

horns on each lower-wing aileron (A). Vertical cables ran up from each lower-wing aileron to its fellow on the upper wing. Lateral rocking of the control column pulled down one pair of ailerons and left the other pair horizontal: there was no provision for raising the ailerons above the horizontal.

The rudder was operated by a T-shaped foot-bar (D) — see first sketch above — which was rocked from side to side, the cables (E,E) being attached to its base.

The Farman system was simple in operation, but it should be pointed out that the ailerons were only downward moving, and hence less satisfactory in lateral control than the Wright, Blériot, Curtiss and Antoinette systems, all of which provided a positive down-travel of aileron or trailing edge on one side, and a negative on the other.

The least satisfactory aspects of the Farman system were the downward-only ailerons, which decreased the sensitivity and speed of response in the machine.

THE CURTISS CONTROL SYSTEM

The control system used by Curtiss in 1909 seems to have derived from the collective suggestions of the Aerial Experiment Association. The system was an ingenious combination of Voisin and Wright elements. The familiar Voisin wheel — now on a vertical column — was pushed forwards to lower the elevator in front, and was pulled backwards to raise it. Turning the wheel, as also in the Voisin, operated the rudder. The ailerons were operated by a shoulder fork derived from the Wrights' hip-cradle, which was also used by Santos-Dumont in his *Demoiselle:* leaning the body to port lowered the starboard aileron and raised the port; and vice versa, when leaning to starboard.

Although an ingenious system, it is clearly not wise for any control surface to be operated by such a movement of the body, since it makes independent bodily movement impossible when sitting in the pilot's seat without the possibility of the machine's flying attitude being affected.

Appendix VII

THE REIMS AVIATION MEETING OF AUGUST 1909

(La Grande Semaine d'Aviation de la Champagne)

The Reims meeting is of such vital importance in aviation history that it seemed essential — in addition to the Survey in the general text of this book — to give here a liberal amount of contemporary comment. Owing again to the kindness of Mr. H. F. King, Editor of *Flight International*, I print here excerpts from what *Flight* published at the time, starting with their correspondent's daily report of the events.

RHEIMS AVIATION MEETING

"It is to be hoped that fine weather will prevail during next week at Rheims, and in view of the storms which broke over the place on Monday and Tuesday nights, it may be anticipated that there is less to come now. Fortunately all the machines were safely under cover, and so no great damage was done, except to the partly-erected shed for the dirigible 'Zodiac III,' which was blown down. During the last few days the official programme has been slightly re-arranged as follows:

Sunday, August 22nd. — Elimination contest for the nomination of the French Aéro Club's champions in the Gordon-Bennett International Aviation Cup Competition; Prix de la Vitesse, first day; Prix du Tour de Piste, first day; Prix des Aéronauts, first day.

Monday, August 23rd. — Grand Prix de la Champagne et de la Ville de Reims, first day; Prix du Tour de Piste, second day; Prix des Aéronauts, second day.

Tuesday, August 24th. — Prix de la Vitesse, second day; Prix du Tour de Piste, third day; Prix des Aéronauts, third day.

Wednesday, August 25th. — Grand Prix de la Champagne et de la Ville de Reims, second day; Prix du Tour de Piste, fourth day; Prix des Aéronauts, fourth day.

Thursday, August 26th. — Grand Prix de la Champagne et de la Ville de Reims, third day; Prix du Tour de Piste, fifth day; Prix des Aéronauts, fifth day; Landing competition for spherical balloons.

Friday, August 27th. — Grand Prix de la Champagne et de la Ville

[319]

de Reims, fourth day; Prix du Tour de Piste, sixth day; Prix des Aéronauts, sixth day.

Saturday, August 28th. — Coupe Internationale d'Aviation Gordon-Bennett; Prix des Passagers, first day; Prix du Tour de Piste, seventh day; Prix des Aéronauts, seventh day.

Sunday, August 29th. — Prix de la Vitesse, third and last day; Prix des Passagers, second and last day; Prix de l'Altitude; Prix du Tour de Piste, eighth and last day; Prix des Aéronauts, eighth and last day.

Most of the competitors have been busily practising during the past few days, some on the Bétheny grounds, and others at their old training quarters at Châlons, among the most successful at Bétheny being MM. Tissandier and Lefebvre on Wright machines, and M. Delagrange on his Blériot flyer. M. Lefebvre has given up the use of the derrick now, and starts by simply running down the rail. Curtiss also made three short flights on Monday, and during a sudden landing slightly damaged his machine, and sprained his right foot rather badly, which may handicap him a little. Mr. Curtiss has now fitted his flyer with a new 8-cyl. V type motor of 35-h.p., in place of the 4-cyl. motor, and he anticipates to get much better results from his machine now. [See note in Sect. 67.]

At Châlons, Latham, having recovered from the accident to his face during his cross-Channel trip, Ruchonnet, Farman, Sommer, and Cockburn have all been doing well, but perhaps the outstanding performance has been that of Henry Fournier, who, on his Itala-engined Voisin machine on Tuesday, on his first attempt at a solo flight, succeeding in circling the parade ground. He then took up M. George Prade, their joint weight being 175 kilogs., and made a fine flight.

The only machines which have been withdrawn are the Santos Dumont flyer, the Austrian representative, one of the Curtiss type, and Esnault-Pelterie's monoplane. This latter has been necessary owing to M. Pelterie being injured while boxing. Besides M. Guffroy, M. Laurens will pilot one of the R.E.P. monoplanes. It is uncertain as to whether Farman will be able to compete. His injuries as the result of the accident, to which we refer elsewhere, are progressing so well that it is hoped he will be able to fly next week, but for other reasons he may decide to abstain from actually taking the air. He is at present trying a very small biplane, with which he will probably compete.

APPENDIX VII

The visit of President Fallières will probably be either on Wednesday or Thursday next.

. . . . .

The Opening day (Sun. Aug. 22nd)

Anything more unpropitious than the weather conditions under which the Rheims aviation meeting opened it would be difficult to imagine. During the previous night and early morning rain had been falling heavily, and on turning out of doors it was found that on the flagstaffs in the Place Royale and elsewhere black flags were displayed, intimating that flying was impossible. Enthusiasm was not so easily quenched. Many, heeding neither the weather nor the black flag, wended their way to the plains at Bétheny. Matters looked less promising there. Mud was hardly the word to apply to the sticky, chalky substance which had formed itself into a veritable quagmire, ankle-deep in places, on the special 'road' which had been made leading to the grand stand. At times some quaint scenes were witnessed in the effort to annex as little as possible of the Bétheny soil. Some relief was later afforded by the laying down of planks over the more frequented points used by the public, so that it became possible to reach the enclosure without getting one's clothes absolutely ruined. Several of the motor cars, however, fared pretty badly, getting stuck in the soft mud, and having to be dragged out by horses. As things ultimately turned out, the crowds were rewarded for their optimism, for all in good time the weather cleared, and the programme as officially laid down was proceeded with, in spite of strong winds and heavy showers.

The first event was the French Eliminating Trials for the Gordon-Bennett Race. For this there were twenty entries, and lots were drawn for starting order, each being allowed a quarter of an hour to get away. First out to the line was one of the red R.E.P. monoplanes, but this was unable to rise, and the first to actually make a start was Tissandier, on a Wright flyer, just before eleven o'clock. He only remained up for 1 min., however, and was followed by Blériot on one of the little cross-Channel monoplanes. He managed to cover about $2\frac{1}{4}$ kiloms., and then Latham had a try. His machine bore the number 13, and to this was attributed his failure to keep going for more than about 500 yards. Lefebvre's turn came next, and he made the best attempt, very nearly completing two laps of the 10 kilom. course. Capt. Ferber (de Rue) and others made attempts but could not get off

[321]

the ground. All this time a nasty gusty wind of about twenty miles an hour was harassing the aviators, and at noon a heavy shower of rain did not improve the position. So it came about that when the time for finishing the trials arrived at two o'clock no one had bettered Lefebvre and Blériot's performances, and they were accordingly announced as the first two French representatives for the Gordon-Bennett Race. The third, it was decided, should be selected according to the pace made in the speed tests in the afternoon, and this secured for Latham the third place, whilst as reserves Tissandier, Lambert, Paulhan, and Sommer, in the order named, were appointed.

A heavy storm at five o'clock made it appear that further flying would be out of the question that day. But quick changes were the order of the day, and half an hour later the weather broke, and immediately all was animation amongst the aviators, who proceeded to bring out their machines for the speed trials. Latham was the first away, he being rapidly followed by others, until the wonderful and unprecedented spectacle was witnessed of seven machines in the air at one time. Five, including Tissandier, Lambert, Lefebvre, Paulhan and Sommer, succeeded in covering the 30 kiloms. for the speed prizes, the three Wright machines and their pilots doing justice to their master by securing the three first places. Moreover, it was vastly interesting to note that the difference between Tissandier, who was first, and Lefebvre and Lambert, who were bracketed second, was only $1\frac{3}{5}$ secs. In addition to the above, Latham, on his Antoinette, twice made a single circuit, and Cockburn, on his Farman, once, the honour of fastest lap time going to Lefebvre, with 8 min. $58\frac{1}{5}$ secs. The longest flight of the day was that of Lefebvre, who remained in the air for 41 mins., and executed some daring manoeuvres, which roused the spectators to enthusiasm. Incidents of intense interest were momentarily occurring, the utter novelty of the entire proceedings rendering the most trivial occurence of moment. A machine dropped down here and there, only to have its place filled by another one, which in its turn, after swooping round for a time, would give place to the next. Motor troubles seemed to be the most fruitful cause of stoppages. Enthusiasm knew no bounds when the crowd were treated to one or two turns of racing, as when Tissandier overhauled and passed Bunau-Varilla, as seen in our photograph on p. 523. Blériot, too, caused a little flutter of excitement by charging a stack of wheat sheaves, resulting in a damaged propeller. Altogether the total distance covered in their flights by various 'bird-men' during the day totalled to 309 kiloms.

Among the spectators were the Right Hon. Lloyd George and Sir Henry Norman, who had motored from Boulogne, stopping the previous night at Compiegne. The Chancellor of the Exchequer was intensely impressed, and did not hesitate to express a wish that such a meeting could be held on Salisbury Plain or some other convenient spot in the British Isles. It is to be hoped that he will be able to impart some of his enthusiasm to other members of the Cabinet, so that aviation may receive a little more encouragement in Great Britain. Sir Henry Norman, who was equally impressed, gave vent to his feelings by expressing the opinion that the world was that day witnessing the birth of a new epoch of human development.

Monday's Events (*Mon. Aug. 23rd*)

What a contrast to the opening morning was the second day's dawn. On the Monday morning all was fair and calm, and to all appearance weather after the aviator's heart was in store. Blériot was up betimes giving his big monoplane a trial run soon after 6 a.m. by traversing one circuit of the course. Nothing further of importance occurred during the morning except the arrival of the dirigible 'Colonel Renard', which M. Kapferer had sailed over from Meaux in a little over $1\frac{1}{2}$ hours, and a flight by M. Paulhan of not quite five circuits of the course. About midday the wind became somewhat gusty, and Bunau-Varilla and one or two others who ventured out failed to accomplish anything very startling. Bunau-Varilla got blown off his course and landed in a field of oats, while M. Fournier was placed *hors de combat* by a gust of wind which caused him to land precipitately on one of his wings, crushing it, the damage being, however, quickly repaired. This was the day of the qualifying trials for the Grand Prix, and the other event was attempts to beat record for the lap time. A start was made at 4.30 p.m., when Lefebvre was first away, quickly followed by Paulhan. Lefebvre covered 21·2 kiloms. in 20 mins. $14\frac{2}{5}$ secs., when he decided to come down, while Paulhan kept going until 56 kiloms. had been covered in 58 mins. $48\frac{4}{5}$ secs. Several of the competitors also attacked the circuit record, and Blériot succeeded in reducing it to 8 mins. $42\frac{2}{5}$ secs., but his victory was shortlived, as Curtiss later, in his American biplane, brought it down to 8 mins $35\frac{3}{5}$ secs. One condition of the Grand Prix was that competitors had to fly a reasonable distance on or before Monday to qualify to take part in the trials on Wednesday, Thursday and Friday. Under this regulation 18 actually qualified.

Before the close of the day's proceedings Lefebvre again provided the crowd with a series of thrills by flying over and under and circling round Paulhan, who was at a height of about 25 feet. Arising out of this, when making one of his dashes under his rival's machine, he swooped so suddenly and so close to *terra firma* that one of the vast brigade of Press photographers who swarmed over the flying ground, and in whose direction Lefebvre was travelling in a bee line, in not unnatural terror flung himself flat on the ground, not realising what was happening, and fearing that his last moment had suddenly arrived. A couple of seconds relieved his anxiety, but a brother 'photo fiend' had recorded the incident in the meantime.

Tuesday's Progress (Tues. Aug. 24th)

Black flags had once more to be hoisted on Tuesday morning, the strong winds blowing rendering flying out of the question. Later on angry and ominous clouds gathered over the ground, and it looked as though a wet reception awaited M. le President, for this was the day he had chosen for his first visit. Just before four o'clock, when President Fallières arrived, however, the weather improved somewhat, but flying was still impossible, so the President spent some time examining the various machines, and receiving their various designers and pilots. He also received the British deputation, headed by General French, and just before five took his seat in the grand stand.

The starting of engines notified that flying was to be attempted, and in a few minutes Bunau-Varilla swept past the grand stand, waving his hat to the distinguished occupants. He, however, only remained up for a few minutes, when his place was taken by Paulhan, who managed to just complete his second lap as the Presidential party started back for the railway station. Altogether he completed three laps, but his time was a good way off the record, which was hardly surprising in view of the strong wind against which he had to contend. The only other aviator to make the three rounds was Latham, whose time was 30 min. 2 sec., but the time officially recorded against him was 5 per cent. more than that — 31 min. $32\frac{1}{5}$ secs. This 'fine' was under the penalisation rule for his unfinished attempt on Sunday. While Latham was flying, Blériot took a turn round for one lap, and by overhauling and passing his cross-Channel rival, demonstrated that he had easily the faster machine. Enthusiasm was intense when it was found that he had handsomely beaten the record, bringing it down to 8 min. $4\frac{2}{5}$ secs. Lefebvre was again flying in the dusk, and once more performed some extraordinary evolutions, the most impressive being a number of sharp double turns and '8's' in front of the grand stand.

APPENDIX VII

On Tuesday night Rheims had been *en fête*, or at least as gay as it could be in face of a heavy downpour of rain. Next morning the black clouds presaged anything but the best weather conditions. However, the wind was very light, and as on several occasions more than one aviator has shown an indifference to rain, it was vainly hoped that some one would venture into the central blue. Until nearly four o'clock, when Paulhan started off on a trial for the Grand Prix, and, as it turned out, made a wonderful performance by shifting the world's record for duration and distance a good way further on, there was nothing of moment to vary the monotony of waiting to record. He did not come down till after half-past six, when he had been up 2h. 43m. 24⅘s., and had traversed 131 kiloms. (82 miles). This is over 6 mins. ahead of Sommer's recently-made unofficial record, and more than 23 mins. better than Wilbur Wright's previous world's record. Naturally, of course, this performance overshadowed all the others during the afternoon, and the scenes around the young aviator upon his return to earth were somewhat disconcerting to his dignity — at least, from a Britisher's point of view. While Paulhan had been pursuing the even tenor of his way, Latham and others had been making attempts to better the circuit times, and Fournier experienced a second tumble, this time much more serious than the first smash. He was flying at a good height and had travelled about half-way round the track, when his Voisin machine, struck by a miniature whirlwind, suddenly swerved, turned over once or twice, and then crashed sideways to the ground. Fournier, with the usual good luck of an aviator, escaped serious injury, and returned to his shed riding the horse of a friendly gendarme. His machine was badly broken up, the tail being severed from the main body. Latham, on his third attempt, succeeded in covering the 30 kiloms., his time, however, being slower than the record for the Prix de Vitesse. While he was in the air a splendid rainbow appeared in the sky, and the spectacular effect of this, in conjunction with the Antoinette dragon-fly, was most impressive and not likely to be soon forgotten by those who were fortunate enough to witness it. In the twilight Curtiss tried to regain the honour of fastest time, and although he improved on his former speed, he could not lower Blériot's record, whilst several aviators, including Delagrange, Rougier and Capt. Ferber (de Rue), were out, but nothing startling, in view of previous exploits, transpired. Truly is it that familiarity breeds, if not contempt in this case, at least indifference, and that very speedily. The marvellous of to-day is but the accepted of to-morrow.

Records Broken on Thursday (Aug. 26th)

A splendid day was experienced on Thursday, and the sensation was Latham's world's distance record of 152 kiloms. (96 miles), his speed also beating all previous efforts, thereby bringing about the curious anomaly of not breaking the duration record. His time for the 150 kiloms. was 2h. 13m. 9⅗s. This splendid effort was made during the afternoon, and followed a preliminary canter of 70 kiloms., which he flew during the morning in 1h. 1m. 51⅖s.

In each case he was forced to come down owing to his petrol supply giving out, but his second marvellous flight easily placed him first for the Grand Prix.

During the long flight there were several exciting incidents. On one occasion Mr. Latham had the opportunity of racing with a passing train for some distance, while at another time he passed over Dela-grange, who was flying round the course on his Blériot.

Another thrill was afforded by Blériot who carried a passenger during a couple of flights, while Curtiss completed four circuits of the course, and Mr. Cockburn also indulged in an exciting race with another passing train.

.   .   .   .   .

In our last issue we had to break the story of the flying at Rheims just at the point where Latham had succeeded in bettering Paulhan's record for distance made on the previous day. This wonderful flight of the Antoinette monoplane was, of course, the outstanding feature of that day; in fact, it might be called an 'Antoinette' day, for in the morning Latham, on his No. 13 machine, flew for 70 kiloms., beating all records for speed. At the start he had notified his intention of running for the Grand Prix, but something going wrong with one of his planes he had to come down after seven laps. Not to be denied so easily, he brought out his No. 29 in the afternoon, and once more started off, circling round the track until his 65 litres of petrol was exhausted, when he glided to earth, after covering 154·5 kiloms. in 2h. 17m. 21⅖s. Count Lambert also made a flight for the Grand Prix, his supply of fuel only carrying him 116 kiloms. in 1h. 50m. 59s. Two mishaps occurred during the day. The first was through the engine on Rougier's machine stopping, whereby he made a sudden drop among the crowd, fortunately without seriously injuring anyone. Several were very much scared, however, by finding themselves brought so suddenly into close quarters with the biplane. The second incident was when Blériot, at the end of his third flight with a passenger, lost control of his machine through the steering-gear failing. The result was a crash into the fence, again fortunately without any serious injury to anyone. Several short flights were made during the day by Legagneux on Capt. Ferber's Voisin, Tissandier, Sommer, Cockburn and Curtiss, the latter covering 30 kiloms. in an attempt for the Grand Prix.

Friday's Record (Aug. 27th)

Farman's record-breaking attempt for the Grand Prix of course overshadowed all else on Friday. It was extraordinary, too, that such success should have been obtained, in view of the fact that the installation of the new Gnome motor was only completed 40 minutes before the time set as the limit for starting. However, the change proved grandly successful, and Farman kept up in the air until well after the official time for declaring the meeting at an end for the day. As will be seen from our tables he was officially credited with having flown 180 kiloms. in 3h. 4m. 56s., but as a matter of fact he only missed completing another lap by a few yards. But the clock had chimed half-past seven, and the official eyes were closed.

The day's proceedings were varied a little by the appearance of the dirigibles 'Col. Renard' and 'Zodiac'. Latham in the course of a trial for the Grand Prix flew close under the car of the former. Paulhan intended trying to regain the world's record. but was rendered *hors de combat* by a mischance. In order to avoid collision with Delagrange he made a sudden drop, with the result that the left side of his machine come into violent contact with the ground and was crumpled up. Both Latham and Tissandier made good flights, each completing ten laps, and Blériot at his first attempt for the Grand Prix traversed 40 kiloms. in about 40 mins. During the day the weather was perfect, and most of the prominent flyers made trials. At the start of Farman's great flight the unusual sight was witnessed of three machines passing each other vertically. Sommer was at the bottom, Farman passed over him, and Latham, travelling much faster, flew by on top.

Saturday's Great Race (Aug. 28th)

Saturday's programme contained the *piece de résistance*, for the first International competition for the Gordon-Bennett Aviation

[327]

Trophy was to be run for on this day. It was a splendid day for flying as there was only a breath of wind. The proceedings opened soon after ten, when Curtiss brought out the machine on which American hopes were fixed, and made a trial for the Circuit Prize. He succeeded in lowering the record to 7 mins. $55\frac{2}{5}$ secs. Then, finding his machine running well, he determined to make his cast for the great event. The two laps were covered in 15 mins. $50\frac{2}{5}$ secs., and this time not being bettered, the Cup crosses the 'herring pond', and the next contest for it will have to be held in America. Cockburn, the British representative, made the next attempt, but he was unable to complete one lap. Lefebvre led the way for France, but he was nearly five minutes too slow. Latham and Blériot did not make their attempts until the afternoon, when the cross-Channel hero just failed to keep the trophy in France. His first lap time was the same as Curtiss' second, but during the second round he was impeded by a squall, which made him some ten precious seconds slower. His total time was 15 mins. $56\frac{1}{5}$ secs., while Latham's was 16 mins. 32 secs. Blériot, however, secured one trophy, that for the fastest circuit, by completing the course in 7 mins. $47\frac{4}{5}$ secs., a figure which was not bettered, The other events of the day were the competition for the Passenger Prize, which was eventually won by Farman, the only aviator to carry two passengers, second place also going to him for the best flight with one companion. Lefebvre covered one lap accompanied by a friend.

The Final Day (Sun., Aug. 29th)

The contests for the two big prizes being over, Sunday, the last day of the first successful flying meeting, was earmarked for the final attempts for the Circuit and Speed Prizes, while the Height Competition also formed part of the day's programme. Ideal weather prevailed and it was anticipated that an exciting duel would be witnessed between Curtiss and Blériot for the Speed Prize. Curtiss placed himself in front by completing the course in 24 mins. $15\frac{2}{5}$ secs. Although he had to submit to a penalisation of 5 per cent. for a previous attempt, he still proved to be the best thus far. Blériot made a determined attempt to capture the prize, but alas, his hopes were soon dashed to the ground. He brought out his fastest machine, but at the far end of the course a sudden descent caused some flexible petrol connections to break. In some way the petrol became ignited, and a few moments later the racer was a wreck. Fortunately, Blériot was able to get clear, but not before his hand had got badly burned.

As will be seen from our tables, several other flyers made attempts for the Circuit and Speed Prizes, but nothing transpired entailing a change in the position of the leaders.

On each day during the week attempts were to have been made for the Dirigible Prize, a race over five laps of the circuit, but it was not till the last day that the 'Col. Renard' made its attempt. Its time for 50 kiloms. was 1 hr. 19 mins. Later the 'Zodiac' went round, but was unable to better the time, so the 'Col. Renard' secured the prize.

The sensational feature of the day was the contest for the Altitude Prize, for which Latham, Paulhan, Farman and Rougier competed. Latham made the most impressive flight, and when he returned to *terra firma* it was found that his barometer registered 155 metres (504 feet) the next best being Farman with 110 metres (358 feet). Although other attempts at flight were made they were of little interest after these wonderful performances, which concluded the Rheims Flying Week.

Closing Scenes (*Mon. Aug. 30th*)

On Monday, the proceedings were officially brought to a conclusion with a banquet offered by the organisers to the competitors, journalists, and others who had taken part. The Marquis d'Polignac presided, and among the honoured guests present were the Mayor of Rheims, Mr. Roger W. Wallace, Chairman of the Aero Club of the U.K., and Mr. Cortland F. Bishop, President of the American Aero Club. Mr. Hubert Latham, on behalf of the competitors, tendered their thanks for the splendid organisation of the meeting, which it was announced would be repeated next year.

―――――――

It taxes the English tongue to the utmost of its reaches adequately to picture the epoch-making events that have marked the progress of the flying races at Rheims. Now they are matters of history, none can gainsay that journeys of over a hundred miles in length can be made by aeroplane without pause; or that the same machine can fly to great heights, or that it can carry comparatively great weights as represented by three persons aboard. On those three counts Henry Farman and his biplane have undoubtedly scored tremendously at the first flying races in the history of the newest phase of scientific manufacturing engineering, as is told in the story that we give of this never-to-be-forgotten meeting at Rheims. But the encouraging feature of the demonstration has been the revelation of the various qualities wherein each system of design proves better than the rest.

APPENDIX VII

The meeting has not shown biplanes as a class to be pronouncedly better than monoplanes, or the other way about. The Antoinette has, perhaps, shown itself to possess more automatic fore-and-aft stability in flight than the little Blériots, that seemed to have the better speed and lift for their wing area and horse-power; the Curtiss doubtless displayed the best speed of the biplanes, and proved the quickest to launch into flight; the Farman shone for weight-carrying, length of flight and ease of alighting; the Wrights made their mark as to quickness in executing turns; the Voisins showed strength and a certain degree of automatic stability, and so forth. Thus it is good for the movement that no one machine should possess a monopoly of good points.

The organisation of the untried thing is rarely an enviable task. It seldom reflects great credit. But in the case of the splendidly successful enterprise, promoted in chief measure by highly praiseworthy local initiation at Rheims, everything was planned with the most brilliantly imaginative foresight, so that, despite the gatherings being greater than on the occasions of any known French military review or race meeting, traffic facilities and accomodation of all sorts were on an adequate scale. Would we could always rely upon doing similar things in equally satisfactory fashion in this country."

From an article entitled "Historic Rheims — and Afterwards", *Flight*. (Issue of Sept. 4, 1909.)

The Flying Races at Rheims
BEING A GOSSIP ABOUT AN HISTORICAL MEETING THAT MARKS AN EPOCH IN THE DEVELOPMENT OF AERIAL LOCOMOTION
(By H. Massac Buist)

"Probably not more than two thousand Britishers, at an outside estimate, witnessed the extraordinary flying machine race meeting that lasted eight days at Rheims. I was there only part of the time, and would not have missed that spectacle if it had cost ten times as much trouble and money. There have been all sorts of estimates as to the crowd. The lowest figure is half a million. But the fact is it is impossible to determine, for the throng stretched for miles and miles round the course. Whether the masses were ten, or twenty, or forty deep you could not tell. No military review has ever drawn such throngs in France. Considering the utterly unprecedented nature of the whole thing, the organisation from every point of view was something to marvel at. It was a fortunate thing, too, that the weather improved

[330]

daily, so that towards the end of the meeting the conditions were absolutely ideal. This point is worth bringing out, because, when so much of a really striking nature has been achieved, there is a risk, as the accounts published in the Press have witnessed, of running to the extreme and exaggerating. Let us not cozen ourselves that more has been done than has actually been accomplished. Of thirty-eight machines entered, scarcely more than a third that number ever rose off the vast plain of Bétheny. Furthermore, for the bulk of the time there was practically no wind, while the absence of hollows and hills, of woods and villages, also furnished the competitors with ideal conditions for handling their machines. Again, from ten o'clock till about noonday there was flying, and as a rule it did not commence again till about four o'clock in the afternoon, so that it will be observed that the most favourable conditions possible were experienced by the competitors. In a word, it must not be assumed that at present anybody who buys an aeroplane can put up quite as good performances with it anywhere about Europe as were witnessed at Bétheny a few days ago. Altogether, apart from physically favourable conditions too, it was very obvious what a deal depends on the pilot, for some who undoubtedly had good machines performed little or not at all with them, while others who had natural aptitude and machines that many deemed to be fairly indifferent, contrived to make them behave as though new life had been infused into them. The more one studied the meeting and the preparations in connection with it, the more one realised that the possession of an aeroplane is only part of the equipment at present necessary to flying. On the ground at Bétheny each firm had a factory in little and a company of mechanics. Their work was no sinecure.

In conversation on returning here one finds that scarcely the least realisation of what the meeting proved obtains in Britain. Here it is thought that we who went over there as enthusiasts, before we arrived on the ground, were so delighted at what we saw that our imaginations enabled us to regard everything as though it were viewed through powerful field-glasses. It may be that the fault of this lies in the news of the meeting having been conveyed for the most part in one or other of two manners. Many of the accounts that have appeared in the Press have been jerky, uninspiring, none too accurate, considerably monotonous, and void of what one may call constructional narrative. At the other extreme there have been the gorgeous impressionist versions in connection with which some facts are certainly rather amusing. For example, when a very interesting incident was occurring during the races, I offered my field-glasses to a man who was sending some very frothy impressions to a London paper. But judge my astonishment when, without raising his eyes from the paper on which he was writing, he told me that he was too busy to look! Those are the sort of people who are supposed to give you truthful ideas about what a meeting is really like. From ten o'clock in the morning till seven at night, with the exception of a luncheon interval, they sit at the table and write steadily, racking their brains for similes and gorgeous phrases all the time. Is it any wonder that the truth is ignored in about every fourth sentence? I cannot see the object of it, except that this is an age of 'fake'. As soon as we see people flying over here, the man in the street will be able to grasp that he has been hoodwinked here or there or in some other fashion. Meantime there is a section of the Press that has undoubtedly trained a large public to delight in nothing unless it is laid on with a trowel. For them the brush of the artist and the dainty slight strokes of truth count for nothing more than niggard-liness — as you might say, a mere minging retailer's method of dealing with a proposition. While on the subject of the written version, too, it is certainly extraordinary that one great English daily paper employed an Italian with a florid style of writing to give a lengthy impressionist version day by day, and his ingenuity in discovering new similes was certainly amazing. What I consider vastly more clever, however, is the fact that his story was telegraphed over to London in Italian, then translated against time into English. The bulk of what credit there is for the version as published is certainly due to the ingenuity of the translator. Meantime, the Italian used to send a paltry little dispatch of a few hundred words only to his own paper in Italy every night. It is a strange age when we talk big about Tariff Reform and have to buy our imagination from Italy.

In view of the large crowds, the train, motor, 'bus, and cab services, and the feeding accomodation, were excellent. The arrangement of the meeting was extraordinary. In the case of any ordinary races, all the competitors can come to the line together, so that the public knows perfectly well which event is taking place. But the difficulties presented by a flying machine meeting are enormous. It had to be left to the individual competitor to choose the moment that seemed to him the most suitable for making his essay, or, at least, that moment which was the earliest by which he could get his machine into readiness for it. It may be that next year the Rheims flying races will see achievement advanced so far that definite hours can be fixed for the start of various events. That time will determine. Meanwhile, it is sufficiently gratifying that the success of the meeting from every point of view has assured that there will be a succeeding one next year.

It was decided wisely that each competitor must make a separate performance for each event. That is to say, if when running in the 30 kilom. or three-lap event you put up one very fast circuit, your time for that circuit could not count for the fastest lap race, nor could any two of your three circuits count for the 20-kilom. Gordon-Bennett Race. Before starting on any given performance every competitor had to announce to the organisers which event he was going for, and his performance only stood him in stead for that particular event. The result was that the organisers had to devise a system of signalling from a flagstaff with yard-arms. It was done in colours and shapes, so that the signals told the onlookers whether there was flying or no flying, what event was being competed for, who was competing for it, whether the record had been beaten or not, whether a good or a bad start or landing had been made, when a landing had been effected without accident, whether the aid of mechanicians was needed, whether a competitor had touched the ground during a flight, or had incorrectly negotiated a corner tower that marked the course, whether any previous sign set up was incorrect; also whether flying was probable, whether there was no flying, or whether there was about to be flying. The whole thing is about the most ingenious imaginable, for by employing the system of signalling by signs representing numbers, a lot of miscellaneous information could be conveyed. For example, a white disc, a red pyramid, and a white oblong would mean, 'Attention! Flights are about to commence'. A white disc, a white oblong, and another white disc, representing the number 171, would mean that a breakdown of the motor had delayed the start. A white disc, a white oblong, and a white pyramid, representing the number 174, would mean that petrol was the cause of a breakdown. A white disc, a white oblong, and a red pyramid meant that the aeroplane had sustained damage to a wing. A white disc, a white oblong, and a red oblong, representing the number 179, would announce that a propeller had been changed; and, similarly, the arrival of the President of the Republic, of a Minister, or of a foreign sovereign, were news that could be conveyed to the public by the sign staff and the simple aid of the excellently printed official programme sold at one franc. That programme should be bought, studied, and practically copied in detail by any organisation attempting to run a flying machine meeting in Britain.

The course was a 10 kilom. (6·2 English statute miles) one, oblong in shape, being 3,750 metres parallel to the grand stand, and 1,250 metres in depth away from it. Therein lies one of the few points of the meeting that experience has now proved should be changed on the next occasion. An aeroplane is such a splendid scouting instrument that it becomes quickly lost to view. In that vast plain, even when following the flights through powerful field-glasses, it was often very difficult to pick out the machines after they had gone into far distance and attention had been diverted from them for a moment. Incidentally, I cannot understand why not one person in a hundred provided himself with glasses. The thing seems scarcely credible. Evidently the vast majority of those who attended the meeting had never seen a flying machine go into the distance before. Undoubtedly they would be very difficult objects to hit, whereas the spherical captive balloons that were used as mark buoys and wind indicators, and the bulky dirigible balloons, were always most glaringly in evidence, owing alike to volume and to the bright yellow colour of the material used in their construction.

When one remembers that 10 minutes was about the average time occupied in completing a lap, and that during about two-thirds of that time one was unable to detect the machines with the naked eye, and, even through the most powerful glasses, the details of their flights were not perceptible, it will be realised that from the spectacular point of view, at any rate, a considerable change is desirable. In any case, now that the meeting has proved the possibility of machines floating one above another and racing side by side, the really interesting spectacular situations would be multiplied many fold by making the course half the length, so that the onlookers would have the machines in good view all the time, and would, therefore, be able to follow every incident throughout the racing. And the incidents of air racing are worth following. As a sport, it is plain that it will surpass everything in point of interest, being already to the full as exciting as steeple-chasing. Some members of the organising committee told me that they were delighted to find that, though the magnificent plain at Bétheny was so vast that the course could have been easily double or treble the size, experience proved that from the spectacular point of view, and without in any way inconveniencing the competitors, it could be made half the size, otherwise 3 miles to the lap, which is amply sufficient when it is borne in mind that not one of the machines achieved a speed of 48 miles an hour, so that once or twice one perceived motor cars bumping along the plain at a faster rate than the aeroplanes could fly overhead. This proof that a 3-mile course is large enough must be greatly encouraging to aviation in England, for it means that an expanse like Brooklands, for example, if made suitable as by the complete clearing of the interior, would serve the purpose excellently well.

The other lesson that is to be learnt from the meeting, albeit writers do not seem to have realised it yet, is that the time has now come for instituting some means of classification for aeroplane races. At Bétheny, folk did not seem to realise that oftentimes they saw a machine that was going about five miles an hour faster than another one that was carrying the same weight with only half its horse-power, and about two-fifths of its wing surface. That is like expecting a cart-horse to outgo a racehorse, a canal barge to be a match for a yacht, a bull-dog for a greyhound, or a voiturette for a full-scale racing motor car. Yet they did not realise that. We want either a division of the machines into classes or a system of handicapping. In either case the obvious means seems to be to make the basis horse-power employed, and wing-surface and weight carried. Such a means as this would be encouraging to the industry because it will educate the public as to the relative merits of different designs from the point of view of efficiency. Had such a system obtained at Rheims, folk would have come away with very different impressions as to the qualifications of the different machines.

Let us take a glance at the preparations that have to be made for flight. You must not think that aeroplaning consists only in the seemingly effortless gliding through the air that you behold when seeing the machines in actual flight. Apart from the problem of design and of manufacture, there is at this early stage of the movement the almost continuous preparation and repreparation, adjustment, repairing and tuning up of the machines before each flight. There is a company of mechanicians for each team of machines, what one may style the most trained troup being the Blériot contingent, that were as smart as gunners at their work, never seeming to need any instruction. As in the case of the Antoinette management, M. Blériot's foreman of mechanics rarely seemed to need any orders. In the sheds the machines were practically in his entire charge. The quickness and systematic fashion in which the Blériot men worked was the admiration of all who studied them.

Quite one of the most interesting and fascinating characters of that meeting is the portly, rugged, imperturbably good humoured M. Levavasseur. When his beloved aeroplanes were on the ground or in their sheds you might have concluded that they had no more to do with him than they had with M. Latham, or with any casual onlooker. If a mechanician discovered any part he thought needed attention, he would shout 'Edouard!' to attract the attention of the foreman. The two would discuss the matter and decide what was to be done, what time neither M. Levavasseur or M. Latham would look over their shoulders. Such indifference towards machines of one's design and using seems absolutely extraordinary. But as soon as they were launched in flight, one could not but remark on the changed attitude of the designer, who scarcely ever took his eyes off them, regarding them with the fond affection of a father for his small children. Among the Farman contingent the mechanics were less numerous, but the aviators worked themselves. Nevertheless, I could not but conclude that in the main the Farman biplanes needed less attention than any of the others. Poor M. Esnault-Pelterie, with his injured hand, toiled all the week with his men at the task of preparing his clever red mono-planes for flight, but he was not able to take part with them in any event, which reveals incidentally how much labour precedes actual launching in the air; while the experiences of M. Blériot in taking a header into the fence with one machine and having another burnt up, suggest that a good stock of aeroplanes requires to be kept at head-quarters if one wants to stand a likely chance of competing in any given event. Blue-eyed Gabriel Voisin, who does not fly, was busy with a troop of mechanics on his various biplanes, with one of which Fournier tried to do cartwheels sideways, with another of which Rougier, who had cut a very poor figure, surprised everybody at the last moment of the competitions by going in for the high flight and actually clearing the minimum height admissible, and with another of which the brilliant young mechanician, Paulhan — who was discovered by Mr. Harry Delacombe and won his machine in a competition of MM. Voisin for the best design for an aeroplane, and who got his Gnome motor for it on the credit basis of undertaking to hand over half his prize money until he could pay for it — put up some sur-prisingly fine performances and showed what these machines are capable of in the hands of a born pilot.

There was always plenty of work going forward before any one of the 'blooming appariels had sortied from its hangar'. Screws were being changed, or chains were being repaired, or torn wings were being sewn up, or, as in one case, the wings themselves were being clipped. That is to say, M. Blériot did better with one of his machines after he had cut an appreciable strip off the back of his planes.

In the hot hours of the day you would see mechanicians sleeping between the sheds or under the shade cast by an aeroplane, while in the shed of M. Roger Sommer, Mr. Charles E. Grey beheld a 'bonne' watching over the slumbers of his two babies on a bed, their sleep being undisturbed until the engine was started up, when the thunder of the open exhaust that is an accompaniment of aeroplaning at present, put an end to their repose. 'Papa,' with his well-groomed beard and conspicuous white boots, can always be singled out from a throng.

It was delightful to see the different methods of tuning up, quite one of the most ingenious being that used by the Blériot machines, that were tied to a stake, and the tractive effort taken by an hydraulic measurer, so that before starting out on a flight it could be ascertained exactly whether or not the machine and propeller were acting with absolute efficiency.

At present there is no set rule for your conduct in starting to aeroplane. Your bulky machine may be taken to a suitable spot by a bevy of willing helpers, including your mechanics, the picture putting one in mind of a lot of ants leading a fly — excuse the pun. Or, the aeroplane may be taken across the ground by a patient farm horse that has long since learnt not to be alarmed by any sudden starting up of an unsilenced engine, while in yet other cases motor cars were used to tow the planes, even as horses came to rescue cars in the beginning of the older movement. There is also the Wright system, which is a laborious one, of placing the machine on two one-wheeled trestles and marching out to the starting rail with it, in which connection it is to be had in mind that, though they used the rail, the starting weight was rarely employed in the case of the Wright machines. The usual Voisin, Blériot and Farman method, was to get to the starting place under their own power.

In regard to launching into flight, some of the machines appeared to be very sensitive, such as the Antoinette, and some of the Voisins, which were usually put head to wind, if there was any, whereas the Farman, the Blériot, and the Curtiss aeroplanes seemed relatively indifferent, because in any case very little wind was blowing. Nevertheless, the variety of the requirements of the machines, accounted for in no mean measure by the differing experiences and aptitudes of their pilots, provided a very interesting spectacle on the taking-off ground, where one would see such persons as Rougier spending the best part of an afternoon in the effort to get going. He was rarely without company. You would see the machines of large spread scurrying and scudding about the ground in all directions, presenting somewhat the appearance of a lot of gigantic fowls fluttering about a vast farmyard.

It needs a deal of practice for the eye to tell exactly when a machine leaves the ground, for it must not be imagined that they leap into the air. Sometimes they go up for a few yards, then come to earth again, and do not lift until they have gone two or three hundred yards further. Plainly, it does not pay to give up just because you do not get off the ground permanently after the first launching. Some proceed half way down the course before they quit the earth. The quickest machine of all to launch in flight was the Curtiss biplane, which was absolutely amazing. Sometimes it would be in mid-air in less than fifty yards going. As a rule the flyers are held back when the engines are started. They are let go after the screw is turning at its proper speed, in which connection one witnessed the same spectacle that was seen again and again at Pau in February. That is to say, people would stand in line with the turn of the screws, so that if a blade broke they were in imminent peril of being killed. Seemingly there were no regulations to prevent their doing this, though I think there ought to be.

I do not propose to describe the competitions, for the detailed results of each have been set forth in another form on other pages of *Flight*. From the point of view of recounting the story of a race, in the case of aeroplanes, at present it is impossible to do so, because the various competitors did not start at the same time. The competitions therefore resolved themselves merely into flights against the clock. Hence, from the spectacular point of view, the interest was in the manner of the flight. Whether the performance had bettered that of another competitor in the same event did not appear until the times were announced twenty minutes afterwards.

The Blériot, the Wright, and — with the exception of Paulhan's — the Voisin machines flew the lowest, while the medium height flyers were the Farman and the Curtiss biplanes, and the normal high flying machines were the Antoinette monoplanes, that usually took a comparatively long time to get launched in flight. One result of these characteristics was that we saw aeroplanes not only outgoing one another when flying side by side on a level, but speeding one over the top of another. In one thrilling moment — a 'minute inoubliable,' as the French say — after rounding a corner tower, three machines appeared in tier fashion. Of course we have had to wait for the Rheims meeting to behold those spectacles, and to learn that such things could happen. It does not matter to the 'top dog,' but the 'under dog' certainly 'feels the draught' of another aeroplane overhead. Henri Farman says that when he was making his record flight of 112½ miles, when machines were flying above him, he felt very distinct tendencies to drive him earthwards.

In regard to tactics, it is plain that these will play a very important part in the future of flying machine races. For example, the quadrangular course was marked out by four wooden towers, each of which had to be passed by competitors on their left. Now, in going for a speed trial you do not want to travel an extra yard by taking a corner wide. At the same time you dare not run the risk of disqualification by going the wrong side of the tower. Gentle and negligible as one would have deemed the breezes to be at Bétheny, nevertheless there were several occasions when one would see an aeroplane approaching a corner tower. When within two hundred yards of it, it would seem to be lifted slightly by an invisible hand, and cast sideways out of its course. In other words, it had been caught in a slight gust, the motion being so fluent that the flyer appeared to be borne on springs. Such occurrences caused the competitors to tack with the utmost promptitude of which they were individually capable. Then they passed the post well before they attempted to turn. In any case, the practice of practically all except the Wright machines — that appeared relatively unaffected by side gusts, but which, in the hands of their pilots, with the possible exception of Lefebvre, described very undulating flight paths at Bétheny — came very wide up to the corner, then turned as quickly as they could. With most, turning seemed to involve a certain loss of speed. Consequently, those pilots concerned each approached the turn at what was for him a relatively high altitude. Having executed the manoeuvre, he would dive down to his normal height so as to pick up speed in the descent.

The control of the various machines differed extraordinarily. That of the Antoinette, that possessed a remarkable degree of fore-and-aft stability, is certainly planned on a very seamanlike system, for each part of the mechanism has a definite movement only, so that, when having to act on a sudden, there is no likelihood of the pilot making a muddle of things, as is so easily possible with the Blériot, the Farman, or the Wright, on each of which machines one hand can execute a more or less universal-lever movement, so that, when confronted with a crisis, it is the easiest thing in the world to thrust out the hand to the wrong point of the compass, as it were. Even the fore-and-aft thrust of the steering pillar to control the elevating planes of a Voisin biplane calls for very nice handling if you are not to make your machine stand on its head. Once launched in flight, the Antoinette needs less skill on the part of the pilot than any other machine. And the firm has a very good demonstrator in Hubert Latham. That is to say, you shall find him coming along the straight in front of the grand stand, and letting go his wheels while he lifts his cap well above his head, and replaces it more comfortably; or he will steer by resting his elbow on one of the wheels and placing his chin on his hand as though he were musing verses in mid-air. On one occasion, when he was overhauling Delagrange on a little Blériot monoplane below him, he let go both side wheels, and, placing a hand on either side of his airboat, raised himself so that he was able to lean over and look down on his aerial rival immediately beneath him. A little after that, too, he caused the onlookers to draw breath because he made the machine dart down as though it were going to pitch to earth head foremost, but when within about 20 feet of the ground, without effort he brought it horizontal again. These are what the Americans style 'stunts.' Yet I do not think that in the case of the particular machine in question in calm weather they are in the nature of foolhardiness, for the Antoinette monoplane has a deal of automatic stability. But I do not imagine any of the other machines represented can approach it in that respect, though the Farman and the Voisin are better than most. The next easiest machine to control appeared to be the Curtiss biplane, which was quite extraordinarily speedy and on which the pilot takes up a position that gives him an obviously comfortable command of the machine. He really looks as though he had control of it, whereas on the Farman and Blériot aeroplanes the intense attention that is necessary on the part of the pilot is very apparent indeed. The honest, stolid Voisins, however, provide a fairly normal and comfortable position for the pilot.

There are wide differences, too, between one aeroplane and another in point of landing. The Farman seemed to come to earth most perfectly and with least shock, for none was softer even when he had two passengers aboard; whereas the Antoinette certainly seemed to have need of all its elaborately ingenious arrangements for absorbing shock when alighting. It comes clumsily to earth. One got a very good notion as to how substantially these seemingly flimsy machines are built when such a man as Rougier alighted. A quintette of mechanicians leapt at different parts of the biplane like so many cats, thrust out their feet before them, and so skidded until they had brought the flyer to a stand.

And the exigencies of space dictate that I should put a period to this gossip, too."

Flight (issue of Sept. 4, 1909)

Appendix VIII

THE FIRST AERODROMES
(1904–09)

The world's first aerodrome, for aeroplanes, was certainly the **Huffman Prairie** (or Pasture), a 90-acre piece of pastureland about 8 miles east of Drayton (Ohio) where the Wright brothers flew in 1904 and 1905. They erected a shed for the machines, and the place was used in exactly the same way as an airfield today.

Issy-les-Moulineaux (Paris). The first European aerodrome in the true sense was the military ground at Issy-les-Moulineaux, then a suburb of Paris, which is on the left bank of the Seine just beyond the Boulevard Victor. Issy was first used by the Vuia I monoplane, which was tested there in August of 1906. This most famous of French aerodromes was to witness many triumphs from 1908 onwards, as well as a short period in 1908 when the ground was temporarily denied to the aviators by the military. Issy was "perfectly level and of a sandy surface" as one contemporary said. The Voisin factory was at Billancourt on the Seine, a little farther down the river and on the other side.

Buc. A "one-man" works and aerodrome was set up by Robert Esnault-Pelterie in 1907 at Buc, 2 miles south-west of Versailles, which in 1909 came to be shared with Maurice Farman. The first machine to be tested there was Esnault-Pelterie's R.E.P. 1 in October 1907. It was "rather inaccessible to any but motorists", but its owners preferred such isolation.

Camp de Châlons. One of the most important centres of French aircraft construction and instruction came to be set up on the great open plain known as the Camp de Châlons, which lies about 12 miles north of Châlons and 16 miles south-east of Reims. This aerodrome became known by a number of names, *i.e.* Mourmelon, Bouy, Châlons, Camp de Châlons, and even Louvercy-Aviation. They all referred to the same area. First to arrive and "settle" was Henri Farman, who brought his Voisin-Farman I-*bis* there in September 1908. He erected his shed on the south-east side of the plain, close to the village of Bouy (which is on the main Châlons-Reims road): then in 1909 when he started building his own machines, and instructing, the shed near Bouy grew to be a factory. The Farman school was generally referred to as being at Mourmelon.

In 1909 there also arrived the Antoinette and Voisin firms, who settled nearby: these three units were grouped within a short distance of one another on the west side of the plain (Camp de Châlons). Grouped in a rough semi-circle to their left were the villages which gave their names to early aviation — Bouy, Louvercy (which some of the locals tried to use for the group under the name Louvercy-Aviation), Mourmelon-le-Petit (which alone boasted a railway station), and the main village of the area, Mourmelon-le-Grand. The Antoinette machines, built at Pouteaux (Seine) were assembled and repaired here, and the Antoinette school was generally referred to as being at Mourmelon. The Voisin machines were built at Billancourt (Seine) and were likewise assembled and repaired here, their school being said to be at Mourmelon or Châlons.

Aerodromes proliferated in the year 1909, when the aeroplane became a practical and accepted vehicle. The most important were the following:

Pau. This southern French resort near the Pyrenees, with its exceptionally fine climate, came to boast two aeroplane aerodromes and an airship station. First to "settle", in January 1909, was Wilbur Wright, who wanted an equable climate in which to continue his flying after his triumphant 1908 season at Auvours, and to train his first pupils. This aerodrome was at Pont-Long, $2\frac{1}{2}$ miles north of Pau, and later became the training aerodrome of the French Wright Company. At the end of 1909 Blériot was to set up his school nearby.

Shellbeach (Leysdown) In England, the Aero Club (which in 1910 became the Royal Aero Club) set up an aerodrome in 1909 at Shellbeach (Leysdown) on the Isle of Sheppey, where the Short Company also became established.

Port-Aviation (Juvisy). The first aerodrome to be deliberately prepared and equipped for aerial displays was Port-Aviation at Juvisy, some 12 miles due south of Paris. It belonged to the Société d'Encouragement à l'Aviation, and was opened with a small inauguratory meeting — "somewhat in the nature of a fiasco" — in May, 1909.

Bétheny (Reims). The plain of Bétheny, five miles north of Reims, was first made famous as an aerodrome by the great aviation meeting of August 1909. It later became also a school aerodrome for the Hanriot firm.

Hammondsport (N.Y.). Back to America, there is the aerodrome at Hammondsport on Lake Keuka (N.Y.) to record, on which the machines of the Aerial Experiment Association were tested in 1908 and 1909. To make matters somewhat confusing, the A.E.A. improperly called their machines "Aerodromes", following Langley (see below).

The word "Aerodrome", in the immediate pre-flight period of powered aviation, was suddenly and inexplicably applied by S. P. Langley to his models and full-size aeroplane; and the word continued to be thus mis-used for "aeroplane" by the A.E.A. and others, for a time. The word "aerodrome" comes from the Greek "aer" (air) and "dromos": the latter can mean a course, race, or running, or the place where such activities take place, but never the man, animal, or machine that runs or races. It is surprising that a man of Langley's status — he was Secretary of the Smithsonian Institution — did not consult one of the many classical scholars in Washington before deciding on a name for his aeroplane.

.   .   .   .   .

PS. The world's first three flying schools* were as follows:

1. The Wright school at Pau (Pont-Long); opened in January 1909; first lesson was given (by Wilbur Wright to Paul Tissandier) on Feb. 4th.
2. The Henry Farman school at Mourmelon (Camp de Châlons); opened Febr. 4th, 1909; first lesson was probably given to the Englishman George Cockburn, date unknown.
3. The Blériot school at Pau (Pont-Long); opened November 24th, 1909.

* It could just be said that the first flying school (but for gliding only) was the Aéronautique-Club, founded in France in 1906, near Palaiseau (S. et O.).

NOTES

(The prefixed numbers refer to the
Sections of the book, not the pages.)

2. CAYLEY'S TRIPLE PAPER OF 1809–10. It is interesting to speculate as to how long Cayley would have waited before publishing his epoch-making paper of 1809–10, had he not read of Degen's attempts to fly, and had not the claim been made that Degen had actually flown under his own power. Cayley was well aware that most of his friends, let alone the general reading public of the day, thought that anyone interested in flying other than by balloon was a crackpot. From the evidence, I would guess that he would have waited quite a time — even years — before publishing his work. His decisive influence in aviation history was to be first through Henson and Stringfellow; then, even more important, through all the more technically-minded men of mid-century in France and England, who were to lead direct to modern aviation. For the ways and means of his influence, see my book *Sir George Cayley's Aeronautics* (Science Museum publication, 1961).

2. DEGEN. Degen has, perhaps, been somewhat underestimated in the past. He deserves credit for enthusiasm and ingenuity, and gratitude for stimulating air-mindedness and precipitating the appearance of Cayley's great triple paper of 1809–10.

3. THE CRYSTAL PALACE EXHIBITION. The exhibition at the Crystal Palace in 1868, at which the Stringfellow triplane model was shown, was staged by the recently founded (1866) Aeronautical Society of Great Britain noted before, who deserve the highest credit for so quickly taking the lead in promoting practical work in aeronautics, and disseminating information and influence among their contemporaries. The exhibition was officially described in *Report of the First Exhibition of the Aeronautical Society of Great Britain*, London, 1868.

9. THE WRIGHTS' THREE MISTAKES. As said in Section 9, one can now with the wisdom of hindsight point to three of the Wrights' mistakes, two major and one minor. Their first major mistake was in deciding to adopt an inherently unstable form of aircraft, and continuing to retain this instability in all their gliders (1900–02) and in their epoch-making powered machines (1903–10). This "unstable" flight philosophy derived from their mistaken belief that stability and controllability were mutually exclusive qualities; and it is very curious that they did not realise — or make tests to establish — that an adequate degree of the sensitivity of control they rightly prized so much, could be retained along with the incorporation of a fair measure of inherent stability, especially longitudinal stability. The Europeans at least realised this desirability, and employed fixed horizontal surfaces from the earliest days, together with their Wright-derived forward elevators. These tailplanes not only acted as stabilising surfaces in themselves, but as dampers for the "de-stabilising" forward elevators. But the Europeans failed to understand the true nature of control, especially dynamic initiatory control, until the Wrights showed them.

The Wrights' second major mistake was the adoption and retention (until 1910) of the forward elevator. It was originally adopted and used at a negative angle of incidence "with the idea of producing inherent stability fore and aft which it should have done had the travel of the centre of pressure been forward [when the angle of incidence was decreasing] as we had been led to believe". When their tests showed that the centre of pressure on cambered wings moved backwards with decreasing incidence, they abandoned the idea of their elevator providing inherent longitudinal stability, but retained it in the forward position "because it absolutely prevented a nose dive such as that in which Lilienthal and many others since have met their deaths". Apart from the fact that Lilienthal — although he had once nose-dived and feared a repetition — was not killed in this way, the Wrights were mistaken about the efficacy of such a forward surface; and its presence, with the lack even of a fixed horizontal tailplane, was a fundamental

NOTES

weakness of all Wright machines until 1909–10. The worst danger from a front elevator — especially on such a short lever arm — is the possibility of it (the elevator itself) becoming stalled at slow speeds, and leading to immediate loss of control of the aircraft. The second danger is in its providing over-sensitive longitudinal control with a continual tendency towards pitching. The third danger is that a down-gust in the path of the aircraft will strike the elevator before it strikes the wings, thus suddenly forcing the machine into a nose-down attitude, where corrective action may be impossible to achieve in time to avert disaster. As to the front elevator "absolutely" preventing a nose-dive, this was completely mistaken, and the Wrights were in fact lucky in the early days of their own flying not to have the elevator precipitate a crash. This curious blind spot of the Wrights was not to be corrected until they abolished the front elevator in 1910.

But there was one excellent reason for the Wrights to have a front elevator on their gliders, at least until they had mastered overall control; for when they were gliding down the Kill Devil Hills, keeping close to the surface, there can be no doubt that a forward elevator — right there before their eyes — made it much easier for them to gauge the effect of elevator movement and keep steadily in the right flying attitude; in addition, it provided a good "psychological support" to have a surface in front of them which they could see.

In the state of knowledge available to the Wrights, the forward elevator was a bad bargain all round in their powered aircraft. Whatever the configuration of the aircraft, the forward elevator would inevitably be a de-stabiliser. Even given the inherent instability of the Wright machines, the forward elevator could only have had the slight advantage that it encountered relatively undisturbed air. But such minor advantage could not compensate for the disadvantages. Incidentally, this one advantage could easily have brought about its own special trouble through its wash affecting the wings. There are some aerodynamicists today who would advocate a forward elevator (canard) configuration for some types of aircraft; but this could only be successful with the knowledge available today.

The third mistake the Wrights made was in their retention of the skid under-carriage, and the track and weight method of launching, long after their initial advantages had disappeared. This, too, was a curious and inexplicable error, considering the ready availability of flat ground and, in 1908–9, of prepared airfields; also the frustrating ritual of track-laying, weight-lifting, and man-handling the machine on dollies, prescribed for the take-off of all Wright machines until 1910, although individual Wright owners were already fitting wheels to the skids in 1909.

11. THE WRIGHTS: 1902. It was this machine (the No. 3 glider modified) of 1902, which figured particularly in Chanute's lecture to the Aéro-Club de France in Paris on April 2nd 1903, and in subsequent articles in the French technical Press, both by Chanute himself and by French writers describing the Chanute lecture. Perhaps the most influential was Chanute's own long article in *L'Aérophile* (Aug. 1903) entitled "La Navigation Aérienne aux États-Unis", in which were repro-duced plans and a photograph of this modified No. 3 glider in flight (see Sect. 16). Incidentally, an erroneous idea that the Wrights were Chanute's pupils gained wide currency in France, not only by some of Chanute's own rather disingenuous remarks, but by the publication in the widely read *La Locomotion* (for April 11, 1903) of photographs of the Wright glider captioned "L'appareil Chanute": no one today can tell how this inexcusable blunder came about.

Illustration 11-E also shows clearly the method of launching. The men at the wing-tips picked up the machine, and ran a short way down the sand-hill before releasing their hold.

12. LANGLEY: 1903. Fred Kelly, the Wrights' biographer, and others have told the unhappy story of how Glenn Curtiss — who had lost the Wrights' patent action against him — was allowed secretly to remove the full-size Langley Aerodrome from the Smithsonian Institution; alter it radically; and then in May-June 1914 test it on Lake Keuka. This was in a disgraceful effort by Curtiss to prove that Langley's machine was "the first aeroplane capable of sustained free flight with a man"; and that, had the catapult device worked properly, it would have flown successfully. Apart from the important structural and control-system alterations made by Curtiss, and the modified propellers he fitted — all of which failed to keep the machine airborne in 1914 for more than 5 seconds at a time — there is now strong evidence to show that the Balzer-Manly engine as originally fitted did not, and could not, deliver nearly enough power to sustain the Aerodrome. In any case, I feel, one must point out that, however creditable the Langley machine was in some ways, it just did not fly in 1903; nor did it at any other time in its original form. The major share of credit for the Aerodrome's remarkable radial engine should go, not to Manly as it so often does, but to S. M. Balzer, the original designer (see in the Bibliography the paper by Robert Meyer of the Smithsonian Institution on early aero engines). The name "Aerodrome" was, incidentally, a curious misnomer, which even for a time was used as a generic term for other powered aeroplanes: *dromos* in Greek can mean a course, a race, the running of such, or the place where such activity takes place, but never the man, animal or machine that runs or races. For a brief description of the Langley Aerodrome and the controversy over it, see pages 222, 223 of GS-A. See also the Smithsonian publication *The 1914 Tests of the Langley Aerodrome* (1942) which was re-published in full in F. C. Kelly's *The Wright Brothers* (1944).

It is sometimes wondered why Langley, some of whose work was contemporary with the Wrights, was not affected by the "climate", or they by his. The answer is twofold; first, Langley had virtually ceased his experiments in 1896 — before the Wrights had started — and thereafter merely extended his results and conclusions into the realm of full-size aircraft: he was naturally set in the ways he had followed so long. Secondly, the Wrights did not approve of Langley's basic design, and were convinced it was not well suited for practical flying: so they set out to follow their own principles and make their own experiments.

13. WRIGHT FLYER I: 1903. The name "Flyer" was given by the Wrights to all their powered machines, and the word later became popular for a short time as a generic term for powered aeroplanes. The name Flyer for a powered aeroplane model was used, curiously enough, by Sir George Cayley as early as 1813, and — also by him — for a full-size flapper-propelled aeroplane in 1849. It used to be widely, and wrongly, believed (including by myself) that the Wrights called their machine "Flyer" after the name of a cycle they built and sold. I cannot trace where this error arose, as the names they chose for their cycles were "Van Cleeve", "St. Clair" and "Wright-Special". It is a great pity that "Kitty Hawk" has now become the accepted name for the historic first Flyer, especially since the 1903 flights took place at the Kill Devil Hills, four miles south of Kitty Hawk.

14. WRIGHT FLYER II: 1904. The complete text of A. I. Root's historic eyewitness account of the flying of this aircraft is given on pages 234–239 of GS-A. Root's account — he was lucky enough to witness the Wrights' first circle on September 20th 1904 — appeared in the issue of *Gleanings in Bee Culture* dated January 1st, 1905, published in Medina (Ohio) where it still flourishes under the control of the Root family. It is surprising how seldom this long and delightful article is read or referred to. It is also, as may be imagined, studiously avoided by the small but vociferous lunatic fringe who still persist in denigrating the Wrights. For the Root article is the first eyewitness account in history of the flight of a powered aeroplane, other than those by the partakers. There are some people who still object to the fact that the Wright powered take-offs from September 7th onwards were by the weight and derrick "catapult", saying that an aeroplane — in order to qualify for flight ability — must take off under its own power. This has never been an accepted criterion of flight for early flying machines: it is of course sustentation beyond the effect of momentum that counts first, and then the machine's capability of being controlled. What is also so often forgotten is that the Europeans could have used catapults if they had wanted to; but as they so lamentably neglected flight control, they would have been in serious danger once they had been suddenly precipitated into the air.

NOTES

15. JATHO: 1903. For a discussion of the claims put forward for Jatho, see page 293 of GS-A.

PHILLIPS: 1904. For a description of Phillips' flight tests in 1904 and 1907, see pages 302–305 of GS-A.

18. THE NAME "ARCHDEACON". A minuscule but irritating problem has plagued me for some years concerning the pronunciation of the famous name Archdeacon. I have consulted a number of Frenchmen and have received contradictory answers: most said it was pronounced "Arsh-dek-ong"; a few said "Arsh-dek". The question was finally settled when I visited Reims in February 1964 to search for local records of the Reims meeting of 1909: I met there a leading figure of the Champagne industry, one of whose family had married an Archdeacon: the name is properly pronounced "Arsh-dek".

20. GABRIEL VOISIN: 1905. The mystery surrounding the part played by Gabriel Voisin in early European aviation is even further from solution now that his autobiography is available in English (*Men, Women and 10,000 Kites*, 1963) translated from the French edition of 1961, entitled *Mes 10,000 Cerfs-volants:* its publication does grave disservice to French aviation history. I reviewed it in *Flight International* (Oct. 17, 1963) and pointed out that, apart from being an ungenerous and mean-spirited book, it contains so many demonstrable absurdities, untruths and misleading statements, that one does not know how much of the rest one can believe. He seeks pathetically to show that it was he alone who invented the practical aeroplane; so he denigrates by word or implication one after another of his great French contemporaries. But the Wrights naturally presented him with his greatest hurdle; so he spends a long last chapter in attacking them. This chapter, I fear, will always rank as one of the most deplorable compositions in the literature of flight. (For other references to this autobiography see notes on Sections 33 and 34.)

It is also difficult to assess Gabriel Voisin's part in the design of the nominally Voisin machines; and F. W. Lanchester, in his paper "The Wright and Voisin Types of Flying Machine: a Comparison", refers to Colliex "who is largely responsible for their (the Voisins') designs".

VOISIN-ARCHDEACON FLOAT-GLIDER. The limited success achieved with the Voisin-Archdeacon float glider of 1905 encouraged the two men to undertake an intensive series of somewhat fruitless tests with this machine on the Lake of Geneva in the Autumn of 1905: for these tests it had been modified, with more camber on wings and tail, and the wings given no less than eight side-curtains (making seven cells): but the tests were not as productive as had been hoped, and in retrospect is appears that most of the time spent working with this glider was not justified by the results.

THE BOX KITE AIRCRAFT CONFIGURATION. It is interesting to note that Hargrave himself made both flat-surfaced and cambered box-kites, now parallelled in 1905 by the Voisin-Archdeacon (flat) and the Voisin-Blériot (cambered).

21. MONTEGOMERY: 1905. The curious claims put forward for Montgomery are discussed in detail in GS-A.

22. THE WRIGHT FLYER III: 1905. It was this 1905 Flyer which was adapted to take two people seated upright for the Wrights' "refresher" flights in May 1908. The warp and rudder mechanism was also changed to the twin-lever system (see notes to Sect. 42). When finally restored and placed in Carillon Park, Dayton, the original prone pilot position was put back, as well as the 1905 warp and rudder mechanism, the former operated by a cradle, the latter by a lever.

25. VUIA MONOPLANE: 1906. Large clear photographs of the Vuia monoplane — with descriptions — were published in *L'Aérophile* in its issues of February 1906 (p. 53) and April 1906 (p. 105), and were seen by all the leading French pioneers.

ELLEHAMMER: 1906. For a new account and assessment of Ellehammer, see GS-A.

NOTES

29. BLÉRIOT: 1907. Contemporary records are contradictory about the nomenclature of Bleriot's three machines of 1907. In choosing to call them the Nos. V, VI, and VII, I am following the most reliable evidence I can find, which also fits in best if one works backwards from the later known numbers. With regard to the VI (*Libellule*) there is a considerable problem concerning the alterations made to it. Dumas even goes so far as to call the first version of the *Libellule* the Blériot V, and the modified version (which was flying the month following the last tests of the V) the Blériot VI. Dumas says the modified machine had less dihedral, a 50 h.p. Antoinette (instead of the 24 h.p. in the first version) and a four-bladed propeller. He does not mention the greatly extended fin which is seen in Fig. D, or other alterations shown in various photographs. I think this was a modification to the first version, and that both my illustrations are of the first version. I cannot yet trace a certain close-up photograph of the second, with its 50 h.p. Antoinette. There is other, and better, evidence to show that Blériot called both versions Blériot VI. It was an illustration of the *Libellule* appearing in the December 1907 issue of the *American Magazine of Aeronautics*, showing its elevons large and clearly, which almost certainly gave the idea of ailerons to the Aerial Experiment Association so that they could hope to evade the Wrights' patent on warping, etc. (see Sect. 40).

31. LANCHESTER: 1907. F. W. Lanchester first started experiments with model gliders at Olton, early in 1892. His first announcement of his circulation theory of sustentation was in a paper entitled *The Soaring of Birds and the Possibilities of Mechanical Flight*, which he read to a meeting of the Birmingham Natural History and Philosophical Society on June 19th 1894. This historic paper was not printed: what is even worse is that Lanchester himself did not preserve a copy. During 1895 and 1896 he revised and expanded this paper, and it was this revision, containing one of the most profound discoveries in scientific history, which was rejected by the Physical Society when Lanchester offered it to them in 1897, a blunder of such magnitude that it is still without explanation. The two famous books *Aerodynamics* and *Aerodonetics*, in which Lanchester expounded his theories, were not published until 1907 and 1908 respectively (see P. W. Kingsford, *F. W. Lanchester: the Life of an Engineer*, London, 1960).

THE BREGUET HELICOPTER: 1907. This machine was known as the Breguet-Richet I, Charles Richet having collaborated with the Breguets in its construction. For the Breguet-Richet II, see Sect. 48.

31. PHILLIPS: 1907. For Phillips' flight tests of 1904 and 1907 see GS-A.

32. DUNNE: 1907. For a note on the chronology of the early Dunne aircraft, see GS-A.

33. VOISIN GLIDER: 1907. This Chanute-type hang-glider was built for Farman, but given back to Voisin in exchange for a powered Voisin. Voisin, Farman, and Colliex flew it at Le Touquet in May, 1907; it was noted and illustrated in *L'Aérophile* for June 1907. It was this glider which was featured in the first two illustrations in the English translation of Gabriel's autobiography and mendaciously dated 1899, in order — presumably — to help persuade the reader that he was active in aviation before his rivals. It was later given by Voisin to the Aéronautique-Club.

EUROPEAN BIPLANE ELEVATORS: 1906–07. One of the minor curiosities of aviation history was the adoption by the Voisins of a Wright-derived biplane elevator forward, rather than the monoplane elevator derived from the Wright gliders (in their first three powered machines). One of the most reliable of contemporaries, Captain Ferber, makes it clear that this was a direct, though long-range, result of the publication in the Paris periodical *L'Auto* for December 24th 1905 of a crude sketch of the No. 3 Wright Flyer. This drawing — one of the first published of a powered Wright machine with any approximation to truth — was pirated by an *Auto* reporter M. Coquelle, in the U.S.A., from an issue of the *Dayton Daily News* which the Wright brothers seem to have succeeded in suppressing, before publication, in an effort to keep their machine secret. Despite the crudity of the sketch, the biplane elevator is plainly shown. Ferber wrote: "Ce dessin a eu une grande importance; il nous montrait les derniers détails que nous ignorions; c'est lui qui est cause que les premiers aéroplanes de Delagrange et Farman, février et juin 1907, ont eu le gouvernail avant cellulaire". It is, incidentally, curious to find the French so often referring erroneously to an open biplane structure as "cellulaire", without realising that the true "cellulaire" structure should be contained by vertical side-curtains, à la Hargrave. In this way, the Wrights' forward monoplane elevator, which was an important feature of their glider designs, which the Europeans had been copying since 1902, evolved into the biplane elevator of the first three powered Voisin machines in 1907. Then, as Farman and others developed their own configurations in 1908–09, the monoplane elevator again came to predominate. The sketch in *L'Auto* also gave a surprisingly accurate idea of the launching rail, the tandem-wheel yoke, and the manner in which the Flyer was placed on the yoke. In its issue of February 7th 1906, *L'Auto* published two more sketches of the Wright 1905 Flyer. One illustration showed the machine in flight from three-quarter rear, and emphasised the double rear rudder; it is, however, probable that some French readers may have taken this structure to be a fixed fin unit. This sketch also showed only one propeller. The forward biplane elevator was also shown; but it appeared very compressed and hence misleading. An attendant vignette also showed a three-quarter view of the aircraft (with the elevator invisible) on the launching rail, with two men steadying the wing-tips before the take-off.

34. VOISIN AND FARMAN: 1907. The clear superiority of Farman's Voisin over Delagrange's, along with other evidence, makes it fairly certain that many of the beneficial modifications carried out on the machine should stand to his credit. Gabriel Voisin, in his autobiography (see note on Sect. 20), claims that Farman was simply the chauffeur who claimed all the glory; but faced with the striking differences in performance between the machines he built for Delagrange and Farman, Gabriel says that he decided to concentrate all his good ideas about modifications on one machine, Farman's. It seems a poor explanation, and since Gabriel includes so many demonstrably misleading and untruthful items in the book, it is likely that much credit should go to Farman. Powerful support for this view is to be found in the fact that as soon as Farman left the Voisins in 1909, after they sold the machine he had ordered to Moore-Brabazon (see sect. 56), he designed and built — almost overnight as it were — his classic No. III, while the Voisins kept on turning out their same old standard type right through 1909, without any lateral control.

35. BLÉRIOT'S AILERONS: 1906–07. Blériot, who had fitted ailerons to his aircraft as early as 1906, was experimenting productively with them before Wilbur Wright flew in France in 1908, but using them primarily as stabilisers. Oddly enough, although he saw them also as aiding in turns, he never got to using them properly with the rudder, and he never made them large enough: instead, he was soon to abandon ailerons altogether, and take to the Wrights' wing-warping. Whereas Farman, having seen and understood the true function of warping, and its co-ordination with rudder control, demonstrated by Wilbur Wright in 1908, took to ailerons. As we know Blériot was assisted by other pioneers, it would be interesting to know what influences led him to abandon ailerons.

36. FARMAN: 1908. *The Times* account of this famous flight is reproduced in full in GS-A.

37. DESIGNATION OF FARMAN'S FLYING FISH: 1908. Farman's *Flying Fish* was originally allocated the designation "Henri Farman No. 2", but this was cancelled when the machine was abandoned, and the name transferred to the Voisin machine specially commissioned by Farman in January 1909. When this machine was sold to Moore-Brabazon by Gabriel Voisin, behind Farman's back, he abandoned the designation "No. 2" for ever, and named the first of his own designs the "Henry Farman III", with a "y" in Henry.

[349]

NOTES

FARMAN IN THE U.S.A.: 1908. Farman went to the United States in July, and at Brighton Beach (near New York) made some 13 take-offs from July 31st to August 9th, 1908. The promoters had unwisely chosen an exhibition ground only 2,520 ft. long, which — with an unlucky combination of wind and rain to prevent flying on four of the appointed days — resulted in a very poor show all round, which was not Farman's fault.

38. ROE: 1908. The claims that A. V. Roe made proper flights at Brooklands in June 1908 — and hence the first flights in Britain — are dealt with in GS-A.

40. THE A.E.A.: 1908. There can be no doubt that the aircraft made by the Aerial Experiment Association in America were not only descended ultimately from the Wrights' gliders — as were the European gliders and powered aircraft of 1902–08 — but had an even closer connection with the brothers. For in January 1908 Selfridge wrote to the Wrights asking for information about both the construction of the Wright gliders and their aerodynamics; the Wrights sent him references to their own articles, their patent, and the published descriptions of their machines following Chanute's 1903 Paris lecture. Unlike the Europeans, the A.E.A. quickly realised the importance of lateral control, and the functioning of the mechanisms to bring it about. Hence the second A.E.A. machine, the *White Wing*, incorporated ailerons in May 1908. It is sometimes said that Curtiss or MacCurdy, or even some other member of the A.E.A., was responsible for thinking out the aileron variation of wing-warping. But an examination of contemporary documents shows that they would almost certainly have got the idea from Blériot. For the *American Magazine of Aeronautics* for December 1907 — which the A.E.A. members certainly read — contained a large and detailed photograph of Blériot's *Libellule* of that year, which clearly showed its wing-tip ailerons (actually elevons) in swivelled positions. It is also possible that they had seen the Esnault-Pelterie elevons in *L'Aérophile* (1905).* The *June Bug* was later fitted with twin floats, and oddly renamed the *Loon*: it was tested by Curtiss in December 1908, but could not take off.

THE A.E.A. DESIGNS. It is still difficult to determine where the true credit lies in the A.E.A. designs, although one member was named as responsible for the design of each aircraft. But it seems likely that each A.E.A. machine was a co-operative effort, with one man in overall charge of the design.

46. FARMAN'S AILERONS: 1908. Until recently, I was not certain that the ailerons were fitted on Farman's machine for its famous flight from Bouy to Reims on October 30th, 1908. From certain photographs and commemorative postcards, it had for some time seemed that he had removed them for this and other flights. Although aware that the newspapers and postcard publishers often republished photographs of machines in earlier forms if there was a lack of on-the-spot coverage, I could find no visual evidence to prove one thing or the other. I have now established, from photographs taken of the machine after it landed on the outskirts of Reims, that the ailerons were in place. Two of these photographs were taken after dark "par magnesium", and show the machine in the company of employees of the Pommery et Greno Champagne firm, on whose property it had landed, and by whose courtesy I was allowed to examine them at Reims.

58. HENRI(Y) FARMAN: 1909. It will be noticed that I am not consistent in using Henri or Henry when spelling Farman's Christian name: this reflects the inconsistency in French usage. The tendency in France was for the name to "progress" from Henri to Henry as aviation became more widespread, and also, I believe, as it became more widely known that Farman was English (see GS-A, page 307). It is interesting, for example, to find that it was "Henri" on the Voisin-built machine, and "Henry" on his own No. III. One of the more significant facts to re-emerge during research for the present book is that the revolutionary rotary Gnome engine was not fitted to Farman's original No. III before the Reims meeting. I had previously supposed that Farman had become dissatisfied with the in-line Vivinus soon after he started testing the machine in April 1909. The

* It is now known that Selfridge had a copy.

[350]

NOTES

Gnome, as mentioned in this Section, was in fact not fitted until midway in the Reims meeting; it was Latham — and not very much to his credit, I fear — who entered an official protest against this change, but was overruled as it was shown that Farman had adhered to the rules of the meeting, and changed the engine with the full approval of the Committee.

However, there were two "production" Henry Farman III's flying by August 1909, and one of them (that commissioned and flown by the Englishman George Cockburn) was fitted with a Gnome from the start. The other machine (Roger Sommer's) had a Vivinus: it was Sommer who, on the last day of the Reims meeting (Sunday, Aug. 29th), was persuaded by Miss Gertrude Bacon to give her the honour of being the first British woman to fly: her flight is delightfully described in her book, *Memories of Land and Sky* (1928).

PS. Since writing the above, Charles Dollfus, who knew Farman well, has told me that he was quite indifferent about the spelling of his Christian name and used both forms indiscriminately in his daily life.

60. THE GOUPY BIPLANE: 1909. There can be little doubt that the developed Goupy biplane of 1909–10 had a powerful influence on British design, especially on A. V. Roe. This influence was exerted first through prominently published photographs in British periodicals, then through the machine being flown in England in 1910. It also appeared in an early cinema newsreel. This seems to have followed the pattern of the Goupy triplane, which was shown under construction in English and French periodicals in 1908, after which Roe (in 1909) abruptly changed to the same type of machine.

62. CURTISS' GOLD BUG AND GOLDEN FLYER: 1909. Few references will be found in the European press to the name *Golden Flyer* — or even for that matter to the name *Gold Bug* for its predecessor — but most American authorities accept them as authentic. A most interesting problem revolves around the engine Curtiss used in the *Golden Flyer* at Reims. On pages 65 and 66 of his book *The Curtiss Aviation Book*, he refers specifically to it as "an eight-cylinder, V-shaped, fifty horse-power motor." But in all the Continental sources, including the many classified tables published of the competing machines, the engine is given as of 30 h.p. or occasionally as 35. It was in fact his 50 h.p. type. It is probable that Curtiss hoped to lull suspicion, and avoid any special European efforts at fitting more powerful engines, by giving the power as that of his standard engines.

65. THE CROSS-CHANNEL FLIGHT: 1909. Few people today, even among historians, give sufficient credit to Lord Northcliffe and his *Daily Mail* — whose air correspondent was Harry Harper — in promoting the cause of early aviation by the award of generous prizes, and by doing everything possible to create air-mindedness in a Britain which was sadly lagging in all matters aeronautical. It is not surprising, therefore, that the most dramatic account of Blériot's Channel-crossing is to be found in the *Daily Mail* of Monday, July 29th, 1909, which includes an amusing translation of Blériot's own account. The most detailed account of the whole Channel "contest", of what led up to it, of Blériot's success and Latham's two failures, is one which I wrote for *Shell Aviation News* (June, 1959) entitled "The Man who came by Air".

66. THE REIMS MEETING: 1909. The best contemporary accounts of the Reims meeting will be found in *The Times*, *Daily Mail* (written by Harry Harper), *Flight*, *Aeronautics*, *Aero* (not the *Aeroplane* which had not started publication), *L'Aérophile*, *The Aeronautical Journal* (reprinted in full in GS-A), and the biography of Harry Harper entitled *Flying Witness*, by Graham Wallace. (London, 1958).

THE FIRST AVIATION MEETINGS. It is correct to describe the Reims meeting as the first "great", or "important", or "significant", aviation meeting of history. For all but the casuist, it is also correct to call this literally epoch-making event simply "the first aviation meeting"; that is to say, from any realistic and mature historical point of view — bearing in mind what the word "meeting" should be taken to imply.

But there were, of course, a number of small locally organised events, as follows:

There was a small but long drawn-out meeting at Douai which ran from June 28th to July 18th, with July 11th–18th the "semaine principale". This was called the "Concours d'Aviation de Douai", in which some good flights were made by Blériot (in his No. XII) and Paulhan, but little else.

There was a "one aeroplane meet" when Ferber (under his pseudonym de Rue) flew at Belfort on July 17th.

The "Semaine d'Aviation de l'Anjou", planned for July 11th–18th, was abandoned by its sponsors well before the time.

Then from July 18th–25th there was "La Grande Semaine d'Aviation de Vichy", which might have been an important occasion, but was marred by a hurricane. Only Paulham and Tissander made good flights.

The inauguration of the aerodrome named "Port-Aviation" at Juvisy (near Paris) was combined with "le meeting de Juvisy" on Sunday May 23rd 1909. It was "somewhat in the nature of a fiasco", as *Flight* put it, as only two machines took off: the Voisin (Delagrange) made a good flight, but the Voisin (Rougier) did not complete a circuit.

Public aviation events on a small scale, races, etc. thereafter took place at Port-Aviation, but not meetings in the proper sense.

Also on May 23rd there was a one aircraft "meeting" at Vienna when Legagneux briefly flew Farman's semi-triplane modification of his famous machine, now sold to an Austrian syndicate.

Short Bibliography

Notes: (1) The works are arranged in chronological order of publication.

    (2) English language works were published in London unless otherwise stated.

    (3) French and German works were published in Paris and Berlin respectively unless otherwise stated.

LILIENTHAL, O. *Der Vogelflug als Grundlage der Fliegekunst* (translated from the second ed. of 1910 as *Bird Flight as a Basis of Aviation* 1911). Berlin, 1889.

CHANUTE, O. *Progress in Flying Machines.* New York, 1894.

AERONAUTICAL ANNUAL. Edited by J. Means. 3 vols. New York, 1895–97.

AERO CLUB OF AMERICA. *Navigating the Air: a scientific Statement of the progress of aeronautical Science up to the present Time.* London, 1907.

MAXIM, Sir H. S. *Artificial and Natural Flight.* 1908.

DUMAS, A. *Stud Book de l'Aviation. Ceux qui ont volé et leurs Appareils.* 1909.

FERBER, F. *L'aviation — ses débuts — son developpement.* 1909.

RUMPLER, E. *Die Flugmaschine.* Berlin, 1909.

PEYREY, F. *L'Idée aérienne: Aviation. Les Oiseaux artificiels.* 1909.

PEYREY, F. *Les premiers hommes-oiseaux: Wilbur and Orville Wright.* 1909.

BERGET, A. *La Route de l'Air.* 1909 (translated as *The Conquest of the Air,* 1909).

LOUGHEED, V. *Vehicles of the Air.* Chicago, 1909 (1910 given on title-page).

JANE, F. T. *All the World's Airships.* 1909.

MOTOR (The). *The Aero Manual.* 1909.

AEROPLANE SUPPLY CO. *The Aeroplane Annual: the first complete Aviation Catalogue.* 1909.

GRAND-CARTERET, J. and DELTEIL, L. *La Conquête de l'Air vue par l'Image* (1495–1909). 1910.

FERRIS, R. *How to Fly; or the Conquest of the Air.* 1910.

WASHINGTON, D.C.: Smithsonian Institution. *Bibliography of Aeronautics.* [From the earliest times to July 1909.] Washingon, D.C., 1910.

GRAHAME-WHITE, C. and HARPER, H. *The Aeroplane, Past, Present and Future* [includes a biographical section on early aviators]. 1911.

[353]

SHORT BIBLIOGRAPHY

LANGLEY, S. P. *Langley Memoir on Mechanical Flight*. (Smithsonian Institution publication) 2 parts. Washington, D.C., 1911.

FRANKFURT a. M.: Exhibition, 1909. *Katalog der historischen Abteilung der ersten Internationalen Luftschiffahrts-Ausstellung* . . . 1909 (including bibliog.). Frankfurt, 1909.

LA VAULX, H. DE *Le Triomphe de la Navigation Aérienne*. 1912.

DOLLFUS, E. H. *Petits Modèles d'Aéroplanes*. 1912.

MAXIM, H. and HAMMER, W. J. *Chronology of Aviation*. New York, 1912.

DUMAS, A. *Les Accidents d'Aviation*. 1913.

VIVIAN, E. C. and MARSH, W. LOCKWOOD. *A History of Aeronautics*. 1921.

BOFFITO, G. *Il Volo in Italia*. Firenze, 1921.

WEISS, J. B. *Gliding and Soaring Flight*. 1922.

MAGOUN, F. A. and HODGINS, E. *A History of Aircraft*. New York, 1931.

DOLLFUS, C. and BOUCHÉ, H. *Histoire de l'Aéronautique*, 1932. (Revised ed. 1942.)

BRETT, R. D. *The History of British Aviation, 1908–14*. 1934.

SUPF, P. *Das Buch der deutschen Fluggeschichte*. 2 vols. Stuttgart, 1935 (new ed. 1956).

UNITED STATES: W.P.A. *Bibliography of Aeronautics*, 50 pts. New York, 1936–40.

DAVY, M. J. B. *Aeronautics: Heavier-than-Air Aircraft. Pt. III. The Propulsion of Aircraft*. (Science Museum Publication.) 1936.

SAHEL, J. *Henry Farman et l'aviation*. 1936.

NEW YORK: Public Library. *History of Aeronautics: a Selected List of References*. New York, 1938.

LONDON: Royal Aeronautical Society. *A List of Books, Periodicals and Pamphlets in the Library*. 1941.

KELLY, F. C. *The Wright Brothers*. 1944.

DAVY, M. J. B. *Aeronautics: Heavier-than-Air Aircraft, Pts. I and II. Historical Survey; Catalogue of the Exhibits*. 2nd ed. (Science Museum publications). 1949.

WRIGHT, W. & O. *The Papers of Wilbur and Orville Wright*. Edited by Marvin W. McFarland. 2 vols. New York, 1953.

PRITCHARD, J. L. "The Wright Brothers and the Royal Aeronautical Society." (*Journal of the Roy. Aeron. Soc.*, December 1953.)

"YEAR." *A Pictorial History of Aviation: The complete Story of man's Conquest of the Air from his earliest Dreams to the present Jet Age*. By the editors of *Year*. Los Angeles and New York, 1953.

[354]

SHORT BIBLIOGRAPHY

HALLE, G. *Otto Lilienthal.* 2nd ed. Düsseldorf, 1956.

WALLACE, G. *Flying Witness: Harry Harper and the Golden Age of Aviation.* 1958.

LASSALLE, E. J. *Les 100 premiers aviateurs brevetés au monde, et la naissance de l'aviation.* 1962(?).

VOISIN, G. Mes dix milles cerfs-volants. 1961. (translated as *Men, Women and 10,000 kites.* 1963).

WYKEHAM, P. *Santos-Dumont.* 1962.

GIBBS-SMITH, C. H. *A Directory and Nomenclature of the First Aeroplanes, 1809–1909.* 1965.

GIBBS-SMITH, C. H. *The Wright Brothers: their Work and Influence, 1899–1910* (in preparation).

GIBBS-SMITH, C. H. *The Aeroplane: An Historical Survey.* 1960 (second edition, 1966).

GIBBS-SMITH, C. H. *The Birth of European Aviation* (in preparation)

· · · · ·

(Periodicals): *L'Aéronaute; Aero; Aeronautics; Aeronautics (U.S.A.); L'Aérophile; L'Aéronautique; L'Année Aéronautique; Flight; Annual Reports of the Aeronautical Society; The Aeronautical Journal; The Journal of the Royal Aeronautical Society; Illustrated London News; L'Illustration; Scientific American; Sphere;* etc., etc.

METRES TO YARDS AND FEET

(taken to the nearest yard and foot for lengths over 20 metres)

Metres (m)	Yards (yds)	feet (ft)
1	1·09	3·28
2	2·19	6·56
3	3·28	9·84
4	4·37	13·12
5	5·47	16·40
6	6·56	19·69
7	7·66	22·97
8	8·75	26·25
9	9·84	29·53
10	10·94	32·80
15	16·40	49·21
20	21·87	65·62
25	27	82
30	33	98
35	38	115
40	44	131
45	49	147
50	55	164
60	66	197
70	77	230
80	87	262
90	98	295
91	100	299
100	109	328
150	164	492
200	219	656
250	273	819
300	328	984
400	437	1311
402	440 (¼ mile)	1320
500	547	1641
600	656	1968
700	766	2298
800	875	2625
805	880 (½ mile)	2640
900	984	2952
1000 (1 Km)	1094	3282
1609	1760 (1 mile)	5280

KILOMETRES TO MILES

Kilometres (Km)	Miles (mi)
1	⅝th (1093·6 yds; 3280 ft)
1·6	1
2	1·2
3	1·9
4	2·5
5	3·1
6	3·7
7	4·4
8	5·0
9	5·6
10	6·2
15	9·3
20	12·4
25	15·5
30	18·6
35	21·7
40	24·9
45	28·0
50	31·1
75	46·6
100	62·1
125	78·0
150	93·2

SQUARE METRES TO SQUARE FEET

(including common wing areas in early aviation)

Square metres	Square Feet
1	10·8
2	21·5
3	32·3
4	43·0
5	53·8
6	64·6
9	96·9
10	107·6
12	129·2
13	139·9
15	161·5
17	183·0
18	193·8
20	215·3
22	236·8
24	258·3
25	269·0
26	279·9
30	322·9
35	376·7
40	430·6
43	462·8
48	516·7
50	538·2
52	559·7
55	592·0
60	645·8

LENGTHS AND DISTANCES OF SOME FAMILIAR
ITEMS AND PLACES

	Km	m	miles	yds	ft
Length of cricket pitch		20·1		22	66
Length of lawn tennis court		23·8		26	78
Length of American football field		91·4		100	300
Length of international soccer field		109·7		120	360
Length of British soccer field		118·8		130	390

In London

	Km	m	miles	yds	ft
Breadth (east-west) of the Round Pond in Kensington Gardens		201·2		220	660
Length of Westminster Bridge		246·9		270	810
From Hyde Park Corner (Apsley House)					
to Dorchester Hotel, Park Lane		402	¼	440	1320
to (just beyond) Grosvenor House		805	½	880	2640
to Marble Arch	1·2	1207	¾	1320	3960
to Exhibition Road	1·6	1609	1	1760	5280
to (a few yards short of) Leicester Square	1·6	1609	1	1760	5280

In Edinburgh

	Km	m	miles	yds	ft
Length of Princes Street	1·6	1609	1	1760	5280

In Paris

	Km	m	miles	yds	ft
Length of the Champs Élysées, from the Place de la Concorde to the Arc de Triomphe	2·0	2012	1¼	2200	6600

In New York

	Km	m	miles	yds	ft
Length of the Brooklyn Bridge		486·2	⅓	531⅔	1595
The English Channel (at its narrowest)	33·8		21		

Index

INDEX